STEPHEN VINCENT BENÉT

Selected Poetry and Prose

———

PS
3503
.E5325
A6
1960

STEPHEN VINCENT BENÉT

Selected Poetry and Prose

EDITED WITH AN INTRODUCTION
BY BASIL DAVENPORT

NEW YORK   *Rinehart & Co., Inc.*   TORONTO

Shenandoah College Library
Winchester, Va.

Ghosts of a Lunatic Asylum: COPYRIGHT 1918 BY STEPHEN VINCENT BENÉT. COPYRIGHT RENEWED 1946 BY ROSEMARY CARR BENÉT. The Retort Discourteous AND Talk: COPYRIGHT 1920 BY STEPHEN VINCENT BENÉT. COPYRIGHT RENEWED 1948 BY ROSEMARY CARR BENÉT. Difference: COPYRIGHT 1921 BY STEPHEN VINCENT BENÉT. The Ballad of William Sycamore: COPYRIGHT 1922 BY STEPHEN VINCENT BENÉT. COPYRIGHT RENEWED 1950 BY ROSEMARY CARR BENÉT. King David: COPYRIGHT 1923 BY STEPHEN VINCENT BENÉT. COPYRIGHT RENEWED 1951 BY ROSEMARY CARR BENÉT. The Mountain Whippoorwill; For All Blasphemers; Architects; The Golden Corpse; To Rosemary; Nomenclature; A Sad Song; A Nonsense Song; To Rosemary, on the Methods by Which She Might Become an Angel; Legend; Dulce Ridentem; AND Illa: COPYRIGHT 1925 BY STEPHEN VINCENT BENÉT. COPYRIGHT RENEWED 1953 BY ROSEMARY CARR BENÉT. American Names: COPYRIGHT 1927 BY STEPHEN VINCENT BENÉT. COPYRIGHT RENEWED 1955 BY ROSEMARY CARR BENÉT. The Barefoot Saint: COPYRIGHT 1929 BY STEPHEN VINCENT BENÉT. COPYRIGHT RENEWED 1957 BY ROSEMARY CARR BENÉT. Mortuary Parlors; Hands; AND 8:30 A.M. on 32nd Street: COPYRIGHT 1931 BY STEPHEN VINCENT BENÉT. COPYRIGHT RENEWED 1959 BY ROSEMARY CARR BENÉT. Southern Ships and Settlers; Captain Kidd; French Pioneers; Thomas Jefferson; John James Audubon; Daniel Boone; AND Western Wagons: COPYRIGHT 1933 BY ROSEMARY AND STEPHEN VINCENT BENÉT. Metropolitan Nightmare: COPYRIGHT 1933 BY STEPHEN VINCENT BENÉT. Ode to Walt Whitman; Nightmare, with Angels; Nightmare Number Three; AND 1935: COPYRIGHT 1935 BY STEPHEN VINCENT BENÉT. The Curfew Tolls: COPYRIGHT 1935 BY STEPHEN VINCENT BENÉT AND THE CURTIS PUBLISHING COMPANY. Glamour: COPYRIGHT 1935 BY ROSEMARY CARR BENÉT. Memory; Notes to Be Left in a Cornerstone; Short Ode; Do You Remember, Springfield?; Sparrow; AND For City Lovers: COPYRIGHT 1936 BY STEPHEN VINCENT BENÉT. The Devil and Daniel Webster: COPYRIGHT 1936 BY STEPHEN VINCENT BENÉT AND THE CURTIS PUBLISHING COMPANY. Johnny Pye and the Fool-Killer: COPYRIGHT 1937 BY STEPHEN VINCENT BENÉT AND THE CURTIS PUBLISHING COMPANY. Nightmare for Future Reference AND Schooner Fairchild's Class: COPYRIGHT 1938 BY STEPHEN VINCENT BENÉT. Jacob and the Indians; The Die-Hard; AND Doc Mellhorn and the Pearly Gates: COPYRIGHT 1938 BY STEPHEN VINCENT BENÉT AND THE CURTIS PUBLISHING COMPANY. Into Egypt: COPYRIGHT 1939 BY STEPHEN VINCENT BENÉT AND THE CURTIS PUBLISHING COMPANY. Minor Litany; Nightmare at Noon; AND Freedom's a Hard-Bought Thing: COPYRIGHT 1940 BY STEPHEN VINCENT BENÉT. They Burned the Books (RADIO SCRIPT): COPYRIGHT 1942 BY STEPHEN VINCENT BENÉT. The Prodigal Children, FROM *The Last Circle* (FARRAR, STRAUS & CUDAHY, INC.): COPYRIGHT 1942 BY THE ESTATE OF STEPHEN VINCENT BENÉT AND THE CURTIS PUBLISHING COMPANY. The Bishop's Beggar: COPYRIGHT 1942 BY THE ESTATE OF STEPHEN VINCENT BENÉT AND THE CURTIS PUBLISHING COMPANY. Memento Mori, FROM *The Last Circle* (FARRAR, STRAUS & CUDAHY, INC.): COPYRIGHT 1943 BY ROSEMARY CARR BENÉT. FOREWORD TO MURIEL RUKEYSER's Theory of Flight: COPYRIGHT 1935 BY YALE UNIVERSITY PRESS. Epic on an American Theme (CORRESPONDENCE WITH THE GUGGENHEIM FOUNDATION), FROM *The New Colophon*: COPYRIGHT 1949 BY DUSCHNES CRAWFORD, INC.

Introduction © 1960 by Basil Davenport. Typography and Cover Design by Stefan Salter. All Rights Reserved. Printed in the United States of America. Library of Congress Catalog Card Number 60-5174.

CONTENTS

INTRODUCTION vii BIBLIOGRAPHY xiv

Poetry

1. BALLADS AND TALES

American Names	3	Captain Kidd	23
Ballad of William Sycamore	4	French Pioneers	23
The Mountain Whippoorwill	7	Thomas Jefferson	24
King David	12	John James Audubon	27
The Retort Discourteous	20	Daniel Boone	28
Southern Ships and Settlers	21	Western Wagons	28

2. YOUNG ADVENTURE

8:30 A.M. on 32nd Street	30	Architects	33
Mortuary Parlors	31	Talk	34
Ghosts of a Lunatic Asylum	32	The Golden Corpse	35
For All Blasphemers	32		

3. MY FAIR LADY

To Rosemary	40	Legend	45
Nomenclature	41	Dulce Ridentem	47
Difference	42	Illa	47
A Sad Song	42	Hands	47
A Nonsense Song	43	Memory	48
To Rosemary, on the Methods by Which She Might Become an Angel	44	Memento Mori	49

4. NIGHTMARES AND VISITANTS

Notes to Be Left in a Cornerstone	50	Do You Remember, Springfield?	56
Short Ode	55	Ode to Walt Whitman	59
Metropolitan Nightmare	70	Nightmare for Future Reference	80
Nightmare, with Angels	73		
Nightmare Number Three	75	Minor Litany	85
1936	77	Nightmare at Noon	87
Sparrow	78	They Burned the Books (radio script)	92
For City Lovers	79		

Prose

1. STORIES OF AMERICA

Jacob and the Indians	109	The Die-Hard	172
The Devil and Daniel Webster	123	Glamour	188
		The Prodigal Children	204
Freedom's a Hard-Bought Thing	138	Schooner Fairchild's Class	217
		Doc Mellhorn and the Pearly Gates	233
Johnny Pye and the Fool-Killer	151		

2. FAR FROM HERE AND NOW

The Barefoot Saint	252	Into Egypt	302
The Bishop's Beggar	265	By the Waters of Babylon	313
The Curfew Tolls	286		

3. CRITICISM AND LETTERS

Foreword to Muriel Rukeyser's *Theory of Flight*	326
Epic on an American Theme (correspondence with the Guggenheim Foundation)	328

INTRODUCTION TO A BENÉT READER

In 1927 Paris was full of American expatriates. Nearly all of them were agreed on one thing, that America was no place for intelligent people to live. Even for those of us who to some extent experienced the expatriate view, it is hard to recall how widespread and how deep that feeling was at the end of the twenties. It was the time of the boom, and a very general money-madness; it was the time of Prohibition, and enormous political corruption; it was the time of the scandals of the Harding administration, and the farce of the Tennessee "monkey trial" (which, it may now be needful to recall, was over the question of whether the theory of evolution could legally be taught in Tennessee). Moreover, there was a prevalent mood of cynicism, the idealism that fought World War I gone sour. This appeared, for instance, in a school of biographical writing that came to have a recognized name, "debunking," which meant portraying great men not merely "warts and all," as Cromwell asked to be painted, but with the composition centered on the warts. For many, this disillusionment began at home, where it found expression in some of the most influential writers of the day. In the bestsellers *Main Street, Babbitt,* and *Elmer Gantry,* Sinclair Lewis portrayed the poverty of American culture. In his magazine *The American Mercury,* H. L. Mencken excoriated what he called "the booboisie," and each month ran a department called "Americana," filled with clippings illustrating American vulgarity and provincialism. And all through the magazine writings of the time runs the charge, repeated again and again, that American life is uniform, monotonous, standardized. People drink Coca-Cola and read *The Saturday Evening Post* in Connecticut and in Georgia, the argument appears to run, and therefore life in Connecticut is just like life in Georgia. Most of the young writers living in Paris were thoroughly disillusioned with America, and convinced that the only place where one could find any originality was in Europe.

There was one young writer living in Paris who was not in the least disillusioned with America. While he was still an undergraduate at Yale, the *Yale Literary Magazine* had published his poem "The Hemp," a ballad of the days of piracy on the American coast. In 1929 he had already written "The Ballad of William Sycamore," "The Mountain Whippoorwill," "American Names," and a group of poems about New York City as it looks to a young man come there to seek his fortune. He was living in Paris not because he was dissatisfied with America, but because living in Paris was cheap. He had been given a Guggenheim Fellowship to enable him to write an epic poem on an American theme, and he wanted to finish it before the money ran out. His name was Stephen Vincent Benét, and the poem was of course *John Brown's Body*. (Here, perhaps, is as good a place as any to say that, though *John Brown's Body* is, of all his work, that for which he is best known and will be longest remembered, it is too long to include as a whole in this volume, and both your editor and your publisher dislike excerpts. We have however included, under the title "Epic on an American Theme," Benét's letters and a progress report to the Guggenheim Foundation, giving his own account of what he hoped to do and how he worked.)

For a writer of an American epic, Benét's background was a fortunate one. His father and his grandfather were both officers in the old Regular Army. In 1845 his grandfather, who became Brigadier General Stephen Vincent Benét, held the first appointment to West Point from the newly created state of Florida, where the Benét family had come from Minorca. James Walker Benét, the son of the first Stephen Vincent Benét and the father of the second, was a colonel in the Regular Army, and a man of keen literary tastes; his son described him as "The Most Unforgettable Character I Ever Met." As the son of an Army officer, young Stephen Vincent Benét had an unusual opportunity to get acquainted with his native country. He was born in Pennsylvania in 1898, spent his childhood in upper New York State, his early boyhood near San Francisco, his later boyhood in Georgia. He spent a summer in the Sierras, and made many visits to his mother's family in Carlisle, Pennsylvania. He went to Yale, which, with such undergraduates as Archibald MacLeish, Thornton Wilder, Philip Barry, and John Farrar, was undergoing what Yale men like to refer to as "a literary renaissance." He has put some of his life at Yale into his novel *The Beginning of Wisdom,* and perhaps even more of his feeling for Yale and the country round it into his sonnet sequence "The Golden Corpse." Altogether, as he grew up he had both the opportunity and the perception to realize that the roots of American culture lie deeper than soft drinks and popular magazines, deeper even than Prohibition and monkey trials.

He was fortunate not only in his upbringing, but in most other respects, or so it seemed to us who knew him. I must qualify that by saying that his health was never good, and while still a young man he was badly bent with arthritis. Also, though *John Brown's Body* earned, by the standard of sales for works of poetry, a small fortune, the bulk of this came just in time to be lost in the crash of '29, and he never knew real financial security. Yet he always made his friends happy, and he always seemed happy himself. The young Napoleon, when someone congratulated him on his good luck, replied calmly, "Le bonheur est aussi une qualité"— "Good luck is also a talent." Taking the word *bonheur* in another sense, happiness too may be called a talent, and it is one that Benét conspicuously possessed. In writing a review of Charles Fenton's recently published biography, *Stephen Vincent Benét,* I spoke of the difficulty he had had to overcome in portraying his subject's character, for it needs to be a portrait almost without shadows.

Benét was certainly happy in the three most important aspects of a man's life—his family, his marriage, and his work. His boyhood, except for one wretched year at a badly chosen boarding school, was almost idyllic. His mother was, according to those who knew her, as delightful as his father. He was the youngest of three literary children; his sister, Laura, was to become a biographer, and his brother, William Rose, a distinguished poet. William Rose Benét was twelve years older than Stephen, old enough to be able to encourage and direct his brother's first efforts in poetry. Between the two brothers there was a warm affection, which was quite untouched by the fact that the reputation of the younger in time surpassed that of the older. Stephen Vincent Benét has expressed something of his feeling for his brother in his poem "Hands."

He was equally blessed in his marriage, which proved to be the most important consequence of a university fellowship. After graduating from Yale in 1919 he went on to take an M.A. in English, and from the Yale Graduate School he received a Scott Hurt Fellowship for the academic year 1920-21, with the stipulation that he need not live at the university—in effect, he was being given his passage to Paris and a little more. With this, and a publisher's advance for his first novel, *The Beginning of Wisdom*, he spent the winter in Paris. Here he met Rosemary Carr, a girl from Chicago who was working on *Vogue*. In November, 1921, they were married, a marriage that was to prove singularly happy. *A Book of Americans*, which they wrote together (some of Benét's contributions to it appear here in the section "Ballads and Tales"), bears the dedication "To Stephanie, Thomas, and Rachel, our other works in collaboration." There is a portrait of Rosemary in the present volume, in the section called "My Fair Lady." People who know that she is a friend of mine have sometimes asked me, with a touch of envy or wistfulness, "Is she really as lovely as his poems make her?" and I have answered, "Yes, quite as lovely."

He was also happy in his work, in that from boyhood he knew what he wanted to do and was able to do it. His first book, *Five Men and Pompey*, was written the summer after his graduation from prep school, and from that time on he was a dedicated writer. Shortly after leaving Yale, and before his marriage, he worked for a few months in an advertising agency, but he soon decided that that was not for him. From then on he trusted to his writing, and succeeded in maintaining a family and educating three children by that alone. Naturally, he did not do this without writing what he would have been the first to call potboilers. He once wrote to Rosemary, the day after she had left for a visit to Chicago, "I try to console myself as best I can by trying to start one of my celebrated, bright, gay stories of gay, bright, dumb young people." But they were good potboilers. I have read all, or nearly all, of his unreprinted magazine stories, and if what you are looking for is entertainment, you will find it in these, and presented with more grace and charm than is usually found in popular fiction.

He was a dedicated writer, devoted to the art of writing. He gave much thought to the problem of writing poetry which belongs to its writer's generation, and belongs also to the central tradition of English poetry—a problem which recurs in every generation, but was especially urgent for his, because of the sharp break with the past which began with World War I. One special aspect of this problem is the technical matter of finding a verse form which bears the same relation to the normal rhythm of our speech that blank verse does to the more formal speech pattern of an earlier time. Benét was one of the first poets to attempt this, and he was still concerned with it at the time of his death, hoping to do better than he had done. Yet the solution that he did achieve, the loose five or six beat line that carries the bulk of *John Brown's Body* and is used in his three "Nightmare" poems, seems to me the best that has been found. It can carry casual conversations without incongruity, and it can deepen into regular blank verse for passages that need a greater dignity. And it passes the great test for existence as a meter: single lines of it stay in your head with a life of their own, lines like:

>It is over now, but they will not let it be over,

or

>He danced with me. He could dance rather well. He is dead.

That is a real meter of our own time.

He was equally concerned with the ventures of others in the art of writing. In 1933 he became editor of the Yale Series of Younger Poets, a series of volumes published annually by the Yale University Press, and chosen from manuscripts submitted in competition. As editor, he assumed the duty of making the final selection. The editors of the Yale Press gave the manuscripts some preliminary screening, but his letters to his co-editors constantly urge them not to try to spare him work, to send him anything that shows signs of promise. Under his fostering care, the series grew until he was reading more than a hundred and fifty manuscripts a year. He advised and encouraged many of these younger poets, who often became warm personal friends. And he made two innovations. Until his time, the winner of each year's competition had received only the recognition of publication, and the usual ten per cent royalty on copies sold. Benét suggested that each winner should receive a prize of a hundred dollars, to be deducted from his own fee as editor; and he increased his own labors by volunteering to contribute an introduction to each volume.

Devoted as he was to writing, he was at the farthest remove from the cloistered devotee of art for art's sake. He was always quietly proud that he came of a family of soldiers. All his life he suffered from extreme nearsightedness, but during World War I, while he was an undergraduate at Yale, he memorized the eye chart used in the Army physical examination and managed to get himself accepted as a private. The next day a sergeant watched his newest recruit peeling potatoes, and, as Benét said later, "decided from the way he was carving things he was likely to nick his nose." Benét's eyesight was examined again with a different chart, and his military career ended three days after it had begun. He then succeeded in getting a job with the State Department, first as a clerk and then as cryptographer for Military Intelligence, returning to Yale to get his degree after the end of the war. When World War II approached he saw what was happening much earlier and more clearly than most people, witness his poem "1936." During these years he was at work on another long narrative poem, *Western Star*, which was to have equalled *John Brown's Body* in length; in 1941 he put the manuscript of this into a safe-deposit drawer, a symbol of the fact that for the duration of the war his pen was to be dedicated to the needs of the nation. He did not live to see the end of the war, and *Western Star* was still unfinished at the time of his death in 1943.

He put forward his own view of the position of the writer in wartime in some lines which appeared in Edward Weeks' literary page in the *Atlantic*, apparently taken, though this is not stated, from a letter to Weeks. He said in part: "I don't think that writing propaganda for a cause you believe in vitiates Milton, who did a good deal of it. . . . It seems to me that the government has as much right to call upon me to use such special abilities as I may have as it has to call upon a chemist to use his." No one, civilian or soldier, used his powers in the war effort more unsparingly than did Benét. His great work in this field was his radio scripts, but he did all other kinds of pieces as well. His health, never robust, was at this time very bad, but he worked constantly for the Writers' War Board, never refusing an assignment or a deadline. In addition, he was constrained to go on writing stories—constrained both by the necessity of the artist to say what is in him, and by the fact that every penny that came from his war writings he turned over to the USO or the Army Fund, and a living had to be earned. The combined pressures proved to be too much. In March 12, 1943, he suffered a heart attack, and died in the arms of his wife.

Essentially he was a romantic. I have stressed his Americanism, both because it is one of his most striking qualities, and because as I have said it is hard now to realize how original his attitude was at the beginning of his career. But he was equally moved by the far away and long ago, by the far hence in time, future as well as past. He had the romantic's sense of the macabre, felt both as humorous and as terrifying—sometimes, as in the "Nightmares," as both at once. His work shows an extraordinary feeling not only for the America of hill and river and countryside, but also for the exhilaration of New York, or as in "Glamour," for the particular atmosphere of an old city backwater. And he has the poet's uncanny gift of being able to show both sides of a coin at the same time. In "Curfew" he can show Napoleon as a good deal of a scoundrel and also as a great man; in "Glamour," again, he can take away the charm of a typical Southern belle and yet leave her somehow more magical than ever.

From such a writer one does not ask a statement of philosophy. In *Out of the Silent Planet*, C. S. Lewis' Martian novel, Mars is inhabited by three rational races. These include the *seroni*, who are devoted to science and philosophy, and the *hrossa*, who are given to hunting and poetry. One of the *hrossa*, trying to explain an idea to the earthman hero, remarks, "One of the *seroni* could say it better than I say it now. Not better than I could say it in a poem." Benét said what he had to say in his stories and his poems. His sense of values is everywhere apparent. Merely from reading him, one can feel him, one can feel the truth of what was said of him by one of his friends, the author William Sloane: "I had rather have *been* Steve Benét than any man I know."

BENÉT BIBLIOGRAPHY

The only full-length study of Benét is Charles A. Fenton's *Stephen Vincent Benét,* which is likely to remain the only one in its field for some time. At the time of Benét's death the *Saturday Review of Literature* devoted the issue of March 27, 1943, to his memory; this contains numerous tributes by friends and critics. The *Saturday Review* also published, on Nov. 15, 1941, an article called "My Brother Steve," by William Rose Benét.

Among Benét's own writings, that for which he will be longest remembered is his *John Brown's Body,* which has appeared in numerous editions. One of these, which first appeared in 1941, is a special educational edition, edited and annotated by Mabel A. Bessey, with an introduction on the historical period by Bert James Loewenberg, and a foreword by Benét. *Selected Works of Stephen Vincent Benét* contains *John Brown's Body* and the historical novel *Spanish Bayonet,* as well as numerous short stories and poems. Benét's novel *The Beginning of Wisdom* is based on his own experiences at prep school and college, and contains many recognizable portraits of his Yale contemporaries. His radio scripts have been brought together in a volume called *We Stand United.*

Poetry

ONE

Ballads and Tales

AMERICAN NAMES

I have fallen in love with American names,
The sharp names that never get fat,
The snakeskin-titles of mining-claims,
The plumed war-bonnet of Medicine Hat,
Tucson and Deadwood and Lost Mule Flat.

Seine and Piave are silver spoons,
But the spoonbowl-metal is thin and worn,
There are English counties like hunting-tunes
Played on the keys of a postboy's horn,
But I will remember where I was born.

I will remember Carquinez Straits,
Little French Lick and Lundy's Lane,
The Yankee ships and the Yankee dates
And the bullet-towns of Calamity Jane.
I will remember Skunktown Plain.

I will fall in love with a Salem tree
And a rawhide quirt from Santa Cruz,
I will get me a bottle of Boston sea
And a blue-gum nigger to sing me blues.
I am tired of loving a foreign muse.

Rue des Martyrs and Bleeding-Heart-Yard,
Senlis, Pisa, and Blindman's Oast,
It is a magic ghost you guard
But I am sick for a newer ghost,
Harrisburg, Spartanburg, Painted Post.

Henry and John were never so
And Henry and John were always right?
Granted, but when it was time to go
And the tea and the laurels had stood all night,
Did they never watch for Nantucket Light?

I shall not rest quiet in Montparnasse.
I shall not lie easy at Winchelsea.
You may bury my body in Sussex grass,
You may bury my tongue at Champmédy.
I shall not be there. I shall rise and pass.
Bury my heart at Wounded Knee.

THE BALLAD OF WILLIAM SYCAMORE

1790-1871

My father, he was a mountaineer,
His fist was a knotty hammer;
He was quick on his feet as a running deer,
And he spoke with a Yankee stammer.

My mother, she was merry and brave,
And so she came to her labor,
With a tall green fir for her doctor grave
And a stream for her comforting neighbor.

And some are wrapped in the linen fine,
And some like a godling's scion;
But I was cradled on twigs of pine
In the skin of a mountain lion.

BALLAD OF WILLIAM SYCAMORE

And some remember a white, starched lap
And a ewer with silver handles;
But I remember a coonskin cap
And the smell of bayberry candles.

The cabin logs, with the bark still rough,
And my mother who laughed at trifles,
And the tall, lank visitors, brown as snuff,
With their long, straight squirrel-rifles.

I can hear them dance, like a foggy song,
Through the deepest one of my slumbers,
The fiddle squeaking the boots along
And my father calling the numbers.

The quick feet shaking the puncheon-floor,
And the fiddle squealing and squealing,
Till the dried herbs rattled above the door
And the dust went up to the ceiling.

There are children lucky from dawn till dusk,
But never a child so lucky!
For I cut my teeth on "Money Musk"
In the Bloody Ground of Kentucky!

When I grew tall as the Indian corn,
My father had little to lend me,
But he gave me his great, old powder-horn
And his woodsman's skill to befriend me.

With a leather shirt to cover my back,
And a redskin nose to unravel
Each forest sign, I carried my pack
As far as a scout could travel.

Till I lost my boyhood and found my wife,
A girl like a Salem clipper!
A woman straight as a hunting-knife
With eyes as bright as the Dipper!

We cleared our camp where the buffalo feed,
Unheard-of streams were our flagons;
And I sowed my sons like the apple-seed
On the trail of the Western wagons.

They were right, tight boys, never sulky or slow,
A fruitful, a goodly muster.
The eldest died at the Alamo.
The youngest fell with Custer.

The letter that told it burned my hand.
Yet we smiled and said, "So be it!"
But I could not live when they fenced the land,
For it broke my heart to see it.

I saddled a red, unbroken colt
And rode him into the day there;
And he threw me down like a thunderbolt
And rolled on me as I lay there.

The hunter's whistle hummed in my ear
As the city-men tried to move me,
And I died in my boots like a pioneer
With the whole wide sky above me.

Now I lie in the heart of the fat, black soil,
Like the seed of a prairie-thistle;
It has washed my bones with honey and oil
And picked them clean as a whistle.

And my youth returns, like the rains of Spring,
And my sons, like the wild-geese flying;
And I lie and hear the meadow-lark sing
And have much content in my dying.

Go play with the towns you have built of blocks,
The towns where you would have bound me!
I sleep in my earth like a tired fox,
And my buffalo have found me.

THE MOUNTAIN WHIPPOORWILL

OR, HOW HILL-BILLY JIM WON THE GREAT FIDDLERS' PRIZE

(*A Georgia Romance*)

Up in the mountains, it's lonesome all the time,
(Sof' win' slewin' thu' the sweet-potato vine).

Up in the mountains, it's lonesome for a child,
(Whippoorwills a-callin' when the sap runs wild).

Up in the mountains, mountains in the fog,
Everythin's as lazy as an old houn' dog.

Born in the mountains, never raised a pet,
Don't want nuthin' an' never got it yet.

Born in the mountains, lonesome-born,
Raised runnin' ragged thu' the cockleburrs and corn.

Never knew my pappy, mebbe never should.
Think he was a fiddle made of mountain laurel-wood.

Never had a mammy to teach me pretty-please.
Think she was a whippoorwill, a-skitin' thu' the trees.

Never had a brother ner a whole pair of pants,
But when I start to fiddle, why, yuh got to start to dance!

Listen to my fiddle—Kingdom Come—Kingdom Come!
Hear the frogs a-chunkin' "Jug o' rum, Jug o' rum!"
Hear that mountain-whippoorwill be lonesome in the air,
An' I'll tell yuh how I traveled to the Essex County Fair.

Essex County has a mighty pretty fair,
All the smarty fiddlers from the South come there.

Elbows flyin' as they rosin up the bow
For the First Prize Contest in the Georgia Fiddlers' Show.

Old Dan Wheeling, with his whiskers in his ears,
King-pin fiddler for nearly twenty years.

Big Tom Sargent, with his blue wall-eye,
An' Little Jimmy Weezer that can make a fiddle cry.

All sittin' roun', spittin' high an' struttin' proud,
(Listen, little whippoorwill, yuh better bug yore eyes!) 30
Tun-a-tun-a-tunin' while the jedges told the crowd
Them that got the mostest claps'd win the bestest prize.

Everybody waitin' for the first tweedle-dee,
When in comes a-stumblin'—hill-billy me!

Bowed right pretty to the jedges an' the rest,
Took a silver dollar from a hole inside my vest,

Plunked it on the table an' said, "There's my callin' card!
An' anyone that licks me—well, he's got to fiddle hard!"

Old Dan Wheeling, he was laughin' fit to holler,
Little Jimmy Weezer said, "There's one dead dollar!" 40

Big Tom Sargent had a yaller-toothy grin,
But I tucked my little whippoorwill spang underneath my chin,
An' petted it an' tuned it till the jedges said, "Begin!"

Big Tom Sargent was the first in line;
He could fiddle all the bugs off a sweet-potato vine.

He could fiddle down a possum from a mile-high tree.
He could fiddle up a whale from the bottom of the sea.

Yuh could hear hands spankin' till they spanked each other raw,
When he finished variations on "Turkey in the Straw."

Little Jimmy Weezer was the next to play;
He could fiddle all night, he could fiddle all day.

He could fiddle chills, he could fiddle fever,
He could make a fiddle rustle like a lowland river.

He could make a fiddle croon like a lovin' woman.
An' they clapped like thunder when he'd finished strummin'.

Then came the ruck of the bob-tailed fiddlers,
The let's go-easies, the fair-to-middlers.

They got their claps an' they lost their bicker,
An' settled back for some more corn-licker.

An' the crowd was tired of their no-count squealing,
When out in the center steps Old Dan Wheeling.

He fiddled high and he fiddled low,
(Listen, little whippoorwill; yuh got to spread yore wings!)
He fiddled with a cheerywood bow.
(Old Dan Wheeling's got bee-honey in his strings.)

He fiddled the wind by the lonesome moon,
He fiddled a most almighty tune.

He started fiddling like a ghost,
He ended fiddling like a host.

He fiddled north an' he fiddled south,
He fiddled the heart right out of yore mouth.

He fiddled here an' he fiddled there.
He fiddled salvation everywhere.

When he was finished, the crowd cut loose,
(Whippoorwill, they's rain on yore breast.)
An' I sat there wonderin', "What's the use?"
(Whippoorwill, fly home to yore nest.)

But I stood up pert an' I took my bow,
An' my fiddle went to my shoulder, so.

An'—they wasn't no crowd to get me fazed—
But I was alone where I was raised.

Up in the mountains, so still it makes yuh skeered.
Where God lies sleepin' in his big white beard.

An' I heard the sound of the squirrel in the pine,
An' I heard the earth a-breathin' thu' the long night-time.

They've fiddled the rose, an' they've fiddled the thorn,
But they haven't fiddled the mountain-corn.

They've fiddled sinful an' fiddled moral,
But they haven't fiddled the breshwood-laurel.

They've fiddled loud, an' they've fiddled still,
But they haven't fiddled the whippoorwill.

I started off with a *dump-diddle-dump*,
(*Oh, hell's broke loose in Georgia!*)
Skunk-cabbage growin' by the bee-gum stump,
(*Whippoorwill, yo're singin' now!*)

Oh, Georgia booze is mighty fine booze,
The best yuh ever poured yuh,
But it eats the soles right offen yore shoes,
For Hell's broke loose in Georgia.

My mother was a whippoorwill pert,
My father, he was lazy,
But I'm Hell broke loose in a new store shirt
To fiddle all Georgia crazy.

Swing yore partners—up an' down the middle!
Sashay now—oh, listen to that fiddle!
Flapjacks flippin' on a red-hot griddle,

An' hell broke loose,
Hell broke loose,
Fire on the mountains—snakes in the grass.
Satan's here a-bilin'—oh, Lordy, let him pass!
Go down Moses, set my people free,
Pop goes the weasel thu' the old Red Sea!
Jonah sittin' on a hickory-bough,
Up jumps a whale—an' where's yore prophet *now*?
Rabbit in the pea-patch, possum in the pot,
Try an' stop my fiddle, now my fiddle's gettin' hot!
Whippoorwill, singin' thu' the mountain hush,
Whippoorwill, shoutin' from the burnin' bush,
Whippoorwill, cryin' in the stable-door,
Sing to-night as yuh never sang before!
Hell's broke loose like a stompin' mountain-shoat,
Sing till yuh bust the gold in yore throat!
Hell's broke loose for forty miles aroun'
Bound to stop yore music if yuh don't sing it **down**.
Sing on the mountains, little whippoorwill,
Sing to the valleys, an' slap 'em with a hill,
For I'm struttin' high as an eagle's quill,
An' Hell's broke loose,
Hell's broke loose,
Hell's broke loose in Georgia!

They wasn't a sound when I stopped bowin',
(*Whippoorwill, yuh can sing no more.*)
But, somewhere or other, the dawn was growin',
(*Oh, mountain whippoorwill!*)

An' I thought, "I've fiddled all night an' lost.
Yo're a good hill-billy, but yuh've been bossed."

So I went to congratulate old man Dan,
—But he put his fiddle into my han'—
An' then the noise of the crowd began.

KING DAVID

David sang to his hook-nosed harp:
"The Lord God is a jealous God!
His violent vengeance is swift and sharp!
And the Lord is King above all gods!

"Blest be the Lord, through years untold,
The Lord Who has blessed me a thousand fold!

"Cattle and concubines, corn and hives
Enough to last me a dozen lives.

"Plump, good women with noses flat,
Marrowful blessings, weighty and fat.

"I wax in His peace like a pious gourd,
The Lord God is a pleasant God,
Break mine enemy's jaw, O Lord!
For the Lord is King above all gods!"

His hand dropped slack from the tunable strings,
A sorrow came on him—a sorrow of kings.

A sorrow sat on the arm of his throne,
An eagle sorrow with claws of stone.

"I am merry, yes, when I am not thinking,
But life is nothing but eating and drinking.

"I can shape my psalms like daggers of jade,
But they do not shine like the first I made.

"I can harry the heathen from North to South,
But no hot taste comes into my mouth.

"My wives are comely as long-haired goats,
But I would not care if they cut their thoats!

"Where are the maids of the desert tents
With lips like flagons of frankincense?

"Where is Jonathan? Where is Saul?
The captain-towers of Zion wall?

"The trees of cedar, the hills of Nod,
The kings, the running lions of God?

"Their words were a writing in golden dust,
Their names are myrrh in the mouths of the just.

"The sword of the slayer could never divide them—
Would God I had died in battle beside them!"

The Lord looked down from a thunder-clap.
(The Lord God is a crafty God.)
He heard the strings of the shrewd harp snap.
(The Lord Who is King above all gods.)

He pricked the king with an airy thorn,
It burnt in his body like grapes of scorn.

The eyelids roused that had drooped like lead.
David lifted his heavy head.

The thorn stung at him, a fiery bee,
"The world is wide. I will go and see
From the roof of my haughty palace," said he.

2

Bathsheba bathed on her vine-decked roof.
(The Lord God is a mighty God.)

Her body glittered like mail of proof.
(And the Lord is King above all gods.)

Her body shimmered, tender and white
As the flesh of aloes in candlelight.

King David forgot to be old or wise.
He spied on her bathing with sultry eyes.

A breath of spice came into his nose.
He said, "Her breasts are like two young roes."

His eyes were bright with a crafty gleam.
He thought, "Her body is soft as cream."   60

He straightened himself like an unbent bow
And called a servant and bade him go.

3

Uriah the Hittite came to his lord,
Dusty with war as a well-used sword.

A close, trim man like a belt, well-buckled;
A jealous gentleman, hard to cuckold.

David entreated him, soft and bland.
Offered him comfits from his own hand.

Drank with him deep till his eyes grew red,
And laughted in his beard as he went to bed.   70

The days slipped by without hurry or strife,
Like apple-parings under a knife,
And still Uriah kept from his wife.

Lean fear tittered through David's psalm,
"This merry husband is far too calm."

David sent for Uriah then,
They greeted each other like pious men.

"Thou hast borne the battle, the dust and the heat.
Go down to thy house and wash thy feet!"

Uriah frowned at the words of the king.
His brisk, hard voice had a leaden ring.

"While the hosts of God still camp in the field
My house to me is a garden sealed.

"How shall I rest while the arrow yet flies?
The dust of the war is still in my eyes."

David spoke with his lion's roar:
"If Peace be a bridle that rubs you sore,
You shall fill your belly with blood and war!"

Uriah departed, calling him kind.
His eyes were serpents in David's mind.

He summoned a captain, a pliable man,
"Uriah the Hittite shall lead the van.

"In the next assault, when the fight roars high,
And the Lord God is a hostile God,

Retire from Uriah that he may die.
For the Lord is King above all gods."

4

The messenger came while King David played
The friskiest ditty ever made.

"News, O King, from our dubious war!
The Lord of Hosts hath prevailed once more!

"His foes are scattered like chirping sparrows,
Their kings lie breathless, feathered with arrows.

"Many are dead of your captains tall.
Uriah the Hittite was first to fall."

David turned from the frolicsome strings
And rent his clothes for the death of kings.

Yet, as he rent them, he smiled for joy.
The sly, wide smile of a wicked boy.

"The powerful grace of the Lord prevails!
He has cracked Uriah between His nails!

"His blessings are mighty, they shall not cease.
And my days henceforth shall be days of peace!"

His mind grew tranquil, smoother than fleece.
He rubbed his body with scented grease.
And his days thenceforward were days of peace.

His days were fair as the flowering lime
—For a little time, for a little time.

And Bathsheba lay in his breast like a dove,
A vessel of amber, made for love.

5

When Bathsheba was great with child,
(The Lord God is a jealous God!)
Portly and meek as a moon grown mild,
(The Lord is King above all gods!)

Nathan, the prophet, wry and dying,
Preached to the king like a locust crying:

KING DAVID

"Hearken awhile to a doleful thing!
There were two men in thy land, O King!

"One was rich as a gilded ram.
One had one treasure, a poor ewe-lamb.

"Rich man wasted his wealth like spittle.　　　　　130
Poor man shared with his lamb spare victual.

"A traveler came to the rich man's door.
'Give me to eat, for I hunger sore!'

"Rich man feasted him fatly, true,
But the meat that he gave him was fiend's meat, too,
Stolen and roasted, the poor man's ewe!

"Hearken, my lord, to a deadly thing!
What shall be done with these men, O King?"

David hearkened, seeing it plain,
His heart grew heavy with angry pain:　　　　　140
"Show me the rich man that he be slain!"

Nathan barked as a jackal can.
"Just, O King! And thou art the man!"

David rose as the thunders rise
When someone in Heaven is telling lies.
But his eyes were weaker than Nathan's eyes.

His huge bulk shivered like quaking sod,
Shoulders bowing to Nathan's rod,
Nathan, the bitter apple of God.

His great voice shook like a runner's, spent,　　　　　150
"My sin has found me! Oh, I repent!"

Answered Nathan, that talkative Jew:
"For many great services, comely and true,
The Lord of Mercy will pardon you.

"But the child in Bathsheba, come of your seed,
Shall sicken and die like a blasted weed."

David groaned when he heard him speak.
The painful tears ran hot on his cheek.

Ashes he cast on his kingly locks.
All night long he lay on the rocks.   160

Beseeching his Lord with a howling cry:
"O Lord God, O my jealous God,
Be kind to the child that it may not die,
For Thou art King above all gods!"

6

Seven long nights he lay there, howling,
A lion wounded, moaning and growling.

Seven long midnights, sorrowing greatly,
While Sin, like a dead man, embraced him straitly.

Till he was abased from his lust and pride
And the child was born and sickened and died.   170

He arose at last. It was ruddy Day.
And his sin like water had washed away.

He cleansed and anointed, took fresh apparel,
And worshiped the Lord in a tuneful carol.

His servants, bearing the child to bury,
Marveled greatly to see him so merry.

He spoke to them mildly as mid-May weather:
"The child and my sin are perished together.

"He is dead, my son. Though his whole soul yearn to me,
I must go to him, he may not return to me.   180

"Why should I sorrow for what was pain?
A cherished grief is an iron chain."

He took up his harp, the sage old chief.
His heart felt clean as a new green leaf.

His soul smelt pleasant as rain-wet clover.
"I have sinned and repented and that's all over.

"In his dealings with heathen, the Lord is hard.
But the humble soul is his spikenard."

His wise thoughts fluttered like doves in the air.
"I wonder is Bathsheba still so fair?   190

"Does she weep for the child that our sin made perish?
I must comfort my ewe-lamb, comfort and cherish.

"The justice of God is honey and balm.
I will soothe her heart with a little psalm."

He went to her chamber, no longer sad,
Walking as light as a shepherd lad.

He found her weeping, her garments rent,
Trodden like straw by God's punishment.
He solaced her out of his great content.

Being but woman, a while she grieved,   200
But at last she was comforted, and conceived.

Nine months later she bore him a son.
(The Lord God is a mighty God!)
The name of that child was SOLOMON.
He was God's tough staff till his days were run!
(And the Lord is King above all gods!)

THE RETORT DISCOURTEOUS

(Italy—16th Century)

But what, by the fur on your satin sleeves,
The rain that drags at my feather
And the great Mercurius, god of thieves,
Are we thieves doing together?

Last night your blades bit deep for their hire,
And we were the sickled barley.
To-night, atoast by the common fire,
You ask me to join your parley.

Your spears are shining like Iceland spar,
The blood-grapes drip for your drinking;
For you folk follow the rising star,
I follow the star that's sinking!

My queen is old as the frosted whins,
Nay, how could her wrinkles charm me?
And the starving bones are bursting the skins
In the ranks of her ancient army.

You marshal a steel-and-silken troop,
Your cressets are fed with spices,
And you batter the world like a rolling hoop
To the goal of your proud devices.

I have rocked your thrones—but your fight is won.
To-night, as the highest bidder,
You offer a share of your brigand-sun,
Consider, old bull, consider!

Ahead, red Death and the Fear of Death,
Your vultures, stoop to the slaughter.

But I shall fight you, body and breath,
Till my life runs out like water!

My queen is wan as the Polar snows.
Her host is a rout of specters.
But I gave her Youth like a burning rose,
And her age shall not lack protectors!

I would not turn for the thunderclap
Or the face of the woman who bore me,
With her battered badge still scarring my cap,
And the drums of defeat before me.

Roll your hands in the honey of life,
Kneel to your white-necked strumpets!
You came to your crowns with a squealing fife
But I shall go out with trumpets!

Poison the steel of the plunging dart,
Holloa your hounds to their station!
I march to my ruin with such a heart
As a king to his coronation.

Your poets roar of your golden feats—
I have herded the stars like cattle.
And you may die in the perfumed sheets,
But I shall die in battle.

SOUTHERN SHIPS AND SETTLERS

1606-1732

O, where are you going, "Goodspeed" and "Discovery"?
With meek "Susan Constant" to make up the three?
We're going to settle the wilds of Virginia,
For gold and adventure we're crossing the sea.

And what will you find there? Starvation and fever.
We'll eat of the adder and quarrel and rail.
All but sixty shall die of the first seven hundred,
But a nation begins with the voyage we sail.

O, what are you doing, my handsome Lord Baltimore?
Where are you sending your "Ark" and your "Dove"?
I'm sending them over the ocean to Maryland
To build up a refuge for people I love.

Both Catholic and Protestant there may find harbor,
Though I am a Catholic by creed and by prayer.
The South is Virginia, the North is New England.
I'll go in the middle and plant my folk there.

O, what do you seek, "Carolina" and "Albemarle",
Now the Stuarts are up and the Roundheads are down?
We'll seek and we'll find, to the South of Virginia,
A site by two rivers and name it Charles Town.

And, in South Carolina, the cockfighting planters
Will dance with their belles by a tropical star.
And, in North Carolina, the sturdy Scotch-Irish
Will prove at King's Mountain the metal they are.

O, what are you dreaming, cock-hatted James Oglethorpe?
And who are the people you take in the "Anne"?
They're poor English debtors whom hard laws imprison,
And poor, distressed Protestants, fleeing a ban.

I'll settle them pleasantly on the Savannah,
With Germans and Highlanders, thrifty and strong.
They shall eat Georgia peaches in huts of palmetto,
And their land shall be fertile, their days shall be long.

All
We're the barques and the sailors, the bread on the waters,
The seed that was planted and grew to be tall,

And the South was first won by our toils and our dangers,
So remember our journeys. Remember us all.

CAPTAIN KIDD

1650?-1701

This person in the gaudy clothes
Is worthy Captain Kidd.
They say he never buried gold.
I think, perhaps, he did.

They say it's all a story that
His favorite little song
Was "Make these lubbers walk the plank!"
I think, perhaps, they're wrong.

They say he never pirated
Beneath the Skull-and-Bones.
He merely traveled for his health
And spoke in soothing tones.
In fact, you'll read in nearly all
The newer history books
That he was mild as cottage cheese
—But I don't like his looks!

FRENCH PIONEERS

1534-1759

New France, New Spain, New England,
Which will it be?
Who will win the new land?
The land across the sea?

They came here, they toiled here,
They broke their hearts afar,

Normandy and Brittany,
Paris and Navarre.

They lost here, at last here,
It wasn't so to be.
Let us still remember them,
Men from oversea.

Marquette and Joliet,
Cartier, La Salle,
Priest, corsair, gentleman,
Gallants one and all.

France was in their quick words,
France was in their veins.
They came here, they toiled here.
They suffered many pains.

Lake and river, stream and wood,
Seigneurs and dames—
They lived here, they died here,
They left singing names.

THOMAS JEFFERSON

1743-1826

Thomas Jefferson,
What do you say
Under the gravestone
Hidden away?

"I was a giver,
I was a molder,
I was a builder
With a strong shoulder."

Six feet and over,
Large-boned and ruddy,
The eyes grey-hazel
But bright with study.

The big hands clever
With pen and fiddle
And ready, ever,
For any riddle.

From buying empires
To planting 'taters,
From Declarations
To trick dumb-waiters.

"I liked the people,
The sweat and crowd of them,
Trusted them always
And spoke aloud of them.

"I liked all learning
And wished to share it
Abroad like pollen
For all who merit.

"I liked fine houses
With Greek pilasters,
And built them surely,
My touch a master's.

"I liked queer gadgets
And secret shelves,
And helping nations
To rule themselves.

"Jealous of others?
Not always candid?
But huge of vision
And open-handed.

"A wild-goose-chaser?
Now and again,
Build Monticello,
You little men!

"Design my plow, sirs,
They use it still,
Or found my college
At Charlottesville.

"And still go questing
New things and thinkers,
And keep as busy
As twenty tinkers.

"While always guarding
The people's freedom—
You need more hands, sir?
I didn't need 'em.

"They call you rascal?
They called me worse.
You'd do grand things, sir,
But lack the purse?

"I got no riches.
I died a debtor.
I died free-hearted
And that was better.

"For life was freakish
But life was fervent,
And I was always
Life's willing servant.

"Life, life's too weighty?
Too long a haul, sir?
I lived past eighty.
I liked it all, sir."

JOHN JAMES AUDUBON

1780-1851

Some men live for warlike deeds,
Some for women's words.
John James Audubon
Lived to look at birds.

Pretty birds and funny birds,
All our native fowl
From the little cedar waxwing
To the Great Horned Owl.

Let the wind blow hot or cold,
Let it rain or snow,
Everywhere the birds went
Audubon would go.

Scrambling through a wilderness,
Floating down a stream,
All around America
In a feathered dream.

Thirty years of traveling,
Pockets often bare,
(Lucy Bakewell Audubon
Patched them up with care).

Followed grebe and meadowlark,
Saw them sing and splash.
(Lucy Bakewell Audubon
Somehow raised the cash).

Drew them all the way they lived
In their habitats.
(Lucy Bakewell Audubon
Sometimes wondered "Cats?")

Colored them and printed them
In a giant book,
"Birds of North America"—
All the world said, "Look!"

Gave him medals and degrees,
Called him noble names,
—Lucy Bakewell Audubon
Kissed her queer John James.

DANIEL BOONE

1735-1820

When Daniel Boone goes by, at night,
The phantom deer arise
And all lost, wild America
Is burning in their eyes.

WESTERN WAGONS

They went with axe and rifle, when the trail was still to blaze,
They went with wife and children, in the prairie-schooner days,
With banjo and with frying pan—Susanna, don't you cry!
For I'm off to California to get rich out there or die!

We've broken land and cleared it, but we're tired of where we are.
They say that wild Nebraska is a better place by far.
There's gold in far Wyoming, there's black earth in Ioway,
So pack up the kids and blankets, for we're moving out today!

The cowards never started and the weak died on the road,
And all across the continent the endless campfires glowed.
We'd taken land and settled—but a traveler passed by—
And we're going West tomorrow—Lordy, never ask us why!

We're going West tomorrow, where the promises can't fail.
O'er the hills in legions, boys, and crowd the dusty trail!
We shall starve and freeze and suffer. We shall die, and tame
 the lands.
But we're going West tomorrow, with our fortune in our hands.

TWO

Young Adventure

8:30 A.M. ON 32ND STREET

*The wind sniffed like a happy cat
At scuttling beetle-people,
The sunshine would have roused a flat
To try and be a steeple.*

*My breakfast in me warm and staunch,
Your letter in my pocket,
The world's a coon that's climbed a branch
And I am David Crockett.*

Time hoards our lives with griping care
And barren is his bursary,
But he'll make diamonds of the air
Upon one anniversary!

Five years ago I saw you first
And knew in every part
The flagrant and immortal thirst
Love salts into the heart.

Five years ago the Pleiad crew
Sang in their starry hive,

Because a miracle like you
Could dare to be alive!

Five years, and still, through earth's degrees
You, like a pageant, pass;
Courageous as invading seas
And careless as the grass.

Pauper poets of rimes grown thin
Mutter their madhouse wrongs.
I have aeons to love you in,
Ages to make you songs!

Pour your rain on the bitter tree!
Harrow the soil with spears!
I shall grow you Felicity,
After a million years!

The street-signs winked like signs at me,
The wind pawed by enchanted!
The sun swung high for all to see
I'd stop him if I wanted!

MORTUARY PARLORS

The smooth, unobtrusive walls say "Hush!" in a voice of honey and meal,
The refined and comforting chairs protest that sorrow may be genteel,
They are all hiding the dead away, they are huddling them off to forget . . .
—I would rather scoop a hole in the sand till my hands ran blood and sweat,
I would rather raise my friend on a pyre for the lightning to do its will,
I would sooner leave my dead to the dogs—they are happy over their kill—

Than to bring them here to this oily place to lie like a numbered sheaf!
—This servants' quiet can have no room for my racked and horrible grief—
The windows smile with the smiles of masks, the curtains are specters walking,
And Death, the obsequious gentleman, comes rubbing black gloves and talking!

GHOSTS OF A LUNATIC ASYLUM

Here, where men's eyes were empty and as bright
As the blank windows set in glaring brick,
When the wind strengthens from the sea—and night
Drops like a fog and makes the breath come thick;

By the deserted paths, the vacant halls,
One may see figures, twisted shades and lean,
Like the mad shapes that crawl an Indian screen,
Or paunchy smears you find on prison walls.

Turn the knob gently! There's the Thumbless Man,
Still weaving glass and silk into a dream,
Although the wall shows through him—and the Khan
Journeys Cathay beside a paper stream.

A Rabbit Woman chitters by the door—
—Chilly the grave-smell comes from the turned sod—
Come—lift the curtain—and be cold before
The silence of the eight men who were God!

FOR ALL BLASPHEMERS

Adam was my grandfather,
A tall, spoiled child,
A red, clay tower
In Eden, green and mild.

He ripped the Sinful Pippin
From its sanctimonious limb.
Adam was my grandfather—
And I take after him.

Noah was my uncle
And he got dead drunk.
There were planets in his liquor-can
And lizards in his bunk.
He fell into the Bottomless
Past Hell's most shrinking star.
Old Aunt Fate has often said
How much alike we are.

Lilith, she's my sweetheart
Till my heartstrings break,
Most of her is honey-pale
And all of her is snake.
Sweet as secret thievery,
I kiss her all I can,
While Somebody Above remarks
"That's not a nice young man!"

Bacchus was my brother,
Nimrod is my friend.
All of them have talked to me
On how such courses end.
But when His Worship takes me up
How can I fare but well?
For who in gaudy Hell will care?
—And I shall be in Hell.

ARCHITECTS

My son has built a fortified house
To keep his pride from the thunder,
And his steadfast heart from the gnawing mouse
That nibbles the roots of wonder.

My daughter's wit has hammered and filed
Her slight and glittering armor.
She hides in its rings like a dragon-child,
And nothing on earth can harm her.

My wife has molded a coffin of lead
From the counterfeit tears of mourners.
She rests in it, calm as a saint long dead,
And the Four Winds kneel at its corners.

I have scooped my den with a crafty thumb
In the guts of an arid acre.
And it may not last till Kingdom Come
—But it will not cripple its maker.

It is six feet long by three feet deep
And some may call it narrow.
But, when I get into it, I can keep
The nakedness of an arrow.

TALK

New words are my desire, new verbs to scan,
Chaste paradigms that never sold themselves,
And adverbs from the leaf-talk of the elves,
With dog-faced articles, unknown to man;
Low-pattered syllables that trot like sheep
Round out my mouth and mind with holy peace,
And I have found redemption and surcease
In Babylonian nouns like bulls asleep.

Who can be hopeless saying "Bethmacoon"?
"Aleery" is an opiate for all pain.
—And I shall swim beneath the Idiot's Moon,
And climb the crags that tower in my brain
To feel the kreeth of Morning touch my lips,
Where Ocean plays with his smaranthian ships.

THE GOLDEN CORPSE

(*Eight Sonnets for Donald Malcolm Campbell*)

Stripped country, shrunken as a beggar's heart,
Inviolate landscape, hardened into steel,
Where the cold soil shatters under heel
Day after day like armor cracked apart.

Winter Connecticut, whose air is clean
As a new icicle to cut the throat,
Whose black and rigid trees will not demean
Themselves to swagger in a crystal coat.

I hate you as a bastard hates his name
When your cramped hills are hostile with the white,
But, every year, when March comes in the same,
A frozen river rolling in the night,

I must go back and hunt among your snow
Something I lost there, much too long ago.

2

It was not innocence, it was not scorn,
And yet it had these names and many more.
It was a champion blowing on a horn,
It was the running of a golden boar.

It was a stallion, trampling the skies
To rags of lightning with his glittering shoes,
It was a childish god with lazy eyes,
It was an indolent and reckless Muse.

More than all these, it was a spirit apart,
Purely of fire and air and the mind.
No fear could eat the temper from its heart
Nor any fleshly bandage make it blind.

It was a silver dagger in the blast.
It was the first of youth, and it has passed.

3

I left it in a bare and windy street
Between two sets of bells whose casual chimes
Answer each other, janglingly and sweet,
Like the concord of long-repeated rhymes.

I left it in a since-demolished bar,
And underneath a rain-streaked paving-stone.
And, men and things being what they are,
The hidden ghost had better couch alone.

I shall not rattle with an iron fist
The relics, scattered into sticks of chalk,
Of what was once the carcass of a hawk
That sat like Wrath on an archangel's wrist.

Nor disinter, to make my house look smart,
That thunder-broken and ferocious heart.

4

Men that dig up a mandrake know dis-ease.
This body is committed to its bones
Down where the taproots of New England trees
Suck bare existence from the broken stones.

All summer cannot quicken it with heat,
Nor Spring perturb it with a budding bough,
Nor all the glittering devils of the sleet
In snowing Winter rack its quiet now.

But, in October, when the apples fall,
And leaves begin to rust before the cold,

THE GOLDEN CORPSE

There may occur, by some unnoticed wall,
A sigh, a whisper in the rotten gold.

A breath that hardly can be called a breath
From Death that will not yet acknowledge Death.

5

Unnoticed—for the years have hardier tasks
Than listening to a whisper or a sigh.
They creep among us with a bag of masks
And fit them to our brows obsequiously.

Some are of iron, to affront the gay,
And some of bronze, to satirize the brave,
But most are merely a compost of clay
Cut in the sleepy features of a slave.

With such astuteness do they counterfeit,
We do not realize the masks are on
Till, gaudy in our folly, bit by bit
We notice that a neighbor's face seems drawn.

And then, with fingers turned to lumps of stone,
Touch the inhuman cast that was our own.

6

There is no doubt such workmanship is sage.
The bound and ordered skies could not abide
A creature formed of elemental rage
For longer than a moment of its pride.

The hand that stooped to Adam from the cloud
And touched his members with a fiery spine
Designed as well the pattern of the shroud
That should convince him he was not divine.

And there are sorceries more excellent
Than the first conflagration of the dust,
But none are quite so single in intent
Or unsophisticated with distrust.

The ripened fruit is golden to the core
But an enchantment fosters it no more.

7

Therefore, in neither anguish nor relief,
I offer to the shadow in the air
No image of a monumental grief
To mock its transience from a stony chair,

Nor any tablets edged in rusty black.
Only a branch of maple, gathered high
When the crisp air first tastes of applejack,
And the blue smokes of Autumn stain the sky.

A branch whose leaves cling to the withering staff
Like precious toys of gilt and scarlet paint,
An emblem Life and Death share half-and-half,
A brittle sceptre for a dying saint.

Unburning fire, an insubstantial Host,
A violence dreamt, a beauty of the ghost.

8

So much in memory. For the future, this.
The checkerboarded house of Day and Night
Is but a cavern where a swallow flies
To beat its wings an instant at the light

And then depart, where the incessant storm
Shepherds the planets like a drunken nurse.
It does not need an everlasting form
To dignify an ecstasy so terse.

But while the swallow fluttered and was quick
I have marked down its passage in the dark
And charred its image on a broken stick
With the brief flame of an uncertain spark.

The fire can have it now, the rain can rain on it,
And the ice harden like a god's disdain on it.

THREE

My Fair Lady

TO ROSEMARY

*If you were gone afar,
And lost the pattern
Of all your delightful ways,
And the web undone,
How would one make you anew,
From what dew and flowers,
What burning and mingled atoms,
Under the sun?*

*Not from too-satin roses,
Or those rare blossoms,
Orchids, scentless and precious
As precious stone.
But out of lemon-verbena,
Rose-geranium,
These alone.*

*Not with running horses,
Or Spanish cannon,
Organs, voiced like a lion,
Clamor and speed.
But perhaps with old music-boxes,*

Young, tawny kittens,
Wild-strawberry-seed.

Even so, it were more
Than a god could compass
To fashion the body merely,
The lovely shroud.
But then—ah, how to recapture
That evanescence,
The fire that cried in pure crystal
Out of its cloud!

NOMENCLATURE

Some people have names like pitchforks, some people have names like cakes,
Names full of sizzling esses like a family quarrel of snakes,
Names black as a cat, vermilion as the cockscomb-hat of a fool—
But your name is a green, small garden, a rush asleep in a pool.

When God looked at the diffident cherubs and dropped them out of the sky,
He named them like Adam's animals, while Mary and Eve stood by,
The poor things huddled before him in scared little naked flocks
—And he gave you a name like sunlight, and clover, and hollyhocks.

For your mouth with its puzzled jesting, for your hair like a dark soft bird,
Shy humor and dainty walking, sweet laughter and subtle word,
As a fairy walks with a mushroom to keep the rain from its things
You carry your name forever, like a scepter alive with wings.

Neither change nor despair shall touch it nor the seasons make it uncouth,
It will burn like an Autumn maple when your proud age talks to your youth,

Wise child, clean friend, adoration, light arrow of God, white flame,
I would break my body to pieces to call you once by your name!

DIFFERENCE

My mind's a map. A mad sea-captain drew it
Under a flowing moon until he knew it;
Winds with brass trumpets, puffy-cheeked as jugs,
And states bright-patterned like Arabian rugs.
"Here there be tygers." "Here we buried Jim."
Here is the strait where eyeless fishes swim
About their buried idol, drowned so cold
He weeps away his eyes in salt and gold.
A country like the dark side of the moon,
A cider-apple country, harsh and boon,
A country savage as a chestnut-rind,
A land of hungry sorcerers.

       Your mind?

—Your mind is water through an April night,
A cherry-branch, plume-feathery with its white,
A lavender as fragrant as your words,
A room where Peace and Honor talk like birds,
Sewing bright coins upon the tragic cloth
Of heavy Fate, and Mockery, like a moth,
Flutters and beats about those lovely things.
You are the soul, enchanted with its wings,
The single voice that raises up the dead
To shake the pride of angels.

       I have said.

A SAD SONG

Rosemary, Rosemary,
Rosemary, Rosemary,
There's a Pig in your garden,

*With silk bristles frizzy
And tushes of snow!*
But Rosemary was cautious,
She said, "Beg your pardon!
I'm really too busy
To look down below."

*Rosemary, Rosemary,
There's a Bird in your kitchen!
His voice is gold water,
He says, "Pretty Poll!"*
But Rosemary heard nothing,
Putting stitch after stitch in
The dress of a daughter,
Her thirty-sixth doll.

*Rosemary, Rosemary,
A silver-winged Rabbit!
He bridles and gentles
And wants you astride!*
"I prefer," said Rosemary,
"To ride a Good Habit."
She went buying black lentils—
She did till she died.

A NONSENSE SONG

Rosemary, Rosemary, let down your hair!
The cow's in the hammock, the crow's in the chair!
I was making you songs out of sawdust and silk,
But they came in to call and they split them like milk.

The cat's in the coffee, the wind's in the east,
He screams like a peacock and whines like a priest
And the saw of his voice makes my blood turn to mice—
So let down your long hair and shut off his advice!

Pluck out the thin hairpins and let the waves stream,
Brown-gold as brook-waters that dance through a dream,
Gentle-curled as young cloudlings, sweet-fragrant as bay,
Till it takes all the fierceness of living away.

Oh, when you are with me, my heart is white steel.
But the bat's in the belfry, the mold's in the meal,
And I think I hear skeletons climbing the stair!
—Rosemary, Rosemary, let down your bright hair!

TO ROSEMARY, ON THE METHODS BY WHICH SHE MIGHT BECOME AN ANGEL

Not where the sober sisters, grave as willows,
Walk like old twilights by the jasper sea,
Nor where the plump hunt of cherubs holly-hilloes
Chasing their ruddy fox, the sun, you'll be!

Not with the stained-glass prophets, bearded grimly,
Not with the fledgling saved, meek Wisdom's lot,
Kissing a silver book that glimmers dimly,
For acolytes are mild and you are not.

They'll give you a curled tuba, tall as Rumor,
They'll sit you on a puff of Autumn cloud,
Gilded-fantastic as your scorn and humor
And let you blow that tuba much too loud.

Against the unceasing chant to sinless Zion,
Three impudent seraph notes, three starry coals,
Sweet as wild grass and happy as a lion
—And all the saints will throw you aureoles.

LEGEND

The trees were sugared like wedding-cake
With a bright hoar frost, with a very cold snow,
When we went begging for Jesus' sake,
Penniless children, years ago.

Diamond weather—but nothing to eat
In that fine, bleak bubble of earth and skies.
Nothing alive in the windy street
But two young children with hungry eyes.

"We must go begging or we will die.
I would sell my soul for an apple-core!"
So we went mendicant, you and I,
Knock-knock-knock at each snow-choked door.

Knock-knock-knock till our fingers froze.
Nobody even replied, "Good day!",
Only the magistrate, toasting his toes,
Howled at us sleepily, "Go away!"

"Rosemary dear, what shall we do?"
"Stephen, I know not. Beseech some saint!
My nose has turned to an icicle blue,
And my belly within me is very faint."

"If there be saints, they are fast asleep,
Lounging in Heaven, in wraps of feather."
"Talk not so, or my eyes will weep
Till the ice-tears rattle and clink together."

"Saints are many—on which shall I call?
He must be kindly, without constraint."
"I think you had better pray to Saint Paul.
I have heard people call him a neighborly saint."

Down he flopped on his cold, bare knees
—Breath that smoked in the bitter air—
Crossing his body with hands afreeze,
He sought Saint Paul in a vehement prayer.

Scarce had these shiverers piped, "Amen,"
Cheeping like fledglings, crying for bread,
When good Saint Paul appeared to them then,
With a wide gold halo around his head.

He waved his episcopal hand, and smiled,
And the ground was spread like a banquet-table!
"Here is much good food for each hungry child,
And I hope you will eat as long as you're able.

"Here are good, thick cloaks for your ragged backs,
And strong, warm boots for your feet," said he,
"And for Stephen, gloves and a little axe,
And a little fur muff for Rosemary."

They thanked him humbly, saying a Pater,
Before they had touched a morsel even,
But he said, "Your thanks are for One far greater"
And pointed his right arm up at Heaven.

"For you are the sparrows around God's door,
He will lift you up like His own great banner.
But the folk who made you suffer so sore—
He shall deal with them in another manner.

"It is His own will to transport those folk
To a region of infinite ice and snow."
And his breath was a taper of incense-smoke,
And he lifted a finger—and it was so.

And the folk were gone—and the saint was fled—
And we stared and stared at the wintry land.
And in front of us there was a banquet spread.
And a little fur muff on Rosemary's hand.

DULCE RIDENTEM

The bee, he has white honey,
The Sunday child her muff,
The rich man lots of money
Though never quite enough,
The apple has a Springtime smell,
The star-fields silver grain,
But I have youth, the cockleshell,
And the sweet laugh of Jane.

The lark's tune goes so clearly
But Jane's is clear wells.
The cuckoo's voice currs cheerly,
But Jane's is new bells.
Whether she chuckles like a dove,
Or laughs like April rain,
It is her heart and hands and love,
The moth-wing soul of Jane.

ILLA

This is only the shadow of what she was once;
The rest is Honor's.
Nevertheless, O Death, be humble in claiming
Even that shadow.

HANDS

My wife's hands are long and thin,
Fit to catch a spirit in,
Fit to set a subtle snare
For something lighter than the air.

My brother's hands are long and fine,
Good at verse and pouring wine,
Good to spend and bad to hoard
And good to hold a singing sword.

My own hands are short and blunt
Being children of affront,
Base mechanics at the most
That have sometimes touched a ghost.

I ask between the running sands,
A blessing upon four hands,
And for mine an iron stake
They can do their best to break.

Now God the Son and God the Sire
And God the triple-handed fire,
Make these blessings come to be
Out of your civility
For four hands of courtesy.

                              Amen.

MEMORY

They can have the names and the dates,
It will do them little service.
They can open the locked chest
And steal the wine and the gold.
There is nothing to be said
But this—the clasp of her body
Was better than milk to the child
Or wisdom to the old.

We die with our first breath.
And, if we die, what matter?
There was a ghost in the flesh,
A ghost that went and came.
Though the moon burn like a lamp

It will not be that brightness—
I said her name in my sleep,
Waking, I said her name.

MEMENTO MORI

FOR US

In the long bed of Time so straitly lying,
Like angels on a shield—
What is this petty artifice called dying?
And when is it revealed?

THIRTY-FIVE

The sun was hot, the day was bright,
And all July was overhead.
I heard the locust first that night.
"Six weeks till frost," it said.

FOR YOU

Sleep in the dust beside me, you
Who never said a faithless word
Or gave a kiss that was not true
No matter how the dust was stirred.

FOUR

Nightmares and Visitants

NOTES TO BE LEFT IN
A CORNERSTONE

This is for you who are to come, with Time,
And gaze upon our ruins with strange eyes.

So, always, there were the streets and the high, clear light
And it was a crowded island and a great city;
They built high up in the air.

I have gone to the museum and seen the pictures.

And yet shall not know this body. It was other;
Though the first sight from the water was even so,
The huge blocks piled, the giants standing together,
Noble with plane and mass and the squareness of stone,
The buildings that had skeletons like a man
And nerves of wire in their bodies, the skyscrapers,
Standing their island, looking toward the sea.
But the maps and the models will not be the same.
They cannot restore that beauty, rapid and harsh,
That loneliness, that passion or that name.

NOTES TO BE LEFT IN A CORNERSTONE

Yet the films were taken?
                    Most carefully and well,
But the skin is not the life but over the life.
The live thing was a different beast, in its time,
And sometimes, in the fall, very fair, like a knife sharpened
On stone and sun and blue shadow. That was the time
When girls in red hats rode down the Avenue
On the tops of busses, their faces bright with the wind,
And the year began again with the first cool days.
All places in that country are fair in the fall.

You speak as if the year began with the fall.

It was so. It began then, not with the calendar.
It was an odd city. The fall brought us new life,
Though there was no festival set and we did not talk of it.

That seems to me strange.
                    It was not strange, in that city.
We had four seasons: the fall of the quick, brief steps
Ringing on stone and the thick crowds walking fast,
The clear sky, the rag of sunset beyond great buildings,
The bronze flower, the resurrection of the year.
The squirrels ran in the dry Park, burying nuts.
The boys came from far places with cardboard suitcases.
It is hard to describe, but the lights looked gay at night then
And everything old and used had been put away.
There were cheap new clothes for the clerks and the clerks' women.
There was frost in the blood and anything could begin.
The shops were slices of honeycomb full of honey,
Full of the new, glassed honey of the year.
It seemed a pity to die then, a great pity.
The great beast glittered like sea-water in the sun,
His heart beating, his lungs full of air and pride,
And the strong shadow cutting the golden towers.

Then the cold fell, and the winter, with grimy snow,
With the overcoatless men with the purple hands
Walking between two signboards in the street

And the sign on their backs said "Winter" and the soiled
    papers
Blew fretfully up and down and froze in the ice
As the lukewarm air blew up from the grated holes.
This lasted a long time, till the skin was dry
And the cheeks hot with the fever and the cough sharp.
On the cold days, the cops had faces like blue meat,
And then there was snow and pure snow and tons of snow
And the whole noise stopping, marvellously and slowly,
Till you could hear the shovels scarping the stone,
Scritch-scratch, scritch-scratch, like the digging of iron mice.
Nothing else but that sound, and the air most pure,
Most pure, most fragrant and most innocent,
And, next day, the boys made dirty balls of the snow.

This season lasted so long we were weary of it.
We were very weary indeed when the spring came to us.
And it came.
I do not know how even yet, but there was a turning,
A change, a melting, a difference, a new smell
Though not that of any flower.
                          It came from both
On a market truck, a girl in a yellow hat
Rivers, I think, or across them. It sneaked in
With a pinched, live face and a bunch of ten-cent narcissus
And the sky was soft and it was easy to dream.
You could count the spring on your fingers, but it came.
Ah, brief it was in that city, but good for love!
The boys got their stick-bats out then, the youths and girls
Talked hoarsely under street lamps, late in the night.

And then it was tiger-summer and the first heat,
The first thunder, the first black pile of aching cloud,
The big warm drops of rain that spatter the dust
And the ripping cloth of lightning.
                          Those were the hot
Nights when the poor lay out on the fire-escapes
And the child cried thinly and endlessly. Many streets
Woke very late in the night, then.

And barbarously the negro night bestrode
The city with great gold rings in his ears
And his strong body glistening with heat.
He had, I think, a phial in one hand
And from it took a syringe, dry as dust,
To dope tired bodies with uneasy sleep.
The backs of my hands are sweating with that sleep
And I have lain awake in the hot bed
And heard the fierce, brief storm bring the relief,
The little coolness, the water on the tongue,
The new wind from the river, dear as rain.

I have not studied the weather-reports intensively.
Should I do so?
                    You will not get it from weather-reports.
There was the drunkard's city and the milkman's,
The city of the starving and the fed,
The city of the night-nurse and the scrubbed wall.
All these locked into each other like sliding rings
And a man, in his time, might inhabit one of them
Or many, as his fate took him, but always, always,
There were the blocks of stone and the windows gazing
And the breath that did not stop. It was never quite still.
You could always hear some sound, though you forgot it,
And the sound entered the flesh and was part of it.

It was high but no one planned it to be so high.
They did not think, when they built so. They did not say,
"This will make life better, this is due to the god,
This will be good to live in." They said "Build!"
And dug steel into the rocks.
                          They were a race
Most nervous, energetic, swift and wasteful,
And maddened by the dry and beautiful light
Although not knowing their madness.
                            So they built
Not as men before but as demons under a whip
And the light was a whip and a sword and a spurning heel
And the light wore out their hearts and they died praising it.

And for money and the lack of it many died,
Leaping from windows or crushed by the big truck.
They shot themselves in washrooms because of money.
They were starved and died on the benches of subway-stations,
The old men, with the caved cheeks, yellow as lard,
The men with the terrible shoes and the open hands,
The eyeing and timid crowd about them gathered.
Yet it is not just to say money was all their god
Nor just to say that machine was all their god.
It is not just to say any one thing about them.
They built the thing very high, far over their heads.
Because of it, they gave up air, earth and stars.

Will you tell me about the people, if you please?

They are all gone, the workers on the high steel,
The best of their kind, cat-footed, walking on space,
The arcs of the red-hot rivet in the air;
They are gone with the empty, arrogant women of price,
The evening women, curried till their flesh shone;
With the big, pale baker, the flour in his creases,
Coming up to breathe from his hell on a summer night;
They are gone as if they were not.
The blue-chinned men of the hotel-lobbies are gone,
Though they sat like gods in their chairs;
Night-watchmen and cleaning-women and millionaires;
The maimed boy, clean and legless and always sitting
On his small, wheeled platform, by the feet of the crowd;
The sharp, sad newsmen, the hackers spinning their wheels;
The ardent, the shy, the brave;
The women who looked from mean windows, every day,
A pillow under their elbows, heavily staring;
They are gone, gone with the long cars and the short ones,
They have dropped as smoothly as coins through the slot of Time,
Mrs. Rausmeyer is gone and Mrs. Costello
And the girl at Goldstein & Brady's who had the hair.

Their lipsticks have made no mark on the evening sky.
It is long ago this all was. It is all forgotten.

And yet, you lie uneasy in the grave.

I cannot well lie easy in the grave.
All cities are the loneliness of man
And this was very lonely, in its time
(Sea-haunted, river-emblemed, O the grey
Water at ends of streets and the boats hooting!
The unbelievable, new, bright, girl moon!), 160
Most cruel also, but I walked it young,
Loved in it and knew night and day in it.
There was the height and the light. It was like no other.
When the gods come, tell them we built this out of steel,
Though men use steel no more.
And tell the man who tries to dig this dust,
He will forget his joy before his loneliness.

SHORT ODE

It is time to speak of these
Who took the long, strange journey overseas,
Who fell through the air in flames.
Their names are many. I will not name their names
Though some were people I knew;
After some years the ghost itself dies, too,
And that is my son's picture on the wall
But his girl has been long married and that is all.
They died in mud, they died in camps of the flu.
They are dead. Let us leave it so. 10
The ones I speak of were not forced, I know.
They were men of my age and country, they were young men
At Belleau, at the seaports, by the Aisne.
They went where their passion took them and are not.
They do not answer mockery or praise.

You may restore the days
They lived beneath and you may well restore
The painted image of that fabled war,
But not those faces, not the living ones
Drowned in the water, blown before the guns   20
In France or Belgium or the bitter sea
(And the foreign grave is far, and men use the name,
But they did not go for votes or the pay they got
Or the brave memorial speech by the D.A.R.)
It is far, the foreign grave. It is very far
And the time is not the same.
But certain things are true
Despite the time, and these were men that I knew,
Sat beside, walked beside,
In the first running of June, in the careless pride.   30
It is hard to think back, to find them, to see their eyes
And none born since shall see those, and the books are lies,
Being either praise or blame.
But they were in their first youth. It is not the same.
You, who are young, remember that youth dies.
Go, stranger, and to Lacedemon tell,
They were shot and rotted, they fell
Burning, on flimsy wings.
And yet it was their thought that they did well.
And yet there are still the tyrants and the kings.   40

DO YOU REMEMBER, SPRINGFIELD?

VACHEL LINDSAY, NOVEMBER 10, 1879—DECEMBER 5, 1931

The Illinois earth is black
(Do you remember, Springfield?)
The State is shaped like a heart,
Shaped like an arrowhead.

The black earth goes deep down.
(Do you remember, Springfield?)

Three feet under the plow
You can find the black earth still.

The towns settled, the woods
Fine in the spring and autumn,
The waters large and rolling,
The black earth ready to hand.

Surely this earth, this air
Should bear the prophet-singers,
Minstrels like colts unbroken,
Minstrels of leaves and corn.

Baltimore gave a stone,
A stone to another singer
(Do you remember, Springfield?)
But that was in years gone by.

A cat to tear at his breast
And a glass to work him madness,
That was the gift to Poe:
But things are different here.

There are votes here to be bought
And rich men here to buy them;
What more could a poet ask
Of the streets where Lincoln strode?

The Board of Health is superb.
The ladies watchful and cultured.
What more could a poet need
Or the heart of man desire?

Gather the leaves with rakes,
The burning autumn, Springfield,
Gather them in with rakes
Lest one of them turn to gold.

A leaf is only a leaf,
It is worth nothing, in Springfield.
It is worth as little as song,
Little as light and air.   40

Trap the lark in the corn,
Let it tell of your bounty, Springfield.
If you burn its eyes with a wire
It still will sing for a space.

A man is another affair.
We understand that, in Springfield.
If he sings, why, let him sing
As long as we need not hear.

He came with singing leaves;
It was really most unfortunate.   50
The Lindsays and the Frazees
Are sturdy pioneer stock.

He came with broncos and clouds
And the cornsilk of the moonlight.
It is not a usual thing
In Springfield, Illinois.

We will show his room and his book
For that brings trade to the city.
We try to use everything.
If you like, you can see his grave.   60

His mouth is stopped with earth,
The deep, black earth of Springfield.
He will not sing any more.
It is fine earth for the mute.

Let us give the Arts their due
And Lincoln a marble courthouse.

Both are respectably dead.
They need not trouble us, now.

Break the colts to the plow
And make them pull their hearts out. 70
Break the broncos of dancing
And sell them for bones and hide.

ODE TO WALT WHITMAN

MAY 31, 1819—MARCH 26, 1892

Now comes Fourth Month and the early buds on the trees.
By the roads of Long Island, the forsythia has flowered,
In the North, the cold will be breaking; even in Maine
The cold will be breaking soon; the young, bull-voiced freshets
Roar from green mountains, gorging the chilly brooks
With the brown, trout-feeding waters, the unlocked springs;
Now Mississippi stretches with the Spring rains. . . .

It is forty years and more,
The time of the ripeness and withering of a man,
Since you lay in the house in Camden and heard, at last, 10
The great, slow footstep, splashing the Third Month snow
In the little, commonplace street
—Town snow, already trampled and growing old,
Soot-flecked and dingy, patterned with passing feet,
The bullet-pocks of rain, the strong urine of horses,
The slashing, bright steel runners of small boys' sleds
Hitching on behind the fast cutters.
They dragged their sleds to the tops of the hills and yelled
The Indian yell of all boyhood, for pure joy
Of the cold and the last gold light and the swift rush down 20
Belly-flopping into darkness, into bedtime.
You saw them come home, late, hungry and burning-cheeked,
The boys and girls, the strong children,

Dusty with snow, their mittens wet with the silver drops of thawed snow.

All winter long, you had heard their sharp footsteps passing,
The skating crunch of their runners,
An old man, tied to a house, after many years,
An old man with his rivery, clean white hair,
His bright eyes, his majestic poverty,
His fresh pink skin like the first strawberry-bloom, 30
His innocent, large, easy old man's clothes
—Brown splotches on the hands of clean old men
At County Farms or sitting on warm park-benches
Like patient flies, talking of their good sons,
"Yes, my son's good to me"—
An old man, poor, without sons, waiting achingly
For spring to warm his lameness,
For spring to flourish,
And yet, when the eyes glowed, neither old nor tied.

All winter long there had been footsteps passing, 40
Steps of postmen and neighbors, quick steps of friends,
All winter long you had waited that great, snow-treading step,
The enemy, the vast comrade,
The step behind, in the wards, when the low lamp flickered
And the sick boy gasped for breath,
"Lean on me! Lean upon my shoulder! By God, you shall not die!"
The step ahead, on the long, wave-thundering beaches of Paumanok,
Invisible, printless, weighty,
The shape half-seen through the wet, sweet sea-fog of youth,
Night's angel and the dark Sea's, 50
The grand, remorseless treader,
Magnificent Death.

"Let me taste all, my flesh and my fat are sweet,
My body hardy as lilac, the strong flower.
I have tasted the calamus; I can taste the nightbane."

ODE TO WALT WHITMAN

Always the water about you since you were born,
The endless lapping of water, the strong motion,
The gulls by the ferries knew you, and the wild sea-birds,
The sandpiper, printing the beach with delicate prints.
At last, old, wheeled to the wharf, you still watched the
    water,
The tanned boys, flat-bodied, diving, the passage of ships,
The proud port, distant, the people, the work of harbors. . . .

"I have picked out a bit of hill with a southern exposure.
I like to be near the trees. I like to be near
The water-sound of the trees."

Now, all was the same in the cluttered, three-windowed room,
Low-ceiled, getting the sun like a schooner's cabin,
The crowding photos hiding the ugly wall-paper.
The floor-litter, the strong chair, timbered like a ship,
The hairy black-and-silver of the old wolfskin;
In the back-yard, neither lilac nor pear yet bloomed
But the branch of the lilac swelling with first sap;
And there, in the house, the figures, the nurse, the woman,
The passing doctor, the friends, the little clan,
The disciple with the notebook who's always there.

All these and the pain and the water-bed to ease you
And you said it rustled of oceans and were glad
And the pain shut and relaxed and shut once more.

"Old body, counsellor, why do you thus torment me?
Have we not been friends from our youth?"

But now it came,
Slow, perceived by no others,
The splashing step through the grey, soft, Saturday rain,
Inexorable footstep of the huge friend.
"Are you there at last, fine enemy?
Ah, haste, friend, hasten, come closer!
Breathe upon me with your grave, your releasing lips!

I have heard and spoken; watched the bodies of boys
Flash in the copper sun and dive to green waters,
Seen the fine ships and the strong matrons and the tall
    axemen, 90
The young girls, free, athletic; the drunkard, retching
In his poor dream; the thief taken by officers;
The President, calm, grave, advising the nation;
The infant, with milk-wet lips in his bee-like slumber.
They are mine; all, all are mine; must I leave them, truly?
I have cherished them in my veins like milk and fruit.
I have warmed them at my bare breast like the eggs of pigeons.
The great plains of the buffalo are mine, the towns, the hills, the
    ship-bearing waters.
These States are my wandering sons.
I had them in my youth; I cannot desert them. 100
The green leaf of America is printed on my heart forever."

Now it entered the house, it marched upon the stair.
By the bedside the faces dimmed, the huge shoulder blotting
    them,
—It is so they die on the plains, the great, old buffalo,
The herd-leaders, the beasts with the kingly eyes,
Innocent, curly-browed,
They sink to the earth like mountains, hairy and silent,
And their tongues are cut by the hunter.

                        Oh, singing tongue!
Great tongue of bronze and salt and the free grasses,
Tongue of America, speaking for the first time, 110
Must the hunter have you at last?

Now, face to face, you saw him
And lifted the right arm once, as a pilot lifts it,
Signalling with the bell,
In the passage at night, on the river known yet unknown,
—Perhaps to touch his shoulder, perhaps in pain—
Then the rain fell on the roof and the twilight darkened
And they said that in death you looked like a marvelous old, wise
    child.

2

It is Fourth Month now and spring in another century,
Let us go to the hillside and ask; he will like to hear us;   120
"Is it good, the sleep?"

"It is good, the sleep and the waking.
I have picked out a bit of hill where the south sun warms me.
I like to be near the trees."

Nay, let him ask, rather.
"Is it well with you, comrades?
The cities great, portentous, humming with action?
The bridges mightily spanning wide-breasted rivers?
The great plains growing the wheat, the old lilac hardy, well-
    budded?
Is it well with these States?"

"The cities are great, portentous, a world-marvel,   130
The bridges arched like the necks of beautiful horses.
We have made the dry land bloom and the dead land blossom."

"Is it well with these States?"

"The old wound of your war is healed and we are one nation.
We have linked the whole land with the steel and the hard high-
    ways.
We have fought new wars and won them. In the French field
There are bones of Texarkana and Little Falls,
Aliens, our own; in the low-lying Belgian ground;
In the cold sea of the English; in dark-faced islands.
Men speak of them well or ill; they themselves are silent."   140

"Is it well with these States?"

"We have made many, fine new toys.
We—
There is a rust on the land.

A rust and a creeping blight and a scaled evil,
For six years eating, yet deeper than those six years,
Men labor to master it but it is not mastered.
There is the soft, grey, foul tent of the hatching worm
Shrouding the elm, the chestnut, the Southern cypress.
There is shadow in the bright sun, there is shadow upon the
    streets.   150
They burn the grain in the furnace while men go hungry.
They pile the cloth of the looms while men go ragged.
We walk naked in our plenty."

                      "My tan-faced children?"

"These are your tan-faced children.
These skilled men, idle, with the holes in their shoes.
These drifters from State to State, these wolvish, bewildered boys
Who ride the blinds and the box-cars from jail to jail,
Burnt in their youth like cinders of hot smokestacks,
Learning the thief's crouch and the cadger's whine,
Dishonored, abandoned, disinherited.   160
These, dying in the bright sunlight they cannot eat,
Or the strong men, sitting at home, their hands clasping nothing,
Looking at their lost hands.
These are your tan-faced children, the parched young,
The old man rooting in waste-heaps, the family rotting
In the flat, before eviction,
With the toys of plenty about them,
The shiny toys making ice and music and light,
But no price for the shiny toys and the last can empty.
The sleepers in blind corners of the night.   170
The women with dry breasts and phantom eyes.
The walkers upon nothing, the four million.
These are your tan-faced children."

                      "But the land?"

"Over the great plains of the buffalo-land,
The dust-storm blows, the choking, sifting, small dust.
The skin of that land is ploughed by the dry, fierce wind

And blown away, like a torrent;
It drifts foot-high above the young sprouts of grain
And the water fouls, the horses stumble and sicken,
The wash-board cattle stagger and die of drought.   180
We tore the buffalo's pasture with the steel blade.
We made the waste land blossom and it has blossomed.
That was our fate; now that land takes its own revenge,
And the giant dust-flower blooms above five States."

"But the gains of the years, who got them?"

                                                         "Many, great gains.
Many, yet few; they robbed us in the broad daylight,
Saying, 'Give us this and that; we are kings and titans;
We know the ropes; we are solid; we are hard-headed;
We will build you cities and railroads.'—as if *they* built them!
They, the preying men, the men whose hearts were like engines,   190
Gouging the hills for gold, laying waste the timber,
The men like band-saws, moving over the land.
And, after them, the others,
Soft-bodied, lacking even the pirate's candor,
Men of paper, robbing by paper, with paper faces,
Rustling like frightened paper when the storm broke.
The men with the jaws of moth and aphis and beetle,
Boring the dusty, secret hole in the corn,
Fixed, sucking the land, with neither wish nor pride
But the wish to suck and continue.   200
They have been sprayed, a little.
But they say they will have the land back again, these men."

"There were many such in my time.
I have seen the rich arrogant and the poor oppressed.
I have seen democracy, also. I have seen
The good man slain, the knave and the fool in power,
The democratic vista botched by the people,
Yet not despaired, loving the giant land,
Though I prophesied to these States."

"Now they say we must have one tyranny or another
And a dark bell rings in our hearts."

"Was the blood spilt for nothing, then?"

3

Under dry winter
Arbutus grows.
It is careless of man.
It is careless of man.

Man can tear it,
Crush it, destroy it;
Uproot the trailers,
The thumb-shaped leafings.

A man in grey clothes
May come there also,
Lie all day there
In weak spring sunlight.

White, firm-muscled,
The flesh of his body;
Wind, sun, earth
In him, possessing him.

In his heart
A flock of birds crying.
In his belly
The new grass growing.

In his skull
Sunlight and silence,
Like a vast room
Full of sunlight and silence.

In the lines of his palms
The roads of America,

In the knots of his hands
The anger of America.   240

In the sweat of his flesh
The sorrows of America,
In the seed of his loins
The glory of America.

The sap of the birch-tree
Is in his pelt,
The maple, the red-bud
Are his nails and parings.

He grows through the earth and is part of it
    like the roots of new grass.

Little arbutus   250
Delicate, tinted,
Tiny, tender,
Fragile, immortal.

If you can grow,
A man can grow
Not like others
But like a man.

Man is a bull
But he has not slain you
And this man lies   260
Like a lover beside you.

Beside the arbutus,
The green-leaved Spring,
He lies like a lover
By his young bride,
In the white hour,
The white, first waking.

4

They say, they say, they say and let them say.
Call you a revolutionist—you were one—
A nationalist—you were one—a man of peace,
A man describing battles, an old fraud,
A Charlus, an adept self-advertiser,
A "good, grey poet"—oh, God save us all!
God save us from the memoirs and the memories!
And yet, they count. They have to. If they didn't
There'd be no Ph.Ds. And each disciple
Jealously guards his own particular store
Of acorns fallen from the oak's abundance
And spits and scratches at the other gatherers.
"I was there when he died!"
                       "He was not there when he died!"
"It was me he trusted, me! X got on his nerves!
He couldn't stand X in the room!"
                       "Y's well-intentioned
But a notorious liar—and, as for Z . . ."

So all disciples, always and forever.
—And the dire court at Longwood, those last years,
The skull of Sterne, grinning at the anatomists,
Poe's hospital-bed, the madness of the Dean,
The bright, coughing blood Keats wrote in to the girl,
The terrible corpse of France, shrunk, naked and solitary—
Oh, yes, you were spared some things.
Though why did Mrs. Davis sue the estate
And what did you mean when you said—
                                And who cares?
You're still the giant lode we quarry
For gold, fools' gold and all the earthy metals,
The matchless mine.
Still the trail-breaker, still the rolling river.

You and your land, your turbulent, seeking land
Where anything can grow.

And they have wasted the pasture and the fresh valley,
Stunk the river, shot the ten thousand sky-darkening
  pigeons
To build sham castles for imitation Medici
And the rugged sons of the rugged sons of death.
The slum, the sharecropper's cabin, the senseless tower,
The factory town with the dirty stoops of twilight,
The yelling cheapness, the bitter want among plenty,
But never Monticello, never again.

And there are many years in the dust of America
And they are not ended yet.

Far north, far north are the sources of the great river,
The headwaters, the cold lakes,
By the little sweet-tasting brooks of the blond country,
The country of snow and wheat,
Or west among the black mountains, the glacial springs.
Far north and west they lie and few come to them, few taste
  them,
But, day and night, they flow south,
By the French grave and the Indian, steadily flowing,
By the forgotten camps of the broken heart,
By the countries of black earth, fertile, and yellow earth and red
  earth,
A growing, a swelling torrent:
Rivers meet it, and tiny rivulets,
Meet it, stain it,
Great rivers, rivers of pride, come bowing their watery heads
Like muddy gift-bearers, bringing their secret burdens,
Rivers from the high horse-plains and the deep, green Eastern
  pastures
Sink into it and are lost and rejoice and shout with it, shout
  within it,
They and their secret gifts,
A fleck of gold from Montana, a sliver of steel from Pittsburg,
A wheat-grain from Minnesota, an apple-blossom from Tennessee,
Roiled, mixed with the mud and earth of the changing bottoms
In the vast, rending floods,

But rolling, rolling from Arkansas, Kansas, Iowa,
Rolling from Ohio, Wisconsin, Illinois,
Rolling and shouting:
Till, at last, it is Mississippi,
The Father of Waters; the matchless; the great flood
Dyed with the earth of States; with the dust and the sun and
    the seed of half the States;
The huge heart-vein, pulsing and pulsing; gigantic; ever broader,
    ever mightier;
It rolls past broken landings and camellia-smelling woods; strange
    birds fly over it;
It rolls through the tropic magic, the almost-jungle, the warm
    darkness breeding the warm, enormous stars;
It rolls to the blue Gulf; ocean; and the painted birds fly.   340
The grey moss mixes with it, the hawk's feather has fallen in it,
The cardinal feather, the feather of the small thrush
Singing spring to New England,
The apple-pip and the pepper-seed and the checkerberry,
And always the water flowing, earthy, majestic,
Fed with snow and heat, dew and moonlight.
Always the wide, sure water,
Over the rotted deer-horn
The gold, Spanish money,
The long-rusted iron of many undertakings,   350
Over De Soto's bones and Joliet's wonder,
And the long forest-years before them, the brief years after,
The broad flood, the eternal motion, the restless-hearted
Always, forever, Mississippi, the god.

April, 1935.

METROPOLITAN NIGHTMARE

It rained quite a lot, that spring. You woke in the morning
And saw the sky still clouded, the streets still wet,
But nobody noticed so much, except the taxis
And the people who parade. You don't, in a city.
The parks got very green. All the trees were green
Far into July and August, heavy with leaf,

METROPOLITAN NIGHTMARE

Heavy with leaf and the long roots boring and spreading,
But nobody noticed that but the city gardeners
And they don't talk.
                      Oh, on Sundays, perhaps, you'd notice:
Walking through certain blocks, by the shut, proud houses
With the windows boarded, the people gone away,
You'd suddenly see the queerest small shoots of green
Poking through cracks and crevices in the stone
And a bird-sown flower, red on a balcony,
But then you made jokes about grass growing in the streets
And politics and grass-roots—and there were songs
And gags and a musical show called "Hot and Wet."
It all made a good box for the papers. When the flamingo
Flew into a meeting of the Board of Estimate,
The new Mayor acted at once and called the photographers.
When the first green creeper crawled upon Brooklyn Bridge,
They thought it was ornamental. They let it stay.

That was the year the termites came to New York
And they don't do well in cold climates—but listen, Joe,
They're only ants and ants are nothing but insects.
It was funny and yet rather wistful, in a way
(As Heywood Broun pointed out in the *World-Telegram*)
To think of them looking for wood in a steel city.
It made you feel about life. It was too divine.
There were funny pictures by all the smart, funny artists
And Macy's ran a terribly clever ad:
"The Widow's Termite" or something.
                                There was no
Disturbance. Even the Communists didn't protest
And say they were Morgan hirelings. It was too hot,
Too hot to protest, too hot to get excited,
An even, African heat, lush, fertile and steamy,
That soaked into bone and mind and never once broke.
The warm rain fell in fierce showers and ceased and fell.
Pretty soon you got used to its always being that way.

You got used to the changed rhythm, the altered beat,
To people walking slower, to the whole bright

Fierce pulse of the city slowing, to men in shorts,
To the new sun-helmets from Best's and the cops' white uniforms,
And the long noon-rest in the offices, everywhere.
It wasn't a plan or anything. It just happened.
The fingers tapped the keys slower, the office-boys
Dozed on their benches, the bookkeeper yawned at his desk.
The A. T. & T. was the first to change the shifts.
And establish an official siesta-room,
But they were always efficient. Mostly it just   50
Happened like sleep itself, like a tropic sleep,
Till even the Thirties were deserted at noon
Except for a few tourists and one damp cop.
They ran boats to see the big lilies on the North River
But it was only the tourists who really noticed
The flocks of rose-and-green parrots and parrakeets
Nesting in the stone crannies of the Cathedral.
The rest of us had forgotten when they first came.

There wasn't any real change, it was just a heat spell,
A rain spell, a funny summer, a weather-man's joke,   60
In spite of the geraniums three feet high
In the tin-can gardens of Hester and Desbrosses.
New York was New York. It couldn't turn inside out.
When they got the news from Woods Hole about the Gulf Stream,
The *Times* ran an adequate story.
But nobody reads those stories but science-cranks.

Until, one day, a somnolent city-editor
Gave a new cub the termite yarn to break his teeth on.
He read all about termites in the Public Library
And it made him sore when they fired him.
The cub was just down from Vermont, so he took the time.
He was serious about it. He went around.   70
                         So, one evening,
Talking with an old watchman, beside the first
Raw girders of the new Planetopolis Building
(Ten thousand brine-cooled offices, each with shower)

He saw a dark line creeping across the rubble
And turned a flashlight on it.
                              "Say, buddy," he said,
"You better look out for those ants. They eat wood, you know,
They'll have your shack down in no time."
                                    The watchman spat.
"Oh, they've quit eating wood," he said, in a casual voice,
"I thought everybody knew that."
                        —and, reaching down,
He pried from the insect jaws the bright crumb of steel.

NIGHTMARE, WITH ANGELS

An angel came to me and stood by my bedside,
Remarking in a professorial-historical-economic and irritated voice,
"If the Romans had only invented a decent explosion-engine!
Not even the best, not even a Ford V-8
But, say, a Model T or even an early Napier,
They'd have built good enough roads for it (they knew how to build roads)
From Cape Wrath to Cape St. Vincent, Susa, Babylon and Moscow,
And the motorized legions never would have fallen,
And peace, in the shape of a giant eagle, would brood over the entire Western World!"
He changed his expression, looking now like a combination of Gilbert Murray, Hilaire Belloc and a dozen other scientists, writers, and prophets,
And continued, in angelic tones,
"If the Greeks had known how to coöperate, if there'd never been a Reformation,
If Sparta had not been Sparta, and the Church had been the Church of the saints,
The Argive peace like a free-blooming olive-tree, the peace of Christ (who loved peace) like a great, beautiful vine enwrapping the spinning earth!
Take it nearer home," he said.

"Take these Mayans and their star-clocks, their carvings and their great cities.
Who sacked them out of their cities, drowned the cities with a green jungle?
A plague? A change of climate? A queer migration?
Certainly they were skilful, certainly they created.
And, in Tenochtitlan, the dark obsidian knife and the smoking heart on the stone but a fair city, 20
And the Incas had it worked out beautifully till Pizarro smashed them.
The collectivist state was there, and the ladies very agreeable.
They lacked steel, alphabet and gunpowder and they had to get married when the government said so.
They also lacked unemployment and overproduction.
For that matter," he said, "take the Cro-Magnons,
The fellows with the big skulls, the handsome folk, the excellent scribers of mammoths,
Physical gods and yet with the sensitive brain (they drew the fine, running reindeer).
What stopped them? What kept us all from being Apollos and Aphrodites
Only with a new taste to the nectar,
The laughing gods, not the cruel, the gods of song, not of war? 30
Supposing Aurelius, Confucius, Napoleon, Plato, Gautama, Alexander—
Just to take half a dozen—
Had ever realized and stabilized the full dream?
How long, O Lord God in the highest? How long, what now, perturbed spirit?"

He turned blue at the wingtips and disappeared as another angel approached me.
This one was quietly but appropriately dressed in cellophane, synthetic rubber and stainless steel,
But his mask was the blind mask of Ares, snouted for gas-masks.
He was neither soldier, sailor, farmer, dictator nor munitions-manufacturer.
Nor did he have much conversation, except to say,

"You will not be saved by General Motors or the pre-fabricated house, 40
You will not be saved by dialectic materialism or the Lambeth Conference.
You will not be saved by Vitamin D or the expanding universe.
In fact, you will not be saved."
Then he showed his hand:
In his hand was a woven, wire basket, full of seeds, small metallic and shining like the seeds of portulaca;
Where he sowed them, the green vine withered, and the smoke and the armies sprang up.

NIGHTMARE NUMBER THREE

We had expected everything but revolt
And I kind of wonder myself when they started thinking—
But there's no dice in that now.
                        I've heard fellows say
They must have planned it for years and maybe they did.
Looking back, you can find little incidents here and there,
Like the concrete-mixer in Jersey eating the wop
Or the roto press that printed "Fiddle-dee-dee!"
In a three-color process all over Senator Sloop,
Just as he was making a speech. The thing about that
Was, how could it walk upstairs? But it was upstairs, 10
Clicking and mumbling in the Senate Chamber.
They had to knock out the wall to take it away
And the wrecking-crew said it grinned.
                                  It was only the best
Machines, of course, the superhuman machines,
The ones we'd built to be better than flesh and bone,
But the cars were in it, of course . . .
                                and they hunted us
Like rabbits through the cramped streets on that Bloody Monday,
The Madison Avenue busses leading the charge.
The busses were pretty bad—but I'll not forget
The smash of glass when the Duesenberg left the show-room 20

And pinned three brokers to the Racquet Club steps
Or the long howl of the horns when they saw men run,
When they saw them looking for holes in the solid ground . . .

I guess they were tired of being ridden in
And stopped and started by pygmies for silly ends,
Of wrapping cheap cigarettes and bad chocolate bars
Collecting nickels and waving platinum hair
And letting six million people live in a town.
I guess it was that. I guess they got tired of us
And the whole smell of human hands.

                                          But it was a shock 30
To climb sixteen flights of stairs to Art Zuckow's office
(Nobody took the elevators twice)
And find him strangled to death in a nest of telephones,
The octopus-tendrils waving over his head,
And a sort of quiet humming filling the air. . . .
Do they eat? . . . There was red . . . But I did not stop to look.
I don't know yet how I got to the roof in time
And it's lonely, here on the roof.

                         For a while, I thought
That window-cleaner would make it, and keep me company.
But they got him with his own hoist at the sixteenth floor   40
And dragged him in, with a squeal.
You see, they coöperate. Well, we taught them that
And it's fair enough, I suppose. You see, we built them.
We taught them to think for themselves.
It was bound to come. You can see it was bound to come.

And it won't be so bad, in the country. I hate to think
Of the reapers, running wild in the Kansas fields,
And the transport planes like hawks on a chickenyard,
But the horses might help. We might make a deal with the horses.
At least, you've more chance, out there.

                                  And they need us, too. 50
They're bound to realize that when they once calm down.
They'll need oil and spare parts and adjustments and tuning up.
Slaves? Well, in a way, you know, we were slaves before.

There won't be so much real difference—honest, there won't.
(I wish I hadn't looked into that beauty-parlor
And seen what was happening there.
But those are female machines and a bit high-strung.)
Oh, we'll settle down. We'll arrange it. We'll compromise.
It wouldn't make sense to wipe out the whole human race.
Why, I bet if I went to my old Plymouth now   60
(Of course you'd have to do it the tactful way)
And said, "Look here! Who got you the swell French horn?"
He wouldn't turn me over to those police cars;
At least I don't think he would.
                              Oh, it's going to be jake.
There won't be so much real difference—honest, there won't—
And I'd go down in a minute and take my chance—
I'm a good American and I always liked them—
Except for one small detail that bothers me
And that's the food proposition. Because, you see,
The concrete-mixer may have made a mistake,   70
And it looks like just high spirits.
But, if it's got so they like the flavor . . . well . . .

1936

All night they marched, the infantrymen under pack,
But the hands gripping the rifles were naked bone
And the hollow pits of the eyes stared, vacant and black,
When the moonlight shone.

The gas mask lay like a blot on the empty chest,
The slanting helmets were spattered with rust and mold,
But they burrowed the hill for the machine-gun nest
As they had of old.

And the guns rolled, and the tanks, but there was no sound,
Never the gasp or rustle of living men
Where the skeletons strung their wire on disputed ground. . . .
I knew them, then.

"It is eighteen years," I cried. "You must come no more."
"We know your names. We know that you are the dead.
Must you march forever from France and the last, blind war?"
"Fool! From the next!" they said.

SPARROW

Lord, may I be
A sparrow in a tree.

No ominous and splendid bird of prey
But something that is fearful every day
Yet keeps its small flesh full of heat and lightness.
Pigeons are better dressed and robins stouter,
The white owl has all winter in his whiteness
And the blue heron is a kingly dream
At evening, by the pale stream,
But, even in the lion's cage, in Zoos,   10
You'll find a sparrow, picking up the crumbs
And taking life precisely as it comes
With the black, wary eye that marks the doubter;
Squabbling in crowds, dust-bathing in the sun,
Small, joyous, impudent, a gutter-child
In Lesbia's bosom or December's chill,
Full of impertinence and hard to kill
As Queen Anne's lace and poppies in the wheat—
I won't pretend the fellow has a Muse
But that he has advice, and good advice,   20
All lovers know who've walked the city's street
And wished the stones were bread.
Peacocks are handsomer and owls more wise.
(At least, by all repute.)
And parrots live on flattery and fruit,
Live to great age. The sparrow's none of these.
The sparrow is a humorist, and dies.
There are so many things that he is not.
He will not tear the stag nor sweep the seas
Nor fall, majestical, to a king's arrow.   30

Yet how he lives, and how he loves in living
Up to the dusty tip of every feather!
How he endures oppression and the weather
And asks for neither justice nor forgiving!
Lord, in your mercy, let me be a sparrow!
His rapid heart's so hot.
And some can sing—song-sparrows, so they say—
And, one thing, Lord—the times are iron, now.
Perhaps you have forgot.
They shoot the wise and brave on every bough.   40
But sparrows are the last things that get shot.

FOR CITY LOVERS

Do not desire to seek who once we were,
Or where we did, or what, or in whose name.
Those buildings have been torn down. When the first wreckers
Tore the house open like a pack of cards
And the sun came in all over, everywhere,
They found some old newspapers and a cork
And footprints on the very dusty floor
But neither mouse nor angel.
                    Then even these
Went, even the little marks of shabby shoes,
The one sharp impress of the naked heel.   10
You cannot call us up there any more.
The number has been changed. There was a card
Downstairs, with names and such, under the bell.
But that's long gone. Yes, and we, they and you
And telegrams and flowers and the years
Went up and down these stairs, day after day,
And kept the stair-rail polished with our hands.
But we have moved to other neighborhoods.

Do not arraign that doorsill with your eyes
Nor try to make your hardened mind recall   20
How the old windows looked when they were lit

Or who the woman was on the third floor.
There are no ghosts to raise. There is the blank
Face of the stone, the hard line of the street,
The boys crying through twilight. That is all.

Go buy yourself a drink and talk about it.
Carry a humming head home through the rain.
But do not wear rosemary, touch cold iron,
Or leave out food before you go to bed.
For there's no fear of ghosts. That boy and girl 30
Are dust the sparrows bathe in, under the sun:
Under the virgin rock their bones lie sunken
Past pave and conduit and hidden waters
Stifled like unborn children in the darkness,
Past light and speech, cable and rooted steel,
Under the caissons, under the foundation.

Peace, peace, for there are people with those names
Somewhere or elsewhere, and you must not vex
Strangers with words about an old address.
But, for those others, do not be afraid 40
They are beyond you. They are too deep down
For steel to pierce, for engines to uncover.
Not all the desperate splitters of the earth,
Nitro or air-drill or the chewing shovel
Shall ever mouth them up from where they lie.

NIGHTMARE FOR FUTURE REFERENCE

That was the second year of the Third World War,
The one between Us and Them.
                                        Well we've gotten used.
We don't talk much about it, queerly enough.
There was all sorts of talk the first years after the Peace,
A million theories, a million wild suppositions,
A million hopeful explanations and plans,
But we don't talk about it, now. We don't even ask.

NIGHTMARE FOR FUTURE REFERENCE

We might do the wrong thing. I don't guess you'd understand that.
But you're eighteen, now. You can take it. You'd better know.

You see, you were born just before the war broke out.
Who started it? Oh, they said it was Us or Them
And it looked like it at the time. You don't know what that's like.
But anyhow, it started and there it was,
Just a little worse, of course, than the one before,
But mankind was used to that. We didn't take notice.
They bombed our capital and we bombed theirs.
You've been to the Broken Towns? Yes, they take you there.
They show you the look of the tormented earth.
But they can't show the smell or the gas or the death
Or how it felt to be there, and a part of it.
But we didn't know. I swear that we didn't know.

I remember the first faint hint there was something wrong,
Something beyond all wars and bigger and strange,
Something you couldn't explain.
                              I was back on leave—
Strange, as you felt on leave, as you always felt—
But I went to see the Chief at the hospital
And there he was, in the same old laboratory,
A little older, with some white in his hair
But the same eyes that went through you and the same tongue.
They hadn't been able to touch him—not the bombs
Nor the ruin of his life's work nor anything.
He blinked at me from behind his spectacles
And said, "Huh. It's you. They won't let me have guinea pigs
Except for the war work, but I steal a few.
And they've made me a colonel—expect me to salute.
Damn fools. A damn-fool business. I don't know how.
Have you heard what Erickson's done with the ductless glands?
The journals are four months late. Sit down and smoke."
And I did and it was like home.
                            He was a great man.
You might remember that—and I'd worked with him.
Well, finally he said to me, "How's your boy?"

"Oh—healthy," I said. "We're lucky."

"Yes," he said,
And a frown went over his face. "He might even grow up,
Though the intervals between wars are getting shorter.
I wonder if it wouldn't simplify things
To declare mankind in a permanent state of siege.
It might knock some sense in their heads."

"You're cheerful," I said.
"Oh, I'm always cheerful," he said. "Seen these, by the way?"
He tapped some charts on a table.

"Seen what?" I said.
"Oh," he said, with that devilish, sidelong grin of his, 50
"Just the normal city statistics—death and birth.
You're a soldier now. You wouldn't be interested.
But the birth rate's dropping—"

"Well, really, sir," I said,
"We know that it's always dropped, in every war."

"Not like this," he said. "I can show you the curve.
It looks like the side of a mountain, going down.
And faster, the last three months—yes, a good deal faster.
I showed it to Lobenheim and he was puzzled.
It makes a neat problem—yes?" He looked at me. 59

"They'd better make peace," he said. "They'd better make peace."

"Well, sir," I said, "if we break through, in the spring—"
"Break through?" he said. "What's that? They'd better make peace.
The stars may be tired of us. No, I'm not a mystic.
I leave that to the big scientists in bad novels.
But I never saw such a queer maternity curve.
I wish I could get to Ehrens, on their side.
He'd tell me the truth. But the fools won't let me do it."

His eyes looked tired as he stared at the careful charts.
"Suppose there are no more babies?" he said. "What then?
It's one way of solving the problem."

"But, sir—" I said. 70

"But, sir!" he said. "Will you tell me, please, what is life?
Why it's given, why it's taken away?
Oh, I know—we make a jelly inside a test tube,
We keep a cock's heart living inside a jar.
We know a great many things and what do we know?
We think we know what finished the dinosaurs,
But do we? Maybe they were given a chance
And then it was taken back. There are other beasts
That only kill for their food. No, I'm not a mystic,
But there's a certain pattern in nature, you know,
And we're upsetting it daily. Eat and mate
And go back to the earth after that, and that's all right.
But now we're blasting and sickening earth itself.
She's been very patient with us. I wonder how long."

Well, I thought the Chief had gone crazy, just at first,
And then I remembered the look of no man's land,
That bitter landscape, pockmarked like the moon,
Lifeless as the moon's face and horrible,
The thing we'd made with the guns.
                              If it were earth,
It looked as though it hated.
                      "Well?" I said,
And my voice was a little thin. He looked hard at me.
"Oh—ask the women," he grunted. "Don't ask me.
Ask them what they think about it."
                                I didn't ask them,
Not even your mother—she was strange, those days—
But, two weeks later, I was back in the lines
And somebody sent me a paper—
Encouragement for the troops and all of that—
All about the fall of Their birth rate on Their side.

I guess you know, now. There was still a day when we fought
And the next day, the women knew. I don't know how
    they knew,
But they smashed every government in the world
Like a heap of broken china, within two days,
And we'd stopped firing by then. And we looked at each other.

We didn't talk much, those first weeks. You couldn't talk.
We started in rebuilding and that was all,
And at first, nobody would even touch the guns,
Not even to melt them up. They just stood there, silent,
Pointing the way they had and nobody there.
And there was a kind of madness in the air,
A quiet, bewildered madness, strange and shy. 110

You'd pass a man who was muttering to himself
And you'd know what he was muttering, and why.
I remember coming home and your mother there.
She looked at me, at first didn't speak at all,
And then she said, "Burn those clothes. Take them off and burn them
Or I'll never touch you or speak to you again."
And then I knew I was still in my uniform.

Well, I've told you, now. They tell you now at eighteen.
There's no use telling before.
      Do you understand?
That's why we have the Ritual of the Earth, 120
The Day of Sorrow, the other ceremonies.
Oh yes, at first people hated the animals
Because they still bred, but we've gotten over that.
Perhaps they can work it better, when it's their turn,
If it's their turn—I don't know. I don't know at all.
You can call it a virus, of course, if you like the word,
But we haven't been able to find it. Not yet. No.
It isn't as if it had happened all at once.
There were a few children born in the last six months
Before the end of the war, so there's still some hope. 130
But they're almost grown. That's the trouble. They're almost grown.
Well, we had a long run. That's something. At first they thought
There might be a nation somewhere—a savage tribe.
But we were all in it, even the Eskimos,
And we keep the toys in the stores, and the colored books,
And people marry and plan and the rest of it,
But, you see, there aren't any children. They aren't born.

MINOR LITANY

This being a time confused and with few clear stars,
Either private ones or public,
Out of its darkness I make a litany
For the lost, for the half-lost, for the desperate,
For all of those who suffer, not in the flesh.
I will say their name, but not yet.
                        This is for those
Who talk to the bearded man in the quiet office,
Sensibly, calmly, explaining just how it was,
And suddenly burst into noisy, quacking tears;
For those who live through the party, wishing for death;
For those who take the sensible country walks,
Wondering if people stare;
For those who try to hook rugs in the big, bright room
And do it badly and are pleased with the praise;
For the night and the fear and the demons of the night;
For the lying back on the couch and the wincing talk.

This is for those who work and those who may not,
For those who suddenly come to a locked door,
And the work falls out of their hands;
For those who step off the pavement into hell,
Having not observed the red light and the warning signals
Because they were busy or ignorant or proud.

This is for those who are bound in the paper chains
That are stronger than links of iron; this is for those
Who each day heave the papier-mache rock
Up the huge and burning hill,
And there is no rock and no hill, but they do not know it.

This is for those who wait till six for the drink,
Till eleven for the tablet;
And for those who cannot wait but go to the darkness;
And for those who long for the darkness but do not go,
Who walk to the window and see the body falling,

Hear the thud of air in the ears,
And then turn back to the room and sit down again,
None having observed the occurrence but themselves.

Christ, have mercy upon us.
Freud, have mercy upon us.
Life, have mercy upon us.

This is for those
Who painfully haul the dark fish out of the dark, 40
The child's old nightmare, embalmed in its own pain,
And, after that, get well or do not get well,
But do not forget the sulphur in the mouth
Or the time when the world was different, not for a while.
And for those also, the veterans
Of another kind of war,
Who say "No thanks" to the cocktails, who say "No thanks.
Well, yes, give me Coca-Cola" with the trained smile,
Those who hid the bottles so cleverly in the trunk,
Who bribed the attendant, who promised to be good, 50
Who woke in the dirty bed in the unknown town.
They are cured, now, very much cured.
They are tanned and fine. Their eyes are their only scars.

This is for those with the light white scars on the wrists,
Who remember the smell of gas and the vomiting,
And it meant little and it is a well-known symptom
And they were always careful to phone, before.
Nevertheless, they remember.
                        This is for those
Who heard the music suddenly get too loud,
Who could not alter the fancy when it came. 60

Chloral, have mercy upon us.
Amytal, have mercy upon us.
Nembutal, have mercy upon us.

This occurs more or less than it did in the past times.
There are statistics. There are no real statistics.

There is also no heroism. There is merely
Fatigue, pain, great confusion, sometimes recovery.

The name, as you know, is Legion.
What's your name, friend? Where are you from and how did
 you get here?
The name is Legion. It's Legion in the case history. 70
Friends, Romans, countrymen,
Mr. and Mrs. Legion is the name.

NIGHTMARE AT NOON

There are no trenches dug in the park, not yet.
There are no soldiers falling out of the sky.
It's a fine, clear day, in the park. It is bright and hot.
The trees are in full, green, summer-heavy leaf.
An airplane drones overhead but no one's afraid.
There's no reason to be afraid, in a fine, big city
That was not built for a war. There is time and time.

There was time in Norway and time, and the thing fell.
When they woke, they saw the planes with the black crosses.
When they woke, they heard the guns rolling in the street. 10
They could not believe, at first. It was hard to believe.
They had been friendly and thriving and inventive.
They had had good arts, decent living, peace for years.
Those were not enough, it seems.
There were people there who wrote books and painted pictures,
Worked, came home tired, liked to be let alone.
They made fun of the strut and the stamp and the stained salute,
They made fun of the would-be Caesars who howl and foam.
That was not enough, it seems. It was not enough.
When they woke, they saw the planes with the black crosses. 20

There is grass in the park. There are children on the long meadow
Watched by some hot, peaceful nuns. Where the ducks are fed
There are black children and white and the anxious teachers

Who keep counting them like chickens. It's quite a job
To take so many school-kids out to the park,
But when they've eaten their picnic, they'll go home.
(And they could have better homes, in a rich city.)
But they won't be sent to Kansas or Michigan
At twenty-four hours' notice,
Dazed, bewildered, clutching their broken toys,
Hundreds on hundreds filling the blacked-out trains.
Just to keep them safe, just so they may live not die.
Just so there's one chance that they may not die but live.
That does not enter our thoughts. There is plenty of time.

In Holland, one hears, some children were less lucky.
It was hard to send them anywhere in Holland.
It is a small country, you see. The thing happened quickly.
The bombs from the sky are quite indifferent to children.
The machine-gunners do not distinguish. In Rotterdam
One quarter of the city was blown to bits.
That included, naturally, ordinary buildings
With the usual furnishings, such as cats and children.
It was an old, peaceful city, Rotterdam,
Clean, tidy, full of flowers.
But that was not enough, it seems.
It was not enough to keep all the children safe.
It was ended in a week, and the freedom ended.

There is no air-raid siren yet, in the park.
All the glass still stands, in the windows around the park.
The man on the bench is reading a Yiddish paper.
He will not be shot because of that, oddly enough.
He will not even be beaten or imprisoned.
Not yet, not yet.
You can be a Finn or a Dane and an American.
You can be German or French and an American,
Jew, Bohunk, Nigger, Mick—all the dirty names
We call each other—and yet American.
We've stuck to that quite a while.
Go into Joe's Diner and try to tell the truckers
You belong to a Master Race and you'll get a laugh.

What's that, brother? Double-talk?
I'm a stranger here myself but it's a free country.
It's a free country . . .
Oh yes, I know the faults and the other side,
The lyncher's rope, the bought justice, the wasted land,
The scale on the leaf, the borers in the corn,
The finks with their clubs, the grey sky of relief,
All the long shame of our hearts and the long disunion.
I am merely remarking—as a country, we try.
As a country, I think we try.

They tried in Spain but the tanks and the planes won out.
They fought very well and long.
They fought to be free but it seems that was not enough.
They did not have the equipment. So they lost.
They tried in Finland. The resistance was shrewd,
Skilful, intelligent, waged by a free folk.
They tried in Greece, and they threw them back for a while
By the soul and spirit and passion of common men.
Call the roll of fourteen nations. Call the roll
Of the blacked-out lands, the lands that used to be free.

But do not call it loud. There is plenty of time.
There is plenty of time, while the bombs on London fall
And turn the world to wind and water and fire.
There is time to sleep while the fire-bombs fall on London.
They are stubborn people in London.

We are slow to wake, good-natured as a country.
(It is our fault and our virtue.) We like to raise
A man to the highest power and then throw bricks at him.
We don't like war and we like to speak our minds.
We're used to speaking our minds.
                              There are certain words,
Our own and others', we're used to—words we've used,
Heard, had to recite, forgotten,
Rubbed shiny in the pocket, left home for keepsakes,
Inherited, stuck away in the back-drawer,
In the locked trunk, at the back of the quiet mind.

Liberty, equality, fraternity.
To none will we sell, refuse or deny, right or justice.
We hold these truths to be self-evident.

I am merely saying—what if these words pass?
What if they pass and are gone and are no more,
Eviscerated, blotted out of the world?
We're used to them, so used that we half-forget,
The way you forget the looks of your own house
And yet you can walk around it, in the darkness.
You can't put a price on sunlight or the air,
You can't put a price on these, so they must be easy.
They were bought with belief and passion, at great cost.
They were bought with the bitter and anonymous blood
Of farmers, teachers, shoemakers and fools
Who broke the old rule and the pride of kings.
And some never saw the end and many were weary,
Some doubtful, many confused.
They were bought by the ragged boys at Valmy mill,
The yokels at Lexington with the long light guns
And the dry, New England faces,
The iron barons, writing a charter out
For their own iron advantage, not the people,
And yet the people got it into their hands
And marked it with their own sweat.
It took long to buy these words.
It took a long time to buy them and much pain.

Thenceforward and forever free.
Thenceforward and forever free.
No man may be bound or fined or slain till he has been judged
    by his peers.
To form a more perfect Union.

The others have their words too, and strong words,
Strong as the tanks, explosive as the bombs.

The State is all, worship the State!
The Leader is all, worship the Leader!

Strength is all, worship strength!
Worship, bow down or die!

I shall go back through the park to my safe house,
This is not London or Paris.
This is the high, bright city, the lucky place,
The place that always had time.
The boys in their shirtsleeves here, the big, flowering girls,
The bicycle-riders, the kids with the model planes,
The lovers who lie on the grass, uncaring of eyes,
As if they lay on an island out of time,
The tough kids, squirting the water at the fountain,
Whistled at by the cop.
The dopes who write "Jimmy's a dope" on the tunnel walls.
These are all quite safe and nothing will happen to them.
Nothing will happen, of course.
Go tell Frank the Yanks aren't coming, in Union Square.
Go tell the new brokers' story about the President.
Whatever it is. That's going to help a lot.
There's time to drink your highball—plenty of time.
Go tell fire it only burns in another country,
Go tell the bombers this is the wrong address,
The hurricane to pass on the other side.
Go tell the earthquake it must not shake the ground.

The bell has rung in the night and the air quakes with it.

I shall not sleep tonight when I hear the plane.

1940.

THEY BURNED THE BOOKS

[*Program opens with a rush of Fire-Music, swelling and then subsiding; as music subsides, a heavy, ominous bell tolls* ONE]

VOICES [*Tense and whispering*]
One!
BELL [*Tolls*]
VOICES
Two!
BELL [*Tolls*]
VOICES
Three!
[*Fire-Music Up and Down*]
BELL [*Louder and quicker*]
VOICES [*Quicker*]
Seven!
BELL [*Tolls*]
VOICES
Eight!
BELL [*Tolls*]
VOICES
Nine!
[*Fire-Music*]

NARRATOR: Nine! Nine iron years of terror and evil!
Nine years since a fire was lighted in a public square, in Berlin.
Nine years since the burning of the books! Do you remember?
Write it down in your calendars, May 10, 1933,
And write it down in red by the light of fire.
 [*Crackle of flames, not too big*]
These are people who work by fire.
The Reichstag went up in flames that February
And in March they got their majority and moved in,
The storm-troopers, the heroes of the beer-hall Putsch,
The boys with a taste for beatings and executions,
The limping doctor, the swollen ex-Army pilot,

92

THEY BURNED THE BOOKS

Gangster and bravo, hoodlum and trigger-man,
Led by the screaming voice that is war and hate,
Moved in on Germany like a cloud of locusts,
Having planned and plotted for long.
They strangled the German Republic and moved in.
   [*Crackle of flames*]
—And people said, "Well, that's interesting, isn't it?"
"Intéressant, n'est-ce pas?"
"My dear fellow, this fellow Hitler, quite extrord'nary.
Wonder what the beggar's up to?"
                              Or people said,
"I see by the papers they had an election in Germany.
Seem to have lots of elections over there.
Say, what do you know about this bank-holiday, Joe?
If you need some cash, I've got a couple of bucks,
But the banks are bound to reopen."

That was March fifth. They burned the books May tenth.

Why bother about the books?
Why bother to go back to that fateful year,
Year that prepared the blood-purge and the wars,
The death of Austria, the trick of Munich,
The bombers over the defenseless towns,
And all we know and all that must be fought
Here, now and always till the score is paid
And from its grim recital pick one instance
Of calculated wrong?
A book's a book. It's paper, ink and print.
If you stab it, it won't bleed.
If you beat it, it won't bruise.
If you burn it, it won't scream.
   [*Crackle of flames*]
Burn a few books—burn hundreds—burn a million—
What difference does that make?
   VOICE OF SCHILLER [*firm, masculine and thoughtful*]:
It does to me.
Excuse me, sir—my name is Friedrich Schiller,
A name once not unknown in Germany,

One of the glories, so they said, of Germany,
A Germany these robbers never knew.
Over a century and a half ago
I spoke and wrote of freedom.
I spoke against oppressors and dictators.
I spoke for every man who lifts his head
And will not bow to tyrants.
And, though I died, my poems and plays spoke on
In every tongue, in every land for freedom,
For that's what books can do.
And now, today, in the land where I was born—

NAZI VOICE: The play, *William Tell*, by Friedrich Schiller shall no longer be performed on the stage. It glorifies a dangerous and unseemly spirit of revolt against conquerors. It shall no longer be performed on the German stage. This is an order!

NARRATOR: That's what they do. That's what they do to the mind.
That's what they do to the books of their own great dead.
That's how they foul the present and the past,
Shut the dead mouth so that it cannot speak
Because it spoke far too well.
Now, here's another ghost,
Pale, frail, satirical, a mocking spirit,
But with the light of freedom in his eyes.
Your name, brave ghost?

HEINE'S VOICE [*sharp and humorous*]: My name? It's Heinrich Heine.
Born to much sorrow, born to be a man.
Out of my laughter and my heart's despair,
I made my little songs—such simple songs
A child could understand them—and grown men
Remember them and love them all their lives.
Some were so funny! Some were pitiful.
And some were trumpet calls for liberty,
For, though I couldn't fight, I was a fighter,
And when my time had come to die, I said
After long torment in my mattress-grave,
"Bury me with a sword upon my coffin
For I have been a soldier of humanity!"

THEY BURNED THE BOOKS

NARRATOR: A soldier of humanity
And you deserved that name,
But now—today—what happens to your songs?
HEINE: Well—there was one about a lorelei,
Just a small song. It went—let's see—like this—
[*He hums the first bars of "The Lorelei" to faint background music*]
You've heard it, maybe? Many people sing it.
They sang it many years along the Rhine.
They sing it still.
NARRATOR: Still?
HEINE: Oh, yes. That one of mine they—haven't burned.
That would be just a little difficult.
Too many Germans know the words by heart.
So, with totalitarian courtesy,
They've kept the song—and blotted out my name.
You see—I was a Jew.
NAZI VOICE: New editions of the works of the Jew, Heinrich Heine, are not desirable. In all textbooks and anthologies where the words of the song "The Lorelei" appear, the name of the Jew, Heine, shall be omitted and the author given as "Author Unknown."
HEINE [*mocking*]: Author well-known—since 1828.
Author unknown—since 1933.
NARRATOR: That's what they do to soldiers of humanity!
That's how they rob the soldier of his sword,
The dead man of the one thing he may keep,
His name—his very name!
Don't think that's all.
Don't think it's just the singers and the poets!
Light the flames—light the flames—and hear them roar!
See what the flames consume!
[*Fire-Music in. Tramp of feet. Crackle of flames*]
They're coming now—the men with the tramping feet,
The hard-faced boys with the truncheons—the new order!
The flames they've lighted howl and leap in the square.
You can't set fire to a Reichstag every day,
But the pyre that they light today shall fling its shadows
In flame and shadow over the whole round world.

Hear them tramp! They're coming! They bring the books to the fire!

NAZI VOICE: The books of the Jew, Albert Einstein—to the flames!

OTHER VOICE: Sieg Heil!

[*Noise of flames*]

NARRATOR: Einstein, the scientist,
Who thought in universes.
Einstein, the man we honor in our land.

NAZI VOICE: To the flames with him—to the flames!

VOICES: Sieg Heil!

NAZI VOICE: The books of Sigmund Freud—to the flames!

[*Noise of flames*]

NARRATOR: Freud, prober of the riddles of man's mind,
World-known, world famous.

[*Noise of flames*]

NAZI VOICE: To the flames—the flames!
Burn them—we don't want thought—we don't want mind.
We want one will, one leader and one folk!

HEINE'S VOICE [*cutting in*]: One vast, inexorable stupidity!

NAZI VOICE: Who said that? Gag him—burn him—to the flames!
To the flames with Heinrich Mann and Thomas Mann,
Gorki the Russian, Schnitzler the Austrian,
Hemingway, Dreiser, the Americans,
And now, to the flames with this!

VOICES: Sieg Heil!

[*Noise of flames*]

NARRATOR: That is the Bible. Would you burn God's word?

NAZI VOICE: We need no Bible but the words of the Leader.
We have no god except the German gods.
We have the tanks, the guns, the bombs, the planes
And that shall be enough!

VOICES: Sieg Heil! Sieg Heil!

HEINE'S VOICE: And yet there shall be weeping for this burning,
Weeping throughout your land.
The weeping of poor women and old men
Who loved and trusted in the word of God

THEY BURNED THE BOOKS

And now are worse than homeless in your world
For you have taken their last failing hope,
The promise of their Father and their Lord.
   NAZI VOICE: How dare you speak?
Exile and Jew, how dare you speak to us?
   HEINE: I speak for all humanity in chains,
Exile, Jew, Christian—for the prison-camps,
And those who dwell in them and bide their time—
For the dishonored, for the dispossessed,
For those you have ground like wheat.
I speak for every honest man of God,
Driven from his own pulpit, by your might,
And for those who saw that happen—and remember it.
I speak for the dark earth and the mute voices
And yet I speak humanity unbound.
   NAZI VOICE: You? You are just a singer,
A worthless singer!
   HEINE: True.
And that is why I speak, because I know,
Being a singer, what moves every heart.
I speak with little barbs and little songs
So simple any child can understand
Just what they say—and yet so memorable
Once you have heard them you will not forget them
But they will stay within your memory,
Sweet as first love, salt as the tears of man,
Free as the winds of heaven in the sky.
And you do well to try to shut my mouth
For, while one little song of mine remains,
All that you hate and would destroy remains,
Humor and grace and human tenderness,
Laughter and mockery and the bare sword,
The sword I wanted on my lonely coffin,
The sword of liberty.
   NAZI VOICE: We'll shut your mouth!
We'll find you in the graveyard where you lie,
Dig up your rotten bones and scatter them
Till there is nobody in all the world
Who's heard of Heinrich Heine!

HEINE [*mocking*]: Dig deep! Dig well!
Scatter my dust, break up my burial stone,
Erase my name with all your thoroughness,
Your lumbering, fat-headed, thoroughness,
Smelling of beer and bombs!
And yet, while there's a book, there will be Heine!
There will be Heine, laughing at you still,
Laughing with all the free—with all the free!
  [*His voice fades. Music*]
  NARRATOR: Yes.
There will be Heine. There will be all those
Whose words lift up man's heart.
But only if we choose.
This battle is not just a battle of lands,
A war of conquest, a balance-of-power war.
It is a battle for the mind of man
Not only for his body. It will decide
What you and you and you can think and say,
Plan, dream, and hope for in your inmost minds
For the next thousand years.
Decide whether man goes forward towards the light,
Stumbling and striving, clumsy—but a man—
Or back to the dark ages, the dark gods,
The old barbaric forest that is fear.
Books are not men, and yet they are alive.
They are man's memory and his aspiration,
The link between his present and his past,
The tools he builds with, all the hoarded thoughts,
Winnowed and sifted from a million minds,
Living and dead to guide him on his way.
Suppose it happened here.
Suppose the books were burned here.
This is a school, somewhere in America.
This is the kind of school we've always had,
Argued about, paid taxes for, kept on with,
Because we want our kids to know some things.
Suppose it happened here.
  [*Typical school bell buzzing. Shuffle of feet, buzz of voices*]
  [*Bell stops*]

VOICE OF A WOMAN TEACHER, MISS WINSLOW: The class will come to order.

[*Noise of class settling down*]

[MISS WINSLOW: This morning we are going to discuss some of the basic American ideas on which our nation was founded—freedom, tolerance, liberty under law. To start the discussion, I am going to ask Joe Barnes to recite the Gettysburg Address to us. Do you think you can do that without looking at your book too much, Joe?

JOE BARNES [*an adolescent voice*]: I—I guess so, Miss Winslow. Studied it last night.

MISS WINSLOW: Very well, Joe. You may begin.

JOE BARNES: The Gettysburg Address. By Abraham Lincoln. "Fourscore and seven years ago our fathers brought forth on this continent a new nation, conceived in liberty and dedicated to the proposition that all men are created equal."

NAZI VOICE: Stop!

JOE BARNES [*continuing uncertainly*]: Now we are engaged— we are engaged—

NAZI VOICE: Stop! The words of the Gettysburg Address can no longer be studied in any school of our glorious new order!

[*Rustle and protesting murmur from class*]

MISS WINSLOW: But those are the words of Lincoln!

JOE BARNES: But Miss Winslow told me—

NAZI VOICE: Miss Winslow is no longer your teacher. I am your teacher. Attention!

[*Rustle of class*]

When I give the command, you will rise and bring your textbooks to my desk. All this nonsense of freedom and tolerance— that is finished. All this nonsense of men being equal—that is finished. We shall give you new textbooks. The old ones will be burned in the schoolyard. Are there any questions?

[*Silence*]

NAZI VOICE: Good. The new order does not like questions.

MISS WINSLOW: I protest! This is infamous! You can't know what you're doing! I have taught here for twenty years!

NAZI VOICE: So I understand. That is a long time, Miss Winslow—too long. You deserve a long rest. We'll see you get it.

No, you needn't bother to say goodbye to your students. Guards!
Take the woman away!

[*Music up and down*]

NARRATOR: Impossible? Fantastic? Sounds that way. Ask the
teachers and books of occupied France,
France, that loved letters—France, once the light of Europe—
Read the list of books the French—can't read any more.
What sort of books?
Well, there are all kinds of course, from detective stories
To the life of a great French queen. But here, for instance,
Is a history of Poland—

NAZI VOICE: Suppressed.

NARRATOR: Why? Well, according to the New Order, Poland
has no history.

NAZI VOICE: Poland has no history.

NARRATOR: And here,
French History for Secondary Schools,
History of France, History of France and Europe,
Contemporary Europe, Legends and Fables
of France for Children—

NAZI VOICE: Suppressed. Withdrawn. On the blacklist.

NARRATOR: But these are not guns or daggers
Stored up against revolt. They're the commonplace
Textbooks, thumbed by a thousand schoolboy fingers,
Inkspotted, dogeared, drowsed above in classrooms,
Familiar and dull and mild.
They must be harmless enough.

NAZI VOICE: They are not harmless. We know what we are
doing.

NARRATOR: Yes. They know what they are doing.
They know, if you take the children of a country
And teach them nothing but lies about the world,
Give them no chance for argument or questions,
Give them no books that show another side,
No word of all the words that speak for freedom,
The man who grows from the child will believe the lies
And never hear of the truth.
                        It's a simple plan,
As simple and efficient as arsenic.

Just rewrite all of the books to suit yourself
And the rest will follow in time—the beatings and burnings,
The massed, mechanical might and the metal men.
Would you like a sample of American history
Nazi style? Can you stand it? You'd better know
What it would be like for your children and their children.
You heard Joe Barnes give the Gettysburg Address.
This is what he'd be like if he'd never heard it
Or anything like it, ever—if all his books
Were the textbooks of the New Order
If our schoolbooks wore swastikas.

Come in Joe, will you?
Looks different in his brown shirt, doesn't he?
Can you tell us about American history, Joe?
Some—names—and dates—and people—

JOE BARNES [*in a mechanical, sullen voice*]: American history dates from the foundation of the New Order.

NARRATOR: Nothing before that?

JOE BARNES: Nothing important.

NARRATOR: Well, come, Joe, there must have been one or two things before that.

JOE BARNES: Nothing important.

NARRATOR: After all, for instance, the discovery of America. That was fairly important. Do you know anything about that?

JOE BARNES: Yes. That is in my book. [*Reciting mechanically*] America was discovered in 1492 by Christopher Columbus, an honorary Aryan.

NARRATOR: An honorary Aryan? I always thought he was an Italian.

JOE BARNES: That was before the New Order. He is now an honorary Aryan of the second class—like Mussolini and Hirohito.

NARRATOR: I wonder how he likes that. However—after Columbus—

JOE BARNES: There came the New Order.

NARRATOR: But weren't there just a few things in between? Wasn't there something called the Declaration of Independence?

JOE BARNES [*scornfully*]: Oh—that! Yes, there was that. But it was all wrong. It said everyone was entitled to life, liberty and the pursuit of happiness. That was all wrong.

NARRATOR: Who wrote it?

JOE BARNES: It is unimportant who wrote it. It is not in my book.

NARRATOR: Didn't you ever hear of a man named Thomas Jefferson?

JOE BARNES: Thomas Jefferson? No. There is no such man in my book.

NARRATOR: Or George Washington?

JOE BARNES: Yes, he was a general. But not a very good one. He was defeated by German might at the battle of Trenton. Afterwards he foolishly became President of the United States instead of ruling his country with a strong, mailed fist.

NARRATOR: But maybe he didn't believe in ruling people with a strong, mailed fist.

JOE BARNES: [*impatiently*]: He may have had some such old-fashioned, sentimental ideas. That is why he is unimportant. The man to study in his period is Benedict Arnold—a man much ahead of his time.

NARRATOR: I always thought Benedict Arnold was a traitor to his country.

JOE BARNES: Traitor? What nonsense! He sensibly tried to collaborate with a stronger power in order to save his countrymen from the horrors of democracy and revolution. He is a very honorary Aryan of the first class, with star. We have many honorary Aryans just like Benedict Arnold.

NARRATOR: I wouldn't be a bit surprised. And—just one last question, Joe.

JOE BARNES: Yes. But hurry, please. I must attend a Strength Through Joy meeting—and it is necessary for me to clean my pistol, first.

NARRATOR: Did you ever hear of a man who said "Government of the people, by the people, for the people?"

JOE BARNES [*violently and fearfully*]: Certainly not! Of course not! It's a lie! You've been spying on me! My father did have the book but I never saw it! It's a long while ago and the teacher has been sent away! I know nothig about Abraham Linc——

[*Music up and down*]

THEY BURNED THE BOOKS

NARRATOR: That's it. That's how they work.
That's what they do to kids.
That's the way they'd like to work here.

NAZI VOICE: That's it, my friend. You see, we can destroy
Houses with bombs and people with starvation,
Outflank defensive lines and tramp ahead.
We can destroy the spirit of a nation
With poisoned doubts and fears,
Erase its history, blot out its past,
Sully its famous names and substitute
Our words for all the words of liberty.
But, while there is a single man alive,
Hidden or starving, who somehow remembers
The vows of freedom, the undying words
That spoke for man's free mind,
Though they were said a thousand years ago,
Our conquest is not perfect.

                              They are terrible,
These immaterial and airy words,
Sharp as edged swords, infectious as the plague.
They travel silently from mind to mind,
Leaving no trace. They live in quiet books
You hardly would suspect unless our leader
Had wisely warned us of them. They hide and creep
In jokes and catchwords under our own noses,
In dots and dashes, in a bar of music.
[*V motif in music*]
And, worse than all,
Within the silent eyes of hungry men,
Waiting their time, waiting their hungry time.
That's why they must be killed.
That's why we burn the books. That's why we burn
All knowledge, all the recollected thought
Gathered in patience through three thousand years
Of civilization. That knowledge is man's brain
And till we've taken an electric wire
And burned the brain cells from his very brain
So he will be a dumb and gaping slave,
We cannot win. And still we mean to win!

Get the fire ready! Bring the books to the fire!

[*Fire-Music, fading into the tolling of a great bell*]

NARRATOR: Nine years ago.

[BELL *tolls*]

NARRATOR: Nine years ago in Berlin.

[BELL *tolls*]

NARRATOR: Nine years ago in a public square in Berlin.

[BELL *tolls*]

NARRATOR: They burned the books and that was the beginning.
We didn't know it then. We know it now.
Hear the books burn.

[*Sound of flames*]

VOICES: Einstein—to the fire!
Mann—Toller—Helen Keller—to the fire!
Old Testament and New—to the fire—to the fire!

[*Fire-Music. Flames. Bell*]

NARRATOR: This is in memory. This is in remembrance.
This is for all the lies that have been told.
The innocent blood, the blood that cries from the ground,
Rise up and speak, you voices!
Voices of dead and living, past and present,
Voices of gagged men, whispering through sore lips,
Voices of children, robbed of their small songs,
Strong voices, chanting of the rights of man,
Rebel and fighter, men of the free heart,
We, too, shall build a fire, though not in fear,
Revenge or barren hate, but such a great
And cleansing fire it shall leap through the world
Like leaping flame!
                  Freedom to speak and pray,
Freedom from want, and fear, freedom for all;
Freedom of thought, freedom of man's bold mind!
Who marches with us?

SCHILLER: I am Friedrich Schiller
And I march with you in the cause of man.

HEINE: I am the soldier of humanity,
The mocking smile upon the face of Time
That men called Heine. And I march with you.

AN ENGLISH VOICE: My name is Milton. I am old and blind.

I knew oppression and defeat and scorn
And the high justice of eternal God,
Paradise lost and paradise regained,
And I march with you.

AN IRISH VOICE: My name is Jonathan Swift,
Dean of St. Patrick's, scourge of knaves and fools,
Though bitter indignation
Tore at my heart and cracked it till it broke,
I never had a patient mind for tyrants,
And I march with you.

AN AMERICAN VOICE: I hailed my sunburnt children in their youth,
Pioneers, pioneers!
I told them Walt would back them to the end.
I said they should be free. I sang democracy,
The new word, the new meaning, the bright day,
And I march with you!

FRENCH VOICE: The miserable shall be lifted up. The tyrants all cast down.

SECOND ENGLISH VOICE: The Parliament of Man, the Federation of the world.

SECOND AMERICAN VOICE: Well, maybe that'll take a while to grow
(My name's Sam Clemens.)
But Pudd'nhead Wilson says
"Cauliflower is just a cabbage with a college education."
And so we might start in.
About this business, now.
I may have made a living, cracking jokes,
But one thing I did hate was cruelty.
One thing I did dislike was pompous fools
Treading on decent people. Count me in.

NARRATOR: Milton and Whitman, Tennyson and Swift,
Mark Twain and Hugo—every one who wrote
With a free pen in words of living fire,
From Plato, dreaming of his bright Republic,
To every exile walking in our streets,
Exiled for truth and faith.
And all of ours, all of our own today,

All those who speak for freedom.
These are our voices. These shall light our fire.
Light the bright candle that shall not be quenched,
That never has been quenched in all man's years
Although all darkness and all tyranny
Have tried to quench it.
                              Call the roll of those
Who tried to quench it!

A COLD, ECHOING VOICE: Darius, the Persian. Darius, the Great King.

NARRATOR: Where is Darius?
COLD VOICE: Dead. Forgotten and dead.
COLD VOICE: Attila the Hun. Attila, devourer of peoples.
NARRATOR: Where is Attila?
COLD VOICE: Bones. Forgotten bones.
COLD VOICE: Alaric the Goth. Alaric, destroyer of Rome.
NARRATOR: Where is Alaric?
COLD VOICE: Dust. Forgotten dust.
NARRATOR: Adolf Hitler, born April 20, 1889.
WHISPERING VOICES: Adolf Hitler.
NARRATOR: Adolf Hitler, burner of books.
WHISPERING VOICES: Adolf Hitler.
NARRATOR: Adolf Hitler, destroyer of thought.
WHISPERING VOICES: Adolf Hitler.
[BELL *tolls*]
VOICES: Adolf Hitler, born 1889.
VOICES: Died. Died. Died. Died. Died.
NARRATOR: We are waiting, Adolf Hitler.
The books are waiting, Adolf Hitler.
The fire is waiting, Adolf Hitler.
The Lord God of Hosts is waiting, Adolf Hitler.

[*Music up to climax*]

(CURTAIN)

Prose

ONE

Stories of America

JACOB AND THE INDIANS

It goes back to the early days—may God profit all who lived then—and the ancestors.

Well, America, you understand, in those days was different. It was a nice place, but you wouldn't believe it if you saw it today. Without busses, without trains, without states, without Presidents, nothing!

With nothing but colonists and Indians and wild woods all over the country and wild animals to live in the wild woods. Imagine such a place! In these days, you children don't even think about it; you read about it in the schoolbooks, but what is that? And I put in a call to my daughter, in California, and in three minutes I am saying "Hello, Rosie," and there it is Rosie and she is telling me about the weather, as if I wanted to know! But things were not always that way. I remember my own days, and they were different. And in the times of my grandfather's grandfather, they were different still. Listen to the story.

My grandfather's grandfather was Jacob Stein, and he came from Rettelsheim, in Germany. To Philadelphia he came, an orphan in a sailing ship, but not a common man. He had learning—he had been to the *chedar*—he could have been a scholar among the scholars. Well, that is the way things happen in this bad world. There was a plague and a new grand duke—things are always so. He would say little of it afterward—they had left his teeth in his mouth, but he would say little of it. He did not have to say—we are children of the Dispersion—we know a black day when it comes.

Yet imagine—a young man with fine dreams and learning, a scholar with a pale face and narrow shoulders, set down in those early days in such a new country. Well, he must work, and he did. It was very fine, his learning, but it did not fill his mouth. He must carry a pack on his back and go from door to door with it. That was no disgrace; it was so that many began. But it was not expounding the Law, and at first he was very homesick. He would sit in his room at night, with the one candle, and read the preacher Koheleth, till the bitterness of the preacher rose in his mouth. Myself, I am sure that Koheleth was a great preacher, but if he had had a good wife he would have been a more cheerful man. They had too many wives in those old days—it confused them. But Jacob was young.

As for the new country where he had come, it was to him a place of exile, large and frightening. He was glad to be out of the ship, but, at first, that was all. And when he saw his first real Indian in the street—well, that was a day! But the Indian, a tame one, bought a ribbon from him by signs, and after that he felt better. Nevertheless, it seemed to him at times that the straps of the pack cut into his very soul, and he longed for the smell of the *chedar* and the quiet streets of Rettelsheim and the good smoked goose-breast pious housewives keep for the scholar. But there is no going back—there is never any going back.

All the same, he was a polite young man, and a hardworking. And soon he had a stroke of luck—or at first it seemed so. It was from Simon Ettelsohn that he got the trinkets for his pack, and one day he found Simon Ettelsohn arguing a point of the Law with a friend, for Simon was a pious man and well thought of in the Congregation Mikveh Israel. Our grandfather's grandfather stood by very modestly at first—he had come to replenish his pack and Simon was his employer. But finally his heart moved within him, for both men were wrong, and he spoke and told them where they erred. For half an hour he spoke, with his pack still upon his shoulders, and never has a text been expounded with more complexity, not even by the great Reb Samuel. Till, in the end, Simon Ettelsohn threw up his hands and called him a young David and a candle of learning. Also, he allowed him a more profitable route of trade. But, best of all, he invited young Jacob to his house, and there Jacob ate well for the first time since he had come to Philadelphia. Also he laid eyes upon Miriam Ettelsohn for the first time, and she was Simon's youngest daughter and a rose of Sharon.

After that, things went better for Jacob, for the protection of the strong is like a rock and a well. But yet things did not go altogether as he wished. For, at first, Simon Ettelsohn made much of him, and there was stuffed fish and raisin wine for the young scholar, though he was a peddler. But there is a look in a man's eyes that says "H'm? Son-in-law?" and that look Jacob did not see. He was modest—he did not expect to win the maiden overnight, though he longed for her. But gradually it was borne in upon him what he was in the Ettelsohn house—a young scholar to be shown before Simon's friends, but a scholar whose learning did not fill his mouth. He did not blame Simon for it, but it was not what he had intended. He began to wonder if he would ever get on in the world at all, and that is not good for any man.

Nevertheless, he could have borne it, and the aches and pains of his love, had it not been for Meyer Kappelhuist. Now, there was a pushing man! I speak no ill of anyone, not even of your Aunt Cora, and she can keep the De Groot silver if she finds it in her heart to do so; who lies down in the straw with a dog, gets up with fleas. But this Meyer Kappelhuist! A big, red-faced fellow from Holland with shoulders the size of a barn door and red hair on the backs of his hands. A big mouth for eating and drinking and telling schnorrer stories—and he talked about the Kappelhuists, in Holland, till you'd think they were made of gold. The crane says, "I am really a peacock—at least on my mother's side." And yet, a thriving man—that could not be denied. He had started with a pack, like our grandfather's grandfather, and now he was trading with the Indians and making money hand over fist. It seemed to Jacob that he could never go to the Ettelsohn house without meeting Meyer and hearing about those Indians. And it dried the words in Jacob's mouth and made his heart burn.

For, no sooner would our grandfather's grandfather begin to expound a text or a proverb, than he would see Meyer Kappelhuist looking at the maiden. And when Jacob had finished his expounding, and there should have been a silence, Meyer Kappelhuist would take it upon himself to thank him, but always in a tone that said: "The Law is the Law and the Prophets are the Prophets, but prime beaver is also prime beaver, my little scholar!" It took the pleasure from Jacob's learning and the joy of the maiden from his heart. Then he would sit silent and burning, while Meyer told a great tale of Indians, slapping his hands on his knees. And in the end he was always careful to ask Jacob how many needles and pins he had sold that day; and when Jacob told him, he would smile and say very smoothly that all things had small beginnings, till the maiden herself could not keep from a little smile. Then, desperately, Jacob would rack his brains for more interesting matter. He would tell of the wars of the Maccabees and the glory of the Temple. But even as he told them, he felt they were far away. Whereas Meyer and his accursed Indians were there, and the maiden's eyes shone at his words.

Finally he took his courage in both hands and went to Simon Ettelsohn. It took much for him to do it, for he had not been brought up to strive with men, but with words. But it seemed to him now that everywhere he went he heard of nothing but Meyer Kappelhuist and his trading with the Indians, till he thought it would drive him mad. So he went to Simon Ettelsohn in his shop.

"I am weary of this narrow trading in pins and needles," he said, without more words.

Simon Ettelsohn looked at him keenly; for while he was an ambitious man, he was kindly as well.

"*Nu,*" he said. "A nice little trade you have and the people like you. I myself started in with less. What would you have more?"

"I would have much more," said our grandfather's grandfather stiffly. "I would have a wife and a home in this new country. But how shall I keep a wife? On needles and pins?"

"*Nu,* it has been done," said Simon Ettelsohn, smiling a little. "You are a good boy, Jacob, and we take an interest in you. Now, if it is a question of marriage, there are many worthy maidens. Asher Levy, the baker, has a daughter. It is true that she squints a little, but her heart is of gold." He folded his hands and smiled.

JACOB AND THE INDIANS

"It is not of Asher Levy's daughter I am thinking," said Jacob, taken aback. Simon Ettelsohn nodded his head and his face grew grave.

"*Nu*, Jacob," he said. "I see what is in your heart. Well, you are a good boy, Jacob, and a fine scholar. And if it were in the old country, I am not saying. But here, I have one daughter married to a Seixas and one to a Da Silva. You must see that makes a difference." And he smiled the smile of a man well pleased with his world.

"And if I were such a one as Meyer Kappelhuist?" said Jacob bitterly.

"Now—well, that is a little different," said Simon Ettelsohn sensibly. "For Meyer trades with the Indians. It is true, he is a little rough. But he will die a rich man."

"I will trade with the Indians too," said Jacob, and trembled.

Simon Ettelsohn looked at him as if he had gone out of his mind. He looked at his narrow shoulders and his scholar's hands.

"Now, Jacob," he said soothingly, "do not be foolish. A scholar you are, and learned, not an Indian trader. Perhaps in a store you would do better. I can speak to Aaron Copras. And sooner or later we will find you a nice maiden. But to trade with Indians—well, that takes a different sort of man. Leave that to Meyer Kappelhuist."

"And your daughter, that rose of Sharon? Shall I leave her, too, to Meyer Kappelhuist?" cried Jacob.

Simon Ettelsohn looked uncomfortable.

"*Nu*, Jacob," he said. "Well, it is not settled, of course. But—"

"I will go forth against him as David went against Goliath," said our grandfather's grandfather wildly. "I will go forth into the wilderness. And God should judge the better man!"

Then he flung his pack on the floor and strode from the shop. Simon Ettelsohn called out after him, but he did not stop for that. Nor was it in his heart to go and seek the maiden. Instead, when he was in the street, he counted the money he had. It was not much. He had meant to buy his trading goods on credit from Simon Ettelsohn, but now he could not do that. He stood in the sunlit street of Philadelphia, like a man bereft of hope.

Nevertheless, he was stubborn—though how stubborn he did

not yet know. And though he was bereft of hope, he found his feet taking him to the house of Raphael Sanchez.

Now, Raphael Sanchez could have bought and sold Simon Ettelsohn twice over. An arrogant old man he was, with fierce black eyes and a beard that was whiter than snow. He lived apart, in his big house with his granddaughter, and men said he was very learned, but also very disdainful, and that to him a Jew was not a Jew who did not come of the pure sephardic strain.

Jacob had seen him, in the Congregation Mikveh Israel, and to Jacob he had looked like an eagle, and fierce as an eagle. Yet now, in his need, he found himself knocking at that man's door.

It was Raphael Sanchez himself who opened. "And what is for sale today, peddler?" he said, looking scornfully at Jacob's jacket where the pack straps had worn it.

"A scholar of the Law is for sale," said Jacob in his bitterness, and he did not speak in the tongue he had learned in this country, but in Hebrew.

The old man stared at him a moment.

"Now am I rebuked," he said. "For you have the tongue. Enter, my guest," and Jacob touched the scroll by the doorpost and went in.

They shared the noon meal at Raphael Sanchez's table. It was made of dark, glowing mahogany, and the light sank into it as sunlight sinks into a pool. There were many precious things in that room, but Jacob had no eyes for them. When the meal was over and the blessing said, he opened his heart and spoke, and Raphael Sanchez listened, stroking his beard with one hand. When the young man had finished, he spoke.

"So, Scholar," he said, though mildly, "you have crossed an ocean that you might live and not die, and yet all you see is a girl's face."

"Did not Jacob serve seven years for Rachel?" said our grandfather's grandfather.

"Twice seven, Scholar," said Raphael Sanchez dryly, "but that was in the blessed days." He stroked his beard again. "Do you know why I came to this country?" he said.

"No," said Jacob Stein.

"It was not for the trading," said Raphael Sanchez. "My house has lent money to kings. A little fish, a few furs—what are they

JACOB AND THE INDIANS

to my house? No, it was for the promise—the promise of Penn—that this land should be an habitation and a refuge, not only for the Gentiles. Well, we know Christian promises. But so far, it has been kept. Are you spat upon in the street here, Scholar of the Law?"

"No," said Jacob. "They call me Jew, now and then. But the Friends, though Gentile, are kind."

"It is not so in all countries," said Raphael Sanchez, with a terrible smile.

"No," said Jacob quietly, "it is not."

The old man nodded. "Yes, one does not forget that," he said. "The spittle wipes off the cloth, but one does not forget. One does not forget the persecutor or the persecuted. That is why they think me mad, in the Congregation Mikveh Israel, when I speak what is in my mind. For, look you"—and he pulled a map from a drawer—"here is what we know of these colonies, and here and here our people make a new beginning, in another air. But here is New France—see it?—and down the great river come the French traders and their Indians."

"Well?" said Jacob in puzzlement.

"Well?" said Raphael Sanchez. "Are you blind? I do not trust the King of France—the king before him drove out the Huguenots, and who knows what he may do? And if they hold the great rivers against us, we shall never go westward."

"We?" said Jacob in bewilderment.

"We," said Raphael Sanchez. He struck his hand on the map. "Oh, they cannot see it in Europe—not even their lords in parliament and their ministers of state," he said. "They think this is a mine, to be worked as the Spaniards worked Potosi, but it is not a mine. It is something beginning to live, and it is faceless and nameless yet. But it is our lot to be part of it—remember that in the wilderness, my young scholar of the Law. You think you are going there for a girl's face, and that is well enough. But you may find something there you did not expect to find."

He paused and his eyes had a different look.

"You see, it is the trade first," he said. "Always the trader, before the settled man. The Gentiles will forget that, and some of our own folk too. But one pays for the land of Canaan; one pays in blood and sweat."

Then he told Jacob what he would do for him and dismissed him, and Jacob went home to his room with his head buzzing strangely. For at times it seemed to him that the Congregation Mikveh Israel was right in thinking Raphael Sanchez half mad. And at other times it seemed to him that the old man's words were a veil, and behind them moved and stirred some huge and unguessed shape. But chiefly he thought of the rosy cheeks of Miriam Ettelsohn.

It was with the Scotchman, McCampbell, that Jacob made his first trading journey. A strange man was McCampbell, with grim features and cold blue eyes, but strong and kindly, though silent, except when he talked of the Ten Lost Tribes of Israel. For it was his contention that they were the Indians beyond the Western Mountains, and on this subject he would talk endlessly.

Indeed, they had much profitable conversation, McCampbell quoting the doctrines of a rabbi called John Calvin, and our grandfather's grandfather replying with Talmud and Torah till McCampbell would almost weep that such a honey-mouthed scholar should be destined to eternal damnation. Yet he did not treat our grandfather's grandfather as one destined to eternal damnation, but as a man, and he, too, spoke of cities of refuge as a man speaks of realities, for his people had also been persecuted.

First they left the city behind them, and then the outlying towns and, soon enough, they were in the wilderness. It was very strange to Jacob Stein. At first he would wake at night and lie awake listening, while his heart pounded, and each rustle in the forest was the step of a wild Indian, and each screech of an owl in the forest the whoop before the attack. But gradually this passed. He began to notice how silently the big man, McCampbell, moved in the woods; he began to imitate him. He began to learn many things that even a scholar of the Law, for all his wisdom, does not know—the girthing of a packsaddle and the making of fires, the look of dawn in the forest and the look of evening. It was all very new to him, and sometimes he thought he would die of it, for his flesh weakened. Yet always he kept on.

When he saw his first Indians—in the woods, not in the town —his knees knocked together. They were there as he had dreamt of them in dreams, and he thought of the spirit, Iggereth-beth-

Mathlan, and her seventy-eight dancing demons, for they were painted and in skins. But he could not let his knees knock together, before heathens and a Gentile, and the first fear passed. Then he found they were grave men, very ceremonious and silent at first, and then when the silence had been broken, full of curiosity. They knew McCampbell, but him they did not know, and they discussed him and his garments with the frankness of children, till Jacob felt naked before them, and yet not afraid. One of them pointed to the bag that hung at Jacob's neck—the bag in which, for safety's sake, he carried his phylactery—then McCampbell said something and the brown hand dropped quickly, but there was a buzz of talk.

Later on, McCampbell explained to him that they, too, wore little bags of deerskin and inside them sacred objects—and they thought, seeing his, that he must be a person of some note. It made him wonder. It made him wonder more to eat deer meat with them, by a fire.

It was a green world and a dark one that he had fallen in—dark with the shadow of the forest, green with its green. Through it ran trails and paths that were not yet roads or highways—that did not have the dust and smell of the cities of men, but another scent, another look. These paths Jacob noted carefully, making a map, for that was one of the instructions of Raphael Sanchez. It seemed a great labor and difficult and for no purpose; yet, as he had promised, so he did. And as they sank deeper and deeper into the depths of the forest, and he saw pleasant streams and wide glades, untenanted but by the deer, strange thoughts came over him. It seemed to him that the Germany he had left was very small and crowded together; it seemed to him that he had not known there was so much width to the world.

Now and then he would dream back—dream back to the quiet fields around Rettelsheim and the red-brick houses of Philadelphia, to the stuffed fish and the raisin wine, the chanting in the *chedar* and the white twisted loaves of calm Sabbath, under the white cloth. They would seem very close for the moment, then they would seem very far away. He was eating deer's meat in a forest and sleeping beside embers in the open night. It was so that Israel must have slept in the wilderness. He had not thought of it as so, but it was so.

Now and then he would look at his hands—they seemed tougher and very brown, as if they did not belong to him any more. Now and then he would catch a glimpse of his own face, as he drank at a stream. He had a beard, but it was not the beard of a scholar—it was wild and black. Moreover, he was dressed in skins, now; it seemed strange to be dressed in skins at first, and then not strange.

Now all this time, when he went to sleep at night, he would think of Miriam Ettelsohn. But, queerly enough, the harder he tried to summon up her face in his thoughts, the vaguer it became.

He lost track of time—there was only his map and the trading and the journey. Now it seemed to him that they should surely turn back, for their packs were full. He spoke of it to McCampbell, but McCampbell shook his head. There was a light in the Scotchman's eyes now—a light that seemed strange to our grandfather's grandfather—and he would pray long at night, sometimes too loudly. So they came to the banks of the great river, brown and great, and saw it, and the country beyond it, like a view across Jordan. There was no end to that country—it stretched to the limits of the sky and Jacob saw it with his eyes. He was almost afraid at first, and then he was not afraid.

It was there that the strong man, McCampbell, fell sick, and there that he died and was buried. Jacob buried him on a bluff overlooking the river and faced the grave to the west. In his death sickness, McCampbell raved of the Ten Lost Tribes again and swore they were just across the river and he would go to them. It took all Jacob's strength to hold him—if it had been at the beginning of the journey, he would not have had the strength. Then he turned back, for he, too, had seen a Promised Land, not for his seed only, but for nations yet to come.

Nevertheless, he was taken by the Shawnees, in a season of bitter cold, with his last horse dead. At first, when misfortune began to fall upon him, he had wept for the loss of the horses and the good beaver. But, when the Shawnees took him, he no longer wept; for it seemed to him that he was no longer himself, but a man he did not know.

He was not concerned when they tied him to the stake and piled the wood around him, for it seemed to him still that it must be happening to another man. Nevertheless he prayed, as was fitting, chanting loudly; for Zion in the wilderness he prayed. He could smell the smell of the *chedar* and hear the voices that he knew—Reb Moses and Reb Nathan, and through them the curious voice of Raphael Sanchez, speaking in riddles. Then the smoke took him and he coughed. His throat was hot. He called for drink, and though they could not understand his words, all men know the sign of thirst, and they brought him a bowl filled. He put it to his lips eagerly and drank, but the stuff in the bowl was scorching hot and burned his mouth. Very angry then was our grandfather's grandfather, and without so much as a cry he took the bowl in both hands and flung it straight in the face of the man who had brought it, scalding him. Then there was a cry and a murmur from the Shawnees and, after some moments, he felt himself unbound and knew that he lived.

It was flinging the bowl at the man while yet he stood at the stake that saved him, for there is an etiquette about such matters. One does not burn a madman, among the Indians; and to the Shawnees, Jacob's flinging the bowl proved that he was mad, for a sane man would not have done so. Or so it was explained to him later, though he was never quite sure that they had not been playing cat-and-mouse with him, to test him. Also they were much concerned by his chanting his death song in an unknown tongue and by the phylactery that he had taken from its bag and bound upon brow and arm for his death hour, for these they thought strong medicine and uncertain. But in any case they released him, though they would not give him back his beaver, and that winter he passed in the lodges of the Shawnees, treated sometimes like a servant and sometimes like a guest, but always on the edge of peril. For he was strange to them, and they could not quite make up their minds about him, though the man with the scalded face had his own opinion, as Jacob could see.

Yet when the winter was milder and the hunting better than it had been in some seasons, it was he who got the credit of it, and the holy phylactery also; and by the end of the winter he was talking to them of trade, though diffidently at first. Ah, our grandfather's grandfather, *selig*, what woes he had! And yet it was not all woe, for he learned much woodcraft from the Shawnees and began to speak in their tongue.

Yet he did not trust them entirely; and when spring came and he could travel, he escaped. He was no longer a scholar then, but a hunter. He tried to think what day it was by the calendar, but he could only remember the Bee Moon and the Berry Moon. Yet when he thought of a feast he tried to keep it, and always he prayed for Zion. But when he thought of Zion, it was not as he had thought of it before—a white city set on a hill—but a great and open landscape, ready for nations. He could not have said why his thought had changed, but it had.

I shall not tell all, for who knows all? I shall not tell of the trading post he found deserted and the hundred and forty French louis in the dead man's money belt. I shall not tell of the half-grown boy, McGillvray, that he found on the fringes of settlement—the boy who was to be his partner in the days to come —and how they traded again with the Shawnees and got much beaver. Only this remains to be told, for this is true.

It was a long time since he had even thought of Meyer Kappelhuist—the big pushing man with red hairs on the backs of his hands. But now they were turning back toward Philadelphia, he and McGillvray, their packhorses and their beaver; and as the paths began to grow familiar, old thoughts came into his mind. Moreover, he would hear now and then, in the outposts of the wilderness, of a red-haired trader. So when he met the man himself not thirty miles from Lancaster, he was not surprised.

Now, Meyer Kappelhuist had always seemed a big man to our grandfather's grandfather. But he did not seem such a big man, met in the wilderness by chance, and at that Jacob was amazed. Yet the greater surprise was Meyer Kappelhuist's, for he stared at our grandfather's grandfather long and puzzledly before he cried out, "But it's the little scholar!" and clapped his hand on his knee. Then they greeted each other civilly and Meyer Kappelhuist drank liquor because of the meeting, but Jacob drank nothing. For, all the time, they were talking, he could see Meyer Kappelhuist's eyes fixed greedily upon his packs of beaver, and he did not like that. Nor did he like the looks of the three tame Indians who traveled with Meyer Kappelhuist and, though he was a man of peace, he kept his hand on his arms, and the boy, McGillvray, did the same.

Meyer Kappelhuist was anxious that they should travel on

together, but Jacob refused, for, as I say, he did not like the look in the red-haired man's eyes. So he said he was taking another road and left it at that.

"And the news you have of Simon Ettelsohn and his family—it is good, no doubt, for I know you are close to them," said Jacob, before they parted.

"Close to them?" said Meyer Kappelhuist, and he looked black as thunder. Then he laughed a forced laugh. "Oh, I see them no more," he said. "The old rascal has promised his daughter to a cousin of the Seixas, a greeny, just come over, but rich, they say. But to tell you the truth, I think we are well out of it, Scholar—she was always a little too skinny for my taste," and he laughed coarsely.

"She was a rose of Sharon and a lily of the valley," said Jacob respectfully, and yet not with the pang he would have expected at such news, though it made him more determined than ever not to travel with Meyer Kappelhuist. And with that they parted and Meyer Kappelhuist went his way. Then Jacob took a fork in the trail that McGillvray knew of and that was as well for him. For when he got to Lancaster, there was news of the killing of a trader by the Indians who traveled with him; and when Jacob asked for details, they showed him something dried on a willow hoop. Jacob looked at the thing and saw the hairs upon it were red.

"Sculped all right, but we got it back," said the frontiersman, with satisfaction. "The red devil had it on him when we caught him. Should have buried it, too, I guess, but we'd buried him already and it didn't seem feasible. Thought I might take it to Philadelphy, sometime—might make an impression on the governor. Say, if you're going there, you might—after all, that's where he come from. Be a sort of memento to his folks."

"And it might have been mine, if I had traveled with him," said Jacob. He stared at the thing again, and his heart rose against touching it. Yet it was well the city people should know what happened to men in the wilderness, and the price of blood. "Yes, I will take it," he said.

Jacob stood before the door of Raphael Sanchez, in Philadelphia. He knocked at the door with his knuckles, and the old man himself peered out at him.

"And what is your business with me, Frontiersman?" said the old man, peering.

"The price of blood for a country," said Jacob Stein. He did not raise his voice, but there was a note in it that had not been there when he first knocked at Raphael Sanchez's door.

The old man stared at him soberly. "Enter, my son," he said at last, and Jacob touched the scroll by the doorpost and went in.

He walked through the halls as a man walks in a dream. At last he was sitting by the dark mahogany table. There was nothing changed in the room—he wondered greatly that nothing in it had changed.

"And what have you seen, my son?" said Raphael Sanchez.

"I have seen the land of Canaan, flowing with milk and honey," said Jacob, Scholar of the Law. "I have brought back grapes from Eshcol, and other things that are terrible to behold," he cried, and even as he cried he felt the sob rise in his throat. He choked it down. "Also there are eighteen packs of prime beaver at the warehouse and a boy named McGillvray, a Gentile, but very trusty," he said. "The beaver is very good and the boy under my protection. And McCampbell died by the great river, but he had seen the land and I think he rests well. The map is not made as I would have it, but it shows new things. And we must trade with the Shawnees. There are three posts to be established —I have marked them on the map—and later, more. And beyond the great river there is country that stretches to the end of the world. That is where my friend McCampbell lies, with his face turned west. But what is the use of talking? You would not understand."

He put his head on his arms, for the room was too quiet and peaceful, and he was very tired. Raphael Sanchez moved around the table and touched him on the shoulder.

"Did I not say, my son, that there was more than a girl's face to be found in the wilderness?" he said.

"A girl's face?" said Jacob. "Why, she is to be married and, I hope, will be happy, for she was a rose of Sharon. But what are girls' faces beside this?" and he flung something on the table. It rattled dryly on the table, like a cast snakeskin, but the hairs upon it were red.

"It was Meyer Kappelhuist," said Jacob childishly, "and he was a strong man. And I am not strong, but a scholar. But I have seen what I have seen. And we must say Kaddish for him."

"Yes, yes," said Raphael Sanchez. "It will be done. I will see to it."

"But you do not understand," said Jacob. "I have eaten deer's meat in the wilderness and forgotten the month and the year. I have been a servant to the heathen and held the scalp of my enemy in my hand. I will never be the same man."

"Oh, you will be the same," said Sanchez. "And no worse a scholar, perhaps. But this is a new country."

"I must be for all," said Jacob. "For my friend McCampbell died also, and he was a Gentile."

"Let us hope," said Raphael Sanchez and touched him again upon the shoulder. Then Jacob lifted his head and he saw that the light had declined and the evening was upon him. And even as he looked, Raphael Sanchez's granddaughter came in to light the candles for Sabbath. And Jacob looked upon her, and she was a dove, with dove's eyes.

THE DEVIL AND DANIEL WEBSTER

It's a story they tell in the border country, where Massachusetts joins Vermont and New Hampshire.

Yes, Dan'l Webster's dead—or, at least, they buried him. But every time there's a thunderstorm around Marshfield, they say you can hear his rolling voice in the hollows of the sky. And they say that if you go to his grave and speak loud and clear, "Dan'l Webster—Dan'l Webster!" the ground'll begin to shiver and the trees begin to shake. And after a while you'll hear a deep voice saying, "Neighbor, how stands the Union?" Then you better answer the Union stands as she stood, rock-bottomed and copper-sheathed, one and indivisible, or he's liable to rear right out of the ground. At least, that's what I was told when I was a youngster.

You see, for a while, he was the biggest man in the country.

He never got to be President, but he was the biggest man. There were thousands that trusted in him right next to God Almighty, and they told stories about him that were like the stories of patriarchs and such. They said, when he stood up to speak, stars and stripes came right out in the sky, and once he spoke against a river and made it sink into the ground. They said, when he walked the woods with his fishing rod, Killall, the trout would jump out of the streams right into his pockets, for they knew it was no use putting up a fight against him; and, when he argued a case, he could turn on the harps of the blessed and the shaking of the earth underground. That was the kind of man he was, and his big farm up at Marshfield was suitable to him. The chickens he raised were all white meat down through the drumsticks, the cows were tended like children, and the big ram he called Goliath had horns with a curl like a morning-glory vine and could butt through an iron door. But Dan'l wasn't one of your gentlemen farmers; he knew all the ways of the land, and he'd be up by candlelight to see that the chores got done. A man with a mouth like a mastiff, a brow like a mountain and eyes like burning anthracite—that was Dan'l Webster in his prime. And the biggest case he argued never got written down in the books, for he argued it against the devil, nip and tuck and no holds barred. And this is the way I used to hear it told.

There was a man named Jabez Stone, lived at Cross Corners, New Hampshire. He wasn't a bad man to start with, but he was an unlucky man. If he planted corn, he got borers; if he planted potatoes, he got blight. He had good-enough land, but it didn't prosper him; he had a decent wife and children, but the the more children he had, the less there was to feed them. If stones cropped up in his neighbor's field, boulders boiled up in his; if he had a horse with the spavins, he'd trade it for one with the staggers and give something extra. There's some folks bound to be like that, apparently. But one day Jabez Stone got sick of the whole business.

He'd been plowing that morning and he'd just broke the plowshare on a rock that he could have sworn hadn't been there yesterday. And, as he stood looking at the plowshare, the off horse began to cough—that ropy kind of cough that means sickness and horse doctors. There were two children down with the measles, his wife was ailing, and he had a whitlow on his thumb. It was about the last straw for Jabez Stone. "I vow," he said, and he looked around him kind of desperate—"I vow it's enough to make a man want to sell his soul to the devil! And I would, too, for two cents!"

Then he felt a kind of queerness come over him at having said what he'd said; though, naturally, being a New Hampshireman, he wouldn't take it back. But, all the same, when it got to be evening and, as far as he could see, no notice had been taken, he felt relieved in his mind, for he was a religious man. But notice is always taken, sooner or later, just like the Good Book says. And, sure enough, next day, about suppertime, a soft-spoken, dark-dressed stranger drove up in a handsome buggy and asked for Jabez Stone.

Well, Jabez told his family it was a lawyer, come to see him about a legacy. But he knew who it was. He didn't like the looks of the stranger, nor the way he smiled with his teeth. They were white teeth, and plentiful—some say they were filed to a point, but I wouldn't vouch for that. And he didn't like it when the dog took one look at the stranger and ran away howling, with his tail between his legs. But having passed his word, more or less, he stuck to it, and they went out behind the barn and made their bargain. Jabez Stone had to prick his finger to sign, and the stranger lent him a silver pin. The wound healed clean, but it left a little white scar.

After that, all of a sudden, things began to pick up and prosper for Jabez Stone. His cows got fat and his horses sleek, his crops were the envy of the neighborhood, and lightning might strike all over the valley, but it wouldn't strike his barn. Pretty soon, he was one of the prosperous people of the county; they asked him to stand for selectman, and he stood for it; there began to be talk of running him for state senate. All in all, you might say the Stone family was as happy and contented as cats in a dairy. And so they were, except for Jabez Stone.

He'd been contented enough, the first few years. It's a great thing when bad luck turns; it drives most other things out of your head. True, every now and then, especially in rainy weather, the little white scare on his finger would give him a twinge. And once a year, punctual as clockwork, the stranger with the handsome buggy would come driving by. But the sixth year, the stranger lighted, and, after that, his peace was over for Jabez Stone.

The stranger came up through the lower field, switching his boots with a cane—they were handsome black boots, but Jabez Stone never liked the look of them, particularly the toes. And, after he'd passed the time of day, he said, "Well, Mr. Stone, you're a hummer! It's a very pretty property you've got here, Mr. Stone."

"Well, some might favor it and others might not," said Jabez Stone, for he was a New Hampshireman.

"Oh, no need to decry your industry!" said the stranger, very easy, showing his teeth in a smile. "After all, we know what's been done, and it's been according to contract and specifications. So when—ahem—the mortgage falls due next year, you shouldn't have any regrets."

"Speaking of that mortgage, mister," said Jabez Stone, and he looked around for help to the earth and the sky, "I'm beginning to have one or two doubts about it."

"Doubts?" said the strange, not quite so pleasantly.

"Why, yes," said Jabez Stone. "This being the U.S.A. and me always having been a religious man." He cleared his throat and got bolder. "Yes, sir," he said, "I'm beginning to have considerable doubts as to that mortgage holding in court."

"There's courts and courts," said the stranger, clicking his teeth. "Still, we might as well have a look at the original document." And he hauled out a big black pocketbook, full of papers. "Sherwin, Slater, Stevens, Stone," he muttered. "I, Jabez Stone, for a term of seven years— Oh, it's quite in order, I think."

But Jabez Stone wasn't listening, for he saw something else flutter out of the black pocketbook. It was something that looked like a moth, but it wasn't a moth. And as Jabez Stone stared at it, it seemed to speak to him in a small sort of piping voice, terrible small and thin, but terrible human. "Neighbor Stone!" it squeaked. "Neighbor Stone! Help me! For God's sake, help me!"

But before Jabez Stone could stir hand or foot, the stranger whipped out a big bandanna handkerchief, caught the creature

THE DEVIL AND DANIEL WEBSTER 127

in it, just like a butterfly, and started tying up the ends of the bandanna.

"Sorry for the interruption," he said. "As I was saying—"

But Jabez Stone was shaking all over like a scared horse.

"That's Miser Stevens' voice!" he said, in a croak. "And you've got him in your handkerchief!"

The stranger looked a little embarrassed.

"Yes, I really should have transferred him to the collecting box," he said with a simper, "but there were some rather unusual specimens there and I didn't want them crowded. Well, well, these little contretemps will occur."

"I don't know what you mean by contertan," said Jabez Stone, "but that was Miser Stevens' voice! And he ain't dead! You can't tell me he is! He was just as spry and mean as a woodchuck, Tuesday!"

"In the midst of life—" said the stranger, kind of pious. "Listen!" Then a bell began to toll in the valley and Jabez Stone listened, with the sweat running down his face. For he knew it was tolled for Miser Stevens and that he was dead.

"These long-standing accounts," said the stranger with a sigh; "one really hates to close them. But business is business."

He still had the bandanna in his hand, and Jabez Stone felt sick as he saw the cloth struggle and flutter.

"Are they all as small as that?" he asked hoarsely.

"Small?" said the stranger. "Oh, I see what you mean. Why, they vary." He measured Jabez Stone with his eyes, and his teeth showed. "Don't worry, Mr. Stone," he said. "You'll go with a very good grade. I wouldn't trust you outside the collecting box. Now, a man like Dan'l Webster, of course—well, we'd have to build a special box for him, and even at that, I imagine the wing spread would astonish you. But, in your case, as I was saying—"

"Put that handkerchief away!" said Jabez Stone, and he began to beg and to pray. But the best he could get at the end was a three years' extension, with conditions.

But till you make a bargain like that, you've got no idea of how fast four years can run. By the last months of those years, Jabez Stone's known all over the state and there's talk of running him for governor—and it's dust and ashes in his mouth.

For every day, when he gets up, he thinks, "There's one more night gone," and every night when he lies down, he thinks of the black pocketbook and the soul of Miser Stevens, and it makes him sick at heart. Till, finally, he can't bear it any longer, and, in the last days of the last year, he hitches up his horse and drives off to seek Dan'l Webster. For Dan'l was born in New Hampshire, only a few miles from Cross Corners, and it's well known that he was a particular soft spot for old neighbors.

It was early in the morning when he got to Marshfield, but Dan'l was up already, talking Latin to the farm hands and wrestling with the ram, Goliath, and trying out a new trotter and working up speeches to make against John C. Calhoun. But when he heard a New Hampshireman had come to see him, he dropped everything else he was doing, for that was Dan'l's way. He gave Jabez Stone a breakfast that five men couldn't eat, went into the living history of every man and woman in Cross Corners, and finally asked him how he could serve him.

Jabez Stone allowed that it was a kind of mortgage case.

"Well, I haven't pleaded a mortgage case in a long time, and I don't generally plead now, except before the Supreme Court," said Dan'l, "but if I can, I'll help you."

"Then I've got hope for the first time in ten years," said Jabez Stone, and told him the details.

Dan'l walked up and down as he listened, hands behind his back, now and then asking a question, now and then plunging his eyes at the floor, as if they'd bore through it like gimlets. When Jabez Stone had finished, Dan'l puffed out his cheeks and blew. Then he turned to Jabez Stone and a smile broke over his face like the sunrise over Monadnock.

"You've certainly given yourself the devil's own row to hoe, Neighbor Stone," he said, "but I'll take your case."

"You'll take it?" said Jabez Stone, hardly daring to believe.

"Yes," said Dan'l Webster. "I've got about seventy-five other things to do and the Missouri Compromise to straighten out, but I'll take your case. For if two New Hampshiremen aren't a match for the devil, we might as well give the country back to the Indians."

Then he shook Jabez Stone by the hand and said, "Did you come down here in a hurry?"

"Well, I admit I made time," said Jabez Stone.

"You'll go back faster," said Dan'l Webster, and he told 'em to hitch up Constitution and Constellation to the carriage. They were matched grays with one white forefoot, and they stepped like greased lightning.

Well, I won't describe how excited and pleased the whole Stone family was to have the great Dan'l Webster for a guest, when they finally got there. Jabez Stone had lost his hat on the way, blown off when they overtook a wind, but he didn't take much account of that. But after supper he sent the family off to bed, for he had most particular business with Mr. Webster. Mrs. Stone wanted them to sit in the front parlor, but Dan'l Webster knew front parlors and said he preferred the kitchen. So it was there they sat, waiting for the stranger, with a jug on the table between them and a bright fire on the hearth—the stranger being scheduled to show up on the stroke of midnight, according to specifications.

Well, most men wouldn't have asked for better company than Dan'l Webster and a jug. But with every tick of the clock Jabez Stone got sadder and sadder. His eyes roved round, and though he sampled the jug you could see he couldn't taste it. Finally, on the stroke of 11:30 he reached over and grabbed Dan'l Webster by the arm.

"Mr. Webster, Mr. Webster!" he said, and his voice was shaking with fear and a desperate courage. "For God's sake, Mr. Webster, harness your horses and get away from this place while you can!"

"You've brought me a long way, neighbor, to tell me you don't like my company," said Dan'l Webster, quite peaceable, pulling at the jug.

"Miserable wretch that I am!" groaned Jabez Stone. "I've brought you a devilish way, and now I see my folly. Let him take me if he wills. I don't hanker after it, I must say, but I can stand it. But you're the Union's stay and New Hampshire's pride! He mustn't get you, Mr. Webster! He mustn't get you!"

Dan'l Webster looked at the distracted man, all gray and shaking in the firelight, and laid a hand on his shoulder.

"I'm obliged to you, Neighbor Stone," he said gently. "It's kindly thought of. But there's a jug on the table and a case in hand. And I never left a jug or a case half finished in my life."

And just at that moment there was a sharp rap on the door.

"Ah, said Dan'l Webster, very coolly, "I thought your clock was a trifle slow, Neighbor Stone." He stepped to the door and opened it. "Come in!" he said.

The stranger came in—very dark and tall he looked in the firelight. He was carrying a box under his arm—a black, japanned box with little air holes in the lid. At the sight of the box, Jabez Stone gave a low cry and shrank into a corner of the room.

"Mr. Webster, I presume," said the stranger, very polite, but with his eyes glowing like a fox's deep in the woods.

"Attorney of record for Jabez Stone," said Dan'l Webster, but his eyes were glowing too. "Might I ask your name?"

"I've gone by a good many," said the stranger carelessly. "Perhaps Scratch will do for the evening. I'm often called that in these regions."

Then he sat down at the table and poured himself a drink from the jug. The liquor was cold in the jug, but it came steaming into the glass.

"And now," said the stranger, smiling and showing his teeth, "I shall call upon you, as a law-abiding citizen, to assist me in taking possession of my property."

Well, with that the argument began—and it went hot and heavy. At first, Jabez Stone had a flicker of hope, but when he saw Dan'l Webster being forced back at point after point, he just scrunched in his corner, with his eyes on that japanned box. For there wasn't any doubt as to the deed or the signature— that was the worst of it. Dan'l Webster twisted and turned and thumped his fist on the table, but he couldn't get away from that. He offered to compromise the case; the stranger wouldn't hear of it. He pointed out the property had increased in value, and state senators ought to be worth more; the stranger stuck to the letter of the law. He was a great lawyer, Dan'l Webster, but we know who's the King of Lawyers, as the Good Book tells us, and it seemed as if, for the first time, Dan'l Webster had met his match.

Finally, the stranger yawned a little. "Your spirited efforts on behalf of your client do you credit, Mr. Webster," he said, "but if you have no more arguments to adduce, I'm rather pressed for time"—and Jabez Stone shuddered.

Dan'l Webster's brow looked dark as a thundercloud.

"Pressed or not, you shall not have this man!" he thundered. "Mr. Stone is an American citizen, and no American citizen may be forced into the service of a foreign prince. We fought England for that in '12 and we'll fight all hell for it again!"

"Foreign?" said the stranger. "And who calls me a foreigner?"

"Well, I never yet heard of the dev—of your claiming American citizenship," said Dan'l Webster with surprise.

"And who with better right?" said the stranger, with one of his terrible smiles. "When the first wrong was done to the first Indian, I was there. When the first slaver put out for the Congo, I stood on her deck. Am I not in your books and stories and beliefs, from the first settlements on? Am I not spoken of, still, in every church in New England? 'Tis true the North claims me for a Southerner and the South for a Northerner, but I am neither. I am merely an honest American like yourself—and of the best descent—for, to tell the truth, Mr. Webster, though I don't like to boast of it, my name is older in this country than yours."

"Aha!" Dan'l Webster, with the veins standing out in his forehead. "Then I stand on the Constitution! I demand a trial for my client!"

"The case is hardly one for an ordinary court," said the stranger, his eyes flickering. "And, indeed, the lateness of the hour——"

"Let it be any court you choose, so it is an American judge and an American jury!" said Dan'l Webster in his pride. "Let it be the quick or the dead; I'll abide the issue!"

"You have said it," said the stranger, and pointed his finger at the door. And with that, and all of a sudden, there was a rushing of wind outside and a noise of footsteps. They came, clear and distinct, through the night. And yet, they were not like the footsteps of living men.

"In God's name, who comes by so late?" cried Jabez Stone, in an ague of fear.

"The jury Mr. Webster demands," cried the stranger, sipping

at his boiling glass. "You must pardon the rough appearance of one or two; they will have come a long way."

And with that the fire burned blue and the door blew open and twelve men entered, one by one.

If Jabez Stone had been sick with terror before, he was blind with terror now. For there was Walter Butler, the loyalist, who spread fire and horror through the Mohawk Valley in the times of the Revolution; and there was Simon Girty, the renegade, who saw white men burned at the stake and whooped with the Indians to see them burn. His eyes were green, like a catamount's, and the stains on his hunting shirt did not come from the blood of the deer. King Philip was there, wild and proud as he had been in life, with the great gash in his head that gave him his death wound, and cruel Governor Dale, who broke men on the wheel. There was Morton of Merry Mount, who so vexed the Plymouth Colony, with his flushed, loose, handsome face and his hate of the godly. There was Teach, the bloody pirate, with his black beard curling on his breast. The Reverend John Smeet, with his strangler's hands and his Geneva gown, walked as daintily as he had to the gallows. The red print of the rope was still around his neck, but he carried a perfumed handkerchief in one hand. One and all, they came into the room with the fires of hell still upon them, and the stranger named their names and their deeds as they came, till the tale of twelve was told. Yet the stranger had told the truth—they had all played a part in America.

"Are you satisfied with the jury, Mr. Webster?" said the stranger mockingly, when they had taken their places.

The sweat stood upon Dan'l Webster's brow, but his voice was clear.

"Quite satisfied," he said. "Though I miss General Arnold from the company."

"Benedict Arnold is engaged upon other business," said the stranger, with a glower. "Ah, you asked for a justice, I believe."

He pointed his finger once more, and a tall man, soberly clad in Puritan garb, with the burning gaze of the fanatic, stalked into the room and took his judge's place.

"Justice Hathorne is a jurist of experience," said the stranger.

"He presided at certain witch trials once held in Salem. There were others who repented of the business later, but not he."

"Repent of such notable wonders and undertakings?" said the stern old justice. "Nay, hang them—hang them all!" And he muttered to himself in a way that struck ice into the soul of Jabez Stone.

Then the trial began, and, as you might expect, it didn't look anyways good for the defense. And Jabez Stone didn't make much of a witness in his own behalf. He took one look at Simon Girty and screeched, and they had to put him back in his corner in a kind of swoon.

It didn't halt the trial, though; the trial went on, as trials do. Dan'l Webster had faced some hard juries and hanging judges in his time, but this was the hardest he'd ever faced, and he knew it. They sat there with a kind of glitter in their eyes, and the stranger's smooth voice went on and on. Every time he'd raise an objection, it'd be "Objection sustained," but whenever Dan'l objected, it'd be "Objection denied." Well, you couldn't expect fair play from a fellow like this Mr. Scratch.

It got to Dan'l in the end, and he began to heat, like iron in the forge. When he got up to speak he was going to flay that stranger with every trick known to the law, and the judge and jury too. He didn't care if it was contempt of court or what would happen to him for it. He didn't care any more what happened to Jabez Stone. He just got madder and madder, thinking of what he'd say. And yet, curiously enough, the more he thought about it, the less he was able to arrange his speech in his mind.

Till, finally, it was time for him to get up on his feet, and he did so, all ready to bust out with lightnings and denunciations. But before he started he looked over the judge and jury for a moment, such being his custom. And he noticed the glitter in their eyes was twice as strong as before, and they all leaned forward. Like hounds just before they got the fox, they looked, and the blue mist of evil in the room thickened as he watched them. Then he saw what he'd been about to do, and he wiped his forehead, as a man might who's just escaped falling into a pit in the dark.

For it was him they'd come for, not only Jabez Stone. He read it in the glitter of their eyes and in the way the stranger hid his mouth with one hand. And if he fought them with their own weapons, he'd fall into their power; he knew that, though he couldn't have told you how. It was his own anger and horror that burned in their eyes; and he'd have to wipe that out or the case was lost. He stood there for a moment, his black eyes burning like anthracite. And then he began to speak.

He started off in a low voice, though you could hear every word. They say he could call on the harps of the blessed when he chose. And this was just as simple and easy as a man could talk. But he didn't start out by condemning or reviling. He was talking about the things that make a country a country, and a man a man.

And he began with the simple things that everybody's known and felt—the freshness of a fine morning when you're young, and the taste of food when you're hungry, and the new day that's every day when you're a child. He took them up and he turned them in his hands. They were good things for any man. But without freedom, they sickened. And when he talked of those enslaved, and the sorrows of slavery, his voice got like a big bell. He talked of the early days of America and the men who had made those days. It wasn't a spread-eagle speech, but he made you see it. He admitted all the wrong that had ever been done. But he showed how, out of the wrong and the right, the suffering and the starvations, something new had come. And everybody had played a part in it, even the traitors.

Then he turned to Jabez Stone and showed him as he was— an ordinary man who'd had hard luck and wanted to change it. And, because he'd wanted to change it, now he was going to be punished for all eternity. And yet there was good in Jabez Stone, and he showed that good. He was hard and mean, in some ways, but he was a man. There was sadness in being a man, but it was a proud thing too. And he showed what the pride of it was till you couldn't help feeling it. Yes, even in hell, if a man was a man, you'd know it. And he wasn't pleading for any one person any more, though his voice rang like an organ. He was telling the story and the failures and the endless journey of mankind. They got tricked and trapped and bamboozled, but it was a great journey. And no demon that was ever foaled could know the inwardness of it—it took a man to do that.

The fire began to die on the hearth and the wind before morning to blow. The light was getting gray in the room when Dan'l Webster finished. And his words came back at the end to New Hampshire ground, and the one spot of land that each man loves and clings to. He painted a picture of that, and to each one of that jury he spoke of things long forgotten. For his voice could search the heart, and that was his gift and his strength. And to one, his voice was like the forest and its secrecy, and to another like the sea and the storms of the sea; and one heard the cry of his lost nation in it, and another saw a little harmless scene he hadn't remembered for years. But each saw something. And when Dan'l Webster finished he didn't know whether or not he'd saved Jabez Stone. But he knew he'd done a miracle. For the glitter was gone from the eyes of judge and jury, and, for the moment, they were men again, and knew they were men.

"The defense rests," said Dan'l Webster, and stood there like a mountain. His ears were still ringing with his speech, and he didn't hear anything else till he heard Judge Hathorne say, "The jury will retire to consider its verdict."

Walter Butler rose in his place and his face had a dark, gay pride on it.

"The jury has considered its verdict," he said, and looked the stranger full in the eye. "We find for the defendant, Jabez Stone."

With that, the smile left the stranger's face, but Walter Butler did not flinch.

"Perhaps 'tis not strictly in accordance with the evidence," he said, "but even the damned may salute the eloquence of Mr. Webster."

With that, the long crow of a rooster split the gray morning sky, and judge and jury were gone from the room like a puff of smoke and as if they had never been there. The stranger turned to Dan'l Webster, smiling wryly.

"Major Butler was always a bold man," he said. "I had not thought him quite so bold. Nevertheless, my congratulations, as between two gentlemen."

"I'll have that paper first, if you please," said Dan'l Webster, and he took it and tore it into four pieces. It was queerly warm to the touch. "And now," he said, "I'll have you!" and his hand came down like a bear trap on the stranger's arm. For he knew that once you bested anybody like Mr. Scratch in fair fight, his power on you was gone. And he could see that Mr. Scratch knew it too.

The stranger twisted and wriggled, but he couldn't get out of that grip. "Come, come, Mr. Webster," he said, smiling palely. "This sort of thing is ridic—ouch!—is ridiculous. If you're worried about the costs of the case, naturally, I'd be glad to pay——"

"And so you shall!" said Dan'l Webster, shaking him till his teeth rattled. "For you'll sit right down at that table and draw up a document, promising never to bother Jabez Stone nor his heirs or assigns nor any other New Hampshireman till doomsday! For any hades we want to raise in this state, we can raise ourselves, without assistance from strangers."

"Ouch!" said the stranger. "Ouch! Well, they never did run very big to the barrel, but—ouch!—I agree!"

So he sat down and drew up the document. But Dan'l Webster kept his hand on his coat collar all the time.

"And, now, may I go?" said the stranger, quite humble, when Dan'l'd seen the document was in proper and legal form.

"Go?" said Dan'l, giving him another shake. "I'm still trying to figure out what I'll do with you. For you've settled the costs of the case, but you haven't settled with me. I think I'll take you back to Marshfield," he said, kind of reflective. "I've got a ram there named Goliath that can butt through an iron door. I'd kind of like to turn you loose in his field and see what he'd do."

Well, with that the stranger began to beg and to plead. And he begged and he pled so humble that finally Dan'l, who was naturally kindhearted, agreed to let him go. The stranger seemed terrible grateful for that and said, just to show they were friends, he'd tell Dan'l's fortune before leaving. So Dan'l agreed to that, though he didn't take much stock in fortune-tellers ordinarily. But, naturally, the stranger was a little different.

Well, he pried and he peered at the lines in Dan'l's hands. And he told him one thing and another that was quite remarkable. But they were all in the past.

THE DEVIL AND DANIEL WEBSTER

"Yes, all that's true, and it happened," said Dan'l Webster. "But what's to come in the future?"

The stranger grinned, kind of happily, and shook his head.

"The future's not as you think it," he said. "It's dark. You have a great ambition, Mr. Webster."

"I have," said Dan'l firmly, for everybody knew he wanted to be President.

"It seems almost within your grasp," said the stranger, "but you will not attain it. Lesser men will be made President and you will be passed over."

"And, if I am, I'll still be Daniel Webster," said Dan'l. "Say on."

"You have two strong sons," said the stranger, shaking his head. "You look to found a line. But each will die in war and neither reach greatness."

"Live or die, they are still my sons," said Dan'l Webster. "Say on."

"You have made great speeches," said the stranger. "You will make more."

"Ah," said Dan'l Webster.

"But the last great speech you make will turn many of your own against you," said the stranger. "They will call you Ichabod; they will call you by other names. Even in New England, some will say you have turned your coat and sold your country, and their voices will be loud against you till you die."

"So, it is an honest speech, it does not matter what men say," said Dan'l Webster. Then he looked at the stranger and their glances locked.

"One question," he said. "I have fought for the Union all my life. Will I see that fight won against those who would tear it apart?"

"Not while you live," said the stranger, grimly, "but it will be won. And after you are dead, there are thousands who will fight for your cause, because of words that you spoke."

"Why, then, you long-barreled, slab-sided, lantern-jawed, fortune-telling note shaver!" said Dan'l Webster, with a great roar of laughter, "be off with you to your own place before I put my mark on you! For, by the thirteen original colonies, I'd go to the Pit itself to save the Union!"

And with that he drew back his foot for a kick that would have stunned a horse. It was only the tip of his shoe that caught the stranger, but he went flying out of the door with his collecting box under his arm.

"And now," said Dan'l Webster, seeing Jabez Stone beginning to rouse from his swoon, "let's see what's left in the jug, for it's dry work talking all night. I hope there's pie for breakfast, Neighbor Stone."

But they say that whenever the devil comes near Marshfield, even now, he gives it a wide berth. And he hasn't been seen in the state of New Hampshire from that day to this. I'm not talking about Massachusetts or Vermont.

FREEDOM'S A HARD-BOUGHT THING

A long time ago, in times gone by, in slavery times, there was a man named Cue. I want you to think about him. I've got a reason.

He got born like the cotton in the boll or the rabbit in the pea patch. There wasn't any fine doings when he got born, but his mammy was glad to have him. Yes. He didn't get born in the Big House, or the overseer's house, or any place where the bearing was easy or the work light. No, Lord. He came out of his mammy in a field hand's cabin one sharp winter, and about the first thing he remembered was his mammy's face and the taste of a piece of bacon rind and the light and shine of the pitch-pine fire up the chimney. Well, now, he got born and there he was.

His daddy worked in the fields and his mammy worked in the fields when she wasn't bearing. They were slaves; they chopped the cotton and hoed the corn. They heard the horn blow before the light came and the horn blow that meant the day's work was done. His daddy was a strong man—strong in his back and his arms. The white folks called him Cuffee. His mammy was a good woman, yes, Lord. The white folks called her Sarah, and she was gentle with her hands and gentle with her voice. She had a voice like the river going by in the night, and at night when she wasn't too tired she'd sing songs to little

FREEDOM'S A HARD-BOUGHT THING 139

Cue. Some had foreign words in them—African words. She couldn't remember what some of them meant, but they'd come to her down out of time.

Now, how am I going to describe and explain about that time when that time's gone? The white folks lived in the Big House and they had many to tend on them. Old Marster, he lived there like Pharaoh and Solomon, mighty splendid and fine. He had his flocks and his herds, his butler and his baker; his fields ran from the river to the woods and back again. He'd ride around the fields each day on his big horse, Black Billy, just like thunder and lightning, and evenings he'd sit at his table and drink his wine. Man, that was a sight to see, with all the silver knives and the silver forks, the glass decanters, and the gentlemen and ladies from all over. It was a sight to see. When Cue was young, it seemed to him that Old Marster must own the whole world, right up to the edge of the sky. You can't blame him for thinking that.

There were things that changed on the plantation, but it didn't change. There were bad times and good times. There was the time young Marse Edward got bit by the snake, and the time Big Rambo ran away and they caught him with the dogs and brought him back. There was a swivel-eyed overseer that beat folks too much, and then there was Mr. Wade, and he wasn't so bad. There was hog-killing time and Christmas and springtime and summertime. Cue didn't wonder about it or why things happened that way; he didn't expect it to be different. A bee in a hive don't ask you how there come to be a hive in the beginning. Cue grew up strong; he grew up smart with his hands. They put him in the blacksmith shop to help Daddy Jake; he didn't like it, at first, because Daddy Jake was mighty cross-tempered. Then he got to like the work; he learned to forge iron and shape it; he learned to shoe a horse and tire a wagon wheel, and everything a blacksmith does. One time they let him shoe Black Billy, and he shod him light and tight and Old Marster praised him in front of Mr. Wade. He was strong; he was black as night; he was proud of his back and his arms.

Now, he might have stayed that way—yes, he might. He heard freedom talk, now and then, but he didn't pay much mind to it. He wasn't a talker or a preacher; he was Cue and he worked in the blacksmith shop. He didn't want to be a field hand, but he didn't want to be a house servant either. He'd rather be Cue than poor white trash or owned by poor white trash. That's the way he felt; I'm obliged to tell the truth about that way.

Then there was a sickness came and his mammy and his daddy died of it. Old Miss got the doctor for them, but they died just the same. After that, Cue felt lonesome.

He felt lonesome and troubled in his mind. He'd seen his daddy and his mammy put in the ground and new slaves come to take their cabin. He didn't repine about that, because he knew things had to be that way. But when he went to bed at night, in the loft over the blacksmith shop, he'd keep thinking about his mammy and his daddy—how strong his daddy was and the songs that his mammy sang. They'd worked all their lives and had children, though he was the only one left, but the only place of their own they had was the place in the burying ground. And yet they'd been good and faithful servants, because Old Marster said so, with his hat off, when he buried them. The Big House stayed, and the cotton and the corn, but Cue's mammy and daddy were gone like last year's crop. It made Cue wonder and trouble.

He began to take notice of things he'd never noticed. When the horn blew in the morning for the hands to go to the fields, he'd wonder who started blowing that horn, in the first place. It wasn't like thunder and lightning; somebody had started it. When he heard Old Marster say, when he was talking to a friend, "This damned epidemic! It's cost me eight prime field hands and the best-trained butler in the state. I'd rather have lost the Flyaway colt than Old Isaac." Cue put that down in his mind and pondered it. Old Marster didn't mean it mean, and he'd sat up with Old Isaac all night before he died. But Isaac and Cue and the Flyaway colt, they all belonged to Old Marster and he owned them, hide and hair. He owned them, like money in his pockets. Well, Cue had known that all his life, but because he was troubled now, it gave him a queer feeling.

Well, now, he was shoeing a horse for young Marster Shepley one day, and he shod it light and tight. And when he was through, he made a stirrup for young Marster Shepley, and young Marster Shepley mounted and threw him a silver bit, with a laughing word. That shouldn't have bothered Cue, because gentlemen sometimes did that. And Old Marster wasn't mean; he didn't object. But all night Cue kept feeling the print of young Marster Shepley's heel in his hands. And yet he liked young Marster Shepley. He couldn't explain it at all.

Finally, Cue decided he must be conjured. He didn't know who had done it or why they'd done it. But he knew what he had to do. He had to go see Aunt Rachel.

Aunt Rachel was an old, old woman, and she lived in a cabin by herself, with her granddaughter, Sukey. She'd seen Old Marster's father and his father, and the tale went she'd seen George Washington with his hair all white, and General Lafayette in his gold-plated suit of clothes that the King of France gave him to fight in. Some folks said she was a conjure and some folks said she wasn't, but everybody on the plantation treated her mighty respectful, because, if she put her eye on you, she mightn't take it off. Well, his mammy had been friends with Aunt Rachel, so Cue went to see her.

She was sitting alone in her cabin by the low light of a fire. There was a pot on the fire, and now and then you could hear it bubble and chunk, like a bullfrog chunking in the swamp, but that was the only sound. Cue made his obleegances to her and asked her about the misery in her back. Then he gave her a chicken he happened to bring along. It was a black rooster, and she seemed pleased to get it. She took it in her thin black hands and it fluttered and clucked a minute. So she drew a chalk line from its beak along a board, and then it stayed still and frozen. Well, Cue had seen that trick done before. But it was different, seeing it done in Aunt Rachel's cabin, with the big pot chunking on the fire. It made him feel uneasy and he jingled the bit in his pocket for company.

After a while, the old woman spoke. "Well, Son Cue," said she, "that's a fine young rooster you've brought me. What else did you bring me, Son Cue?"

"I brought you trouble," said Cue, in a husky voice, because that was all he could think of to say.

She nodded her head as if she'd expected that. "They mostly brings me trouble," she said. "They mostly brings trouble to Aunt Rachel. What kind of trouble, Son Cue? Man trouble or woman trouble?"

"It's my trouble," said Cue, and he told her the best way he could. When he'd finished, the pot on the fire gave a bubble and a croak, and the old woman took a long spoon and stirred it.

"Well, Son Cue, son of Cuffee, son of Shango," she said, "you've got a big trouble, for sure."

"Is it going to kill me dead?" said Cue.

"I can't tell you right about that," said Aunt Rachel. "I could give you lies and prescriptions. Maybe I would, to some folks. But your Grandaddy Shango was a powerful man. It took three men to put the irons on him, and I saw the irons break his heart. I won't lie to you, Son Cue. You've got a sickness."

"Is it a bad sickness?" said Cue.

"It's a sickness in your blood," said Aunt Rachel. "It's a sickness in your liver and your veins. Your daddy never had it that I knows of—he took after his mammy's side. But his daddy was a Corromantee, and they is bold and free, and you takes after him. It's the freedom sickness, Son Cue."

"The freedom sickness?" said Cue.

"The freedom sickness," said the old woman, and her little eyes glittered like sparks. "Some they break and some they tame down," she said, "and some is neither to be tamed or broken. Don't I know the signs and the sorrow—me, that come through the middle passage on the slavery ship and seen my folks scattered like sand? Ain't I seen it coming, Lord—O Lord, ain't I seen it coming?"

"What's coming?" said Cue.

"A darkness in the sky and a cloud with a sword in it," said the old woman, stirring the pot, "because they hold our people and they hold our people."

Cue began to tremble. "I don't want to get whipped," he said. "I never been whipped—not hard."

"They whipped your Grandaddy Shango till the blood ran twinkling down his back," said the old woman, "but some you can't break or tame."

"I don't want to be chased by dogs," said Cue. "I don't want to hear the dogs belling and the paterollers after me."

The old woman stirred the pot.

"Old Marster, he's a good marster," said Cue. "I don't want to do him no harm. I don't want no trouble or projecting to get me into trouble."

The old woman stirred the pot and stirred the pot.

"O God, I want to be free," said Cue. "I just ache and hone to be free. How I going to be free, Aunt Rachel?"

"There's a road that runs underground," said the old woman. "I never seen it, but I knows of it. There's a railroad train that runs, sparking and snorting, underground through the earth. At least that's what they tell me. But I wouldn't know for sure," and she looked at Cue.

Cue looked back at her bold enough, for he'd heard about the Underground Railroad himself—just mentions and whispers. But he knew there wasn't any use asking the old woman what she wouldn't tell.

"How I going to find that road, Aunt Rachel?" he said.

"You look at the rabbit in the brier and you see what he do," said the old woman. "You look at the owl in the woods and you see what he do. You look at the star in the sky and you see what she do. Then you come back and talk to me. Now I'm going to eat, because I'm hungry."

That was all the words she'd say to him that night; but when Cue went back to his loft, her words kept boiling around in his mind. All night he could hear that train of railroad cars, snorting and sparking underground through the earth. So, next morning, he ran away.

He didn't run far or fast. How could he? He'd never been more than twenty miles from the plantation in his life; he didn't know the roads or the ways. He ran off before the horn, and Mr. Wade caught him before sundown. Now, wasn't he a stupid man, that Cue?

When they brought him back, Mr. Wade let him off light, because he was a good boy and never run away before. All the same, he got ten, and ten laid over the ten. Yellow Joe, the head driver, laid them on. The first time the whip cut into him, it was just like a fire on Cue's skin, and he didn't see how he could stand it. Then he got to a place where he could.

After it was over, Aunt Rachel crope up to his loft and had her granddaughter, Sukey, put salve on his back. Sukey, she was sixteen, and golden-skinned and pretty as a peach on a peach tree. She worked in the Big House and he never expected her to do a thing like that.

"I'm mighty obliged," he said, though he kept thinking it was Aunt Rachel got him into trouble and he didn't feel as obliged as he might.

"Is that all you've got to say to me, Son Cue?" said Aunt Rachel, looking down at him. "I told you to watch three things. Did you watch them?"

"No'm," said Cue. "I run off in the woods just like I was a wild turkey. I won't never do that no more."

"You're right, Son Cue," said the old woman. "Freedom's a hard-bought thing. So, now you've been whipped, I reckon you'll give it up."

"I been whipped," said Cue, "but there's a road running underground. You told me so. I been whipped, but I ain't beaten."

"Now you're learning a thing to remember," said Aunt Rachel, and went away. But Sukey stayed behind for a while and cooked Cue's supper. He never expected her to do a thing like that, but he liked it when she did.

When his back got healed, they put him with the field gang for a while. But then there was blacksmith work that needed to be done and they put him back in the blacksmith shop. And things went on for a long time just the way they had before. But there was a difference in Cue. It was like he'd lived up till now with his ears and his eyes sealed over. And now he began to open his eyes and his ears.

He looked at the rabbit in the brier and he saw it could hide. He looked at the owl in the woods and he saw it went soft through the night. He looked at the star in the sky and he saw she pointed north. Then he began to figure.

He couldn't figure things fast, so he had to figure things slow. He figure the owl and the rabbit got wisdom the white folks don't know about. But he figure the white folks got wisdom he don't know about. They got reading and writing wisdom, and it seem mighty powerful. He ask Aunt Rachel if that's so, and she say it's so.

That's how come he learned to read and write. He ain't supposed to. But Sukey, she learned some of that wisdom, along with the young misses, and she teach him out of a little book she tote from the Big House. The little book, it's all about bats and rats and cats, and Cue figure whoever wrote it must be sort of touched in the head not to write about things folks would want to know, instead of all those trifling animals. But he put himself to it and he learn. It almost bust his head, but he learn. It's a proud day for him when he write his name, "Cue," in the dust with the end of a stick and Sukey tell him that's right.

Now he began to hear the first rumblings of that train running underground—that train that's the Underground Railroad. Oh, children, remember the names of Levi Coffin and John Hansen! Remember the Quaker saints that hid the fugitive! Remember the names of all those that helped set our people free!

There's a word dropped here and a word dropped there and a word that's passed around. Nobody know where the word come from or where it goes, but it's there. There's many a word spoken in the quarters that the Big House never hears about. There's a heap said in front of the fire that never flies up the chimney. There's a name you tell to the grapevine that the grapevine don't tell back.

There was a white man, one day, came by, selling maps and pictures. The quality folks, they looked at his maps and pictures and he talked with them mighty pleasant and respectful. But while Cue was tightening a bolt on his wagon, he dropped a word and a word. The word he said made that underground train come nearer.

Cue meet that man one night, all alone, in the woods. He's a quiet man with a thin face. He hold his life in his hands every day he walk about, but he don't make nothing of that. Cue's seen bold folks and bodacious folks, but it's the first time he's seen a man bold that way. It makes him proud to be a man. The man ask Cue questions and Cue give him answers. While he's seeing that man, Cue don't just think about himself any more. He think about all his people that's in trouble.

The man say something to him; he say, "No man own the earth. It's too big for one man." He say, "No man own another man; that's too big a thing too." Cue think about those words and ponder them. But when he gets back to his loft, the courage drains out of him and he sits on his straw tick, staring at the wall.

That's the time the darkness comes to him and the shadow falls on him.

He aches and he hones for freedom, but he aches and he hones for Sukey too. And Long Ti's cabin is empty, and it's a good cabin. All he's got to do is to go to Old Marster and take Sukey with him. Old Marster don't approve to mix the field hand with the house servant, but Cue's different; Cue's a blacksmith. He can see the way Sukey would look, coming back to her in the evening. He can see the way she'd be in the morning before the horn. He can see all that. It ain't freedom, but it's what he's used to. And the other way's long and hard and lonesome and strange.

"Oh Lord, why you put this burden on a man like me?" say Cue. Then he listen a long time for the Lord to tell him, and it seem to him, at last, that he get an answer. The answer ain't in any words, but it's a feeling in his heart.

So when the time come and the plan ripe and they get to the boat on the river and they see there's one too many for the boat, Cue know the answer. He don't have to hear the quiet white man say, "There's one too many for the boat." He just pitch Sukey into it before he can think too hard. He don't say a word or a groan. He know it's that way and there's bound to be a reason for it. He stand on the bank in the dark and see the boat pull away, like Israel's children. Then he hear the shouts and the shot. He know what he's bound to do then, and the reason for it. He know it's the paterollers, and he show himself. When he get back to the plantation, he's worn and tired. But the paterollers, they've chased him, instead of the boat.

He creep by Aunt Rachel's cabin and he see the fire at her window. So he scratch at the door and go in. And there she is, sitting by the fire, all hunched up and little.

"You looks poorly, Son Cue," she say, when he come in, though she don't take her eye off the pot.

"I'm poorly, Aunt Rachel," he say. "I'm sick and sorry and distressed."

"What's the mud on your jeans, Son Cue?" she say, and the pot, it bubble and croak.

"That's the mud of the swamp where I hid from the paterollers," he say.

"What's the hole in your leg, Son Cue?" she say, and the pot, it croak and bubble.

"That's the hole from the shot they shot at me," say Cue. "The blood most nearly dried, but it make me lame. But Israel's children, they's safe."

"They's across the river?" say the old woman.

"They's across the river," say Cue. "They ain't room for no more in the boat. But Sukey, she's across."

"And what will you do now, Son Cue?" say the old woman. "For that was your chance and your time, and you give it up for another. And tomorrow morning, Mr. Wade, he'll see that hole in your leg and he'll ask question. It's a heavy burden you've laid on yourself, Son Cue."

"It's a heavy burden," say Cue, "and I wish I was shut of it. I never asked to take no such burden. But freedom's a hard-bought thing."

The old woman stand up sudden, and for once she look straight and tall. "Now bless the Lord!" she say. "Bless the Lord and praise him! I come with my mammy in the slavery ship—I come through the middle passage. There ain't many that remember that, these days, or care about it. There ain't many that remember the red flag that witched us on board or how we used to be free. Many thousands gone, and the thousands of many thousands that lived and died in slavery. But I remember. I remember them all. Then they took me into the Big House—me that was a Mandingo and a witch woman—and the way I live in the Big House, that's between me and my Lord. If I done wrong, I done paid for it— I paid for it with weeping and sorrow. That's before Old Miss' time and I help raise up Old Miss. They sell my daughter to the South and my son to the West, but I raise up Old Miss and tend on her. I ain't going to repine of that. I count the hairs on Old Miss' head when she's young, and she turn to me, weak and helpless. And for that there'll be a kindness between me and the Big House—a kindness that folks will remember. But my children's children shall be free."

"You do this to me," say Cue, and he look at her, and he look dangerous. "You do this to me, old woman," he say, and his breath come harsh in his throat, and his hands twitch.

"Yes," she say, and look him straight in the eyes. "I do to you what I never even do for my own. I do it for your Granddaddy Shango, that never turn to me in the light of the fire. He turn to that soft Eboe woman, and I have to see it. He roar like a lion in the chains, and I have to see that. So, when you come, I try you and I test you, to see if you fit to follow after him. And because you fit to follow after him, I put freedom in your heart, Son Cue."

"I never going to be free," say Cue, and look at his hands. "I done broke all the rules. They bound to sell me now."

"You'll be sold and sold again," say the old woman. "You'll know the chains and the whip. I can't help that. You'll suffer for your people and with your people. But while one man's got freedom in his heart, his children bound to know the tale."

She put the lid on the pot and it stop bubbling.

"Now I come to the end of my road," she say, "but the tale don't stop there. The tale go backward to Africa and it go forward, like clouds and fire. It go, laughing and grieving forever, through the earth and the air and the waters—my people's tale."

Then she drop her hands in her lap and Cue creep out of the cabin. He know then he's bound to be a witness, and it make him feel cold and hot. He know then he's bound to be a witness and tell that tale. O Lord, it's hard to be a witness, and Cue know that. But it help him in the days to come.

Now, when he got sold, that's when Cue feel the iron in his heart. Before that, and all his life, he despise bad servants and bad masters. He live where the master's good; he don't take much mind of other places. He's a slave, but he's Cue, the blacksmith, and Old Marster and Old Miss, they tend to him. Now he know the iron in his heart and what it's like to be a slave.

He know that on the rice fields in the hot sun. He know that, working all day for a handful of corn. He know the bad marsters and the cruel overseers. He know the bite of the whip and the gall of the iron on the ankle. Yes, Lord, he know tribulation. He know his own tribulation and the tribulation of his people. But all the time, somehow, he keep freedom in his heart. Freedom mighty hard to root out when it's in the heart.

He don't know the day or the year, and he forget, half the time, there ever was a gal named Sukey. All he don't forget is

FREEDOM'S A HARD-BOUGHT THING

the noise of the train in his ears, the train snorting and sparking underground. He think about it at nights till he dream it carry him away. Then he wake up with the horn. He feel ready to die then, but he don't die. He live through the whip and the chain; he live through the iron and the fire. And finally he get away.

When he get away, he ain't like the Cue he used to be—not even back at Old Marster's place. He hide in the woods like a rabbit; he slip through the night like an owl. He go cold and hungry, but the star keep shining over him and he keep his eyes on the star. They set the dogs after him and he hear the dogs belling and yipping through the woods.

He's scared when he hear the dogs, but he ain't scared like he used to be. He ain't more scared than any man. He kill the big dog in the clearing—the big dog with the big voice—and he do it with his naked hands. He cross water three times after that to kill the scent, and he go on.

He got nothing to help him—no, Lord—but he got a star. The star shine in the sky and the star shine—the star point north with its shining. You put that star in the sky, O Lord; you put it for the prisoned and the humble. You put it there—you ain't never going to blink it out.

He hungry and he eat green corn and cowpeas. He thirsty and he drink swamp water. One time he lie two days in the swamp, too puny to get up on his feet, and he know they hunting around him. He think that's the end of Cue. But after two days he lift his head and his hand. He kill a snake with a stone, and after he's cut out the poison bag, he eat the snake to strengthen him, and go on.

He don't know what the day is when he come to the wide, cold river. The river yellow and foaming, and Cue can't swim. But he hide like a crawdad on the bank; he make himself a little raft with two logs. He know this time's the last time and he's obliged to drown. But he put out on the raft and it drift him to the freedom side. He mighty weak by then.

He mighty weak, but he careful. He know tales of Billy Shea, the slave catcher; he remember those tales. He slide into the town by night, like a shadow, like a ghost. He beg broken victuals at a door; the woman give them to him, but she look at him suspicious. He make up a tale to tell her, but he don't think she believe the tale. In the gutter he find a newspaper; he pick it up and look at the notices. There's a notice about a runaway man named Cue. He look at it and it make the heart beat in his breast.

He patient; he mighty careful. He leave that town behind. He got the name of another town. Cincinnati, and a man's name in that town. He don't know where it is; he have to ask his way, but he do it mighty careful. One time he ask a yellow man directions; he don't like the look on the yellow man's face. He remember Aunt Rachel; he tell the yellow man he conjure his liver out if the yellow man tell him wrong. Then the yellow man scared and tell him right. He don't hurt the yellow man; he don't blame him for not wanting trouble. But he make the yellow man change pants with him, because his pants mighty ragged.

He patient; he very careful. When he get to the place he been told about, he look all about that place. It's a big house; it don't look right. He creep around to the back—he creep and he crawl. He look in a window; he see white folks eating their supper. They just look like any white folks. He expect them to look different. He feel mighty bad. All the same, he rap at the window the way he been told. They don't nobody pay attention and he just about to go away. Then the white man get up from the table and open the back door a crack. Cue breathe in the darkness.

"God bless the stranger the Lord sends us," say the white man in a low, clear voice, and Cue run to him and stumble, and the white man catch him. He look up and it's a white man, but he ain't like thunder and lightning.

He take Cue and wash his wounds and bind them up. He feed him and hide him under the floor of the house. He ask him his name and where he's from. Then he send him on. O Lord, remember thy tried servant, Asaph Brown! Remember his name!

They send him from there in a wagon, and he's hidden in the straw at the bottom. They send him from the next place in a closed cart with six others, and they can't say a word all night. One time a tollkeeper ask them what's in the wagon, and the driver say, "Southern calico," and the tollkeeper laugh. Cue always recollect that.

One time they get to big water—so big it look like the ocean. They cross that water in a boat; they get to the other side. When they get to the other side, they sing and pray, and white folks look on, curious. But Cue don't feel happy; he just feel he want to sleep.

He sleep like he never sleep before—not for days and years. When he wake up, he wonder; he hardly recollect where he is. He lying in the loft of a barn. Ain't nobody around him. He get up and go out in the air. It's a fine sunny day.

He get up and go out. He say to himself, *I'm free,* but it don't take hold yet. He say to himself, *This is Canada and I'm free,* but it don't take hold. Then he start to walk down the street.

The first white man he meet on the street, he scrunch up in himself and start to run across the street. But the white man don't pay him any mind. Then he know.

He say to himself in his mind, *I'm free. My name's Cue—John H. Cue. I got a strong back and strong arms. I got freedom in my heart. I got a first name and a last name and a middle name. I never had them all before.*

He say to himself, *My name's Cue—John H. Cue. I got a name and a tale to tell. I got a hammer to swing. I got a tale to tell my people. I got recollection. I call my first son 'John Freedom Cue.' I call my first daughter 'Come-Out-of-the-Lion's-Mouth.'*

Then he walk down the street, and he pass a blacksmith shop. The blacksmith, he's an old man and he lift the hammer heavy. Cue look in that shop and smile.

He pass on; he go his way. And soon enough he see a girl like a peach tree—a girl named Sukey—walking free down the street.

JOHNNY PYE AND THE FOOL-KILLER

You don't hear so much about the Fool-Killer these days, but when Johnny Pye was a boy there was a good deal of talk about him. Some said he was one kind of person, and some said another, but most people agreed that he came around fairly regular. Or, it seemed so to Johnny Pye. But then, Johnny was an adopted child, which is, maybe, why he took it so hard.

The miller and his wife had offered to raise him, after his own folks died, and that was a good deed on their part. But, as soon as he lost his baby teeth and started acting the way most boys act, they began to come down on him like thunder, which wasn't so good. They were good people, according to their lights, but their lights were terribly strict ones, and they believed that the harder you were on a youngster, the better and brighter he got. Well, that may work with some children, but it didn't with Johnny Pye.

He was sharp enough and willing enough—as sharp and willing as most boys in Martinsville. But, somehow or other, he never seemed to be able to do the right things or say the right words— at least when he was home. Treat a boy like a fool and he'll act like a fool, I say, but there's some folks need convincing. The miller and his wife thought the way to smarten Johnny was to treat him like a fool, and finally they got so he pretty much believed it himself.

And that was hard on him, for he had a boy's imagination, and maybe a little more than most. He could stand the beatings and he did. But what he couldn't stand was the way things went at the mill. I don't suppose the miller intended to do it. But, as long as Johnny Pye could remember, whenever he heard of the death of somebody he didn't like, he'd say, "Well, the Fool-Killer's come for so-and-so," and sort of smack his lips. It was, as you might say, a family joke, but the miller was a big man with a big red face, and it made a strong impression on Johnny Pye. Till, finally, he got a picture of the Fool-Killer, himself. He was a big man, too, in a checked shirt and corduroy trousers, and he went walking the ways of the world, with a hickory club that had a lump of lead in the end of it. I don't know how Johnny Pye got that picture so clear, but, to him, it was just as plain as the face of any human being in Martinsville. And, now and then, just to test it, he'd ask a grown-up person, kind of timidly, if that was the way the Fool-Killer looked. And, of course, they'd generally laugh and tell him it was. Then Johnny would wake up at night, in his room over the mill, and listen for the Fool-Killer's step on the road and wonder when he was coming. But he was brave enough not to tell anybody that.

Finally, though, things got a little more than he could bear. He'd done some boy's trick or other—let the stones grind a little fine, maybe, when the miller wanted the meal ground coarse—

JOHNNY PYE AND THE FOOL-KILLER

just carelessness, you know. But he'd gotten two whippings for it, one from the miller and one from his wife, and, at the end of it, the miller had said, "Well, Johnny Pye, the Fool-Killer ought to be along for you most any day now. For I never did see a boy that was such a fool." Johnny looked to the miller's wife to see if she believed it, too, but she just shook her head and looked serious. So he went to bed that night, but he couldn't sleep, for every time a bough rustled or the mill wheel creaked, it seemed to him it must be the Fool-Killer. And, early next morning, before anybody was up, he packed such duds as he had in a bandanna handkerchief and ran away.

He didn't really expect to get away from the Fool-Killer very long—as far as he knew, the Fool-Killer got you wherever you went. But he thought he'd give him a run for his money, at least. And when he got on the road, it was a bright spring morning, and the first peace and quiet he'd had in some time. So his spirits rose, and he chunked a stone at a bullfrog as he went along, just to show he was Johnny Pye and still doing business.

He hadn't gone more than three or four miles out of Martinsville, when he heard a buggy coming up the road behind him. He knew the Fool-Killer didn't need a buggy to catch you, so he wasn't afraid of it, but he stepped to the side of the road to let it pass. But it stopped, instead, and a black-whiskered man with a stovepipe hat looked out of it.

"Hello, bub," he said. "Is this the road for East Liberty?"

"My name's John Pye and I'm eleven years old," said Johnny, polite but firm, "and you take the next left fork for East Liberty. They say it's a pretty town—I've never been there myself." And he sighed a little, because he thought he'd like to see the world before the Fool-Killer caught up with him.

"H'm," said the man. "Stranger here, too, eh? And what brings a smart boy like you on the road so early in the morning?"

"Oh," said Johnny Pye, quite honestly, "I'm running away from the Fool-Killer. For the miller says I'm a fool and his wife says I'm a fool and almost everybody in Martinsville says I'm a fool except little Susie Marsh. And the miller says the Fool-Killer's after me—so I thought I'd run away before he came."

The black-whiskered man sat in his buggy and wheezed for a while. When he got his breath back, "Well, jump in, bub," he said. "The miller may say you're a fool, but I think you're a right smart boy to be running away from the Fool-Killer all by yourself. And I don't hold with small-town prejudices and I need a right smart boy, so I'll give you a lift on the road."

"But, will I be safe from the Fool-Killer, if I'm with you?" said Johnny. "For, otherwise, it don't signify."

"Safe?" said the black-whiskered man, and wheezed again. "Oh, you'll be safe as houses. You see, I'm a herb doctor—and some folks think, a little in the Fool-Killer's line of business, myself. And I'll teach you a trade worth two of milling. So jump in, bub."

"Sounds all right the way you say it," said Johnny, "but my name's John Pye," and he jumped into the buggy. And they went rattling along toward East Liberty with the herb doctor talking and cutting jokes till Johnny thought he'd never met a pleasanter man. About half a mile from East Liberty, the doctor stopped at a spring.

"What are we stopping here for?" said Johnny Pye.

"Wait and see," said the doctor, and gave him a wink. Then he got a haircloth trunk full of empty bottles out of the back of the buggy and made Johnny fill them with spring water and label them. Then he added a pinch of pink powder to each bottle and shook them up and corked them and stowed them away.

"What's that?" said Johnny, very interested.

"That's Old Doctor Waldo's Unparalleled Universal Remedy," said the doctor, reading from the label.

"Made from the purest snake oil and secret Indian herbs, it cures rheumatism, blind staggers, headache, malaria, five kinds of fits, and spots in front of the eyes. It will also remove oil or grease stains, clean knives and silver, polish brass, and is strongly recommended as a general tonic and blood purifier. Small size, one dollar—family bottle, two dollars and a half."

"But I don't see any snake oil in it," said Johnny, puzzled, "or any secret Indian herbs."

"That's because you're not a fool," said the doctor, with another wink. "The Fool-Killer wouldn't, either. But most folks will."

And, that very same night, Johnny saw. For the doctor made his pitch in East Liberty and he did it handsome. He took a couple of flaring oil torches and stuck them on the sides of the buggy; he put on a diamond stickpin and did card tricks and told funny stories till he had the crowd goggle-eyed. As for Johnny, he let him play on the tambourine. Then he started talking about Doctor Waldo's Universal Remedy, and, with Johnny to help him, the bottles went like hot cakes. Johnny helped the doctor count the money afterward, and it was a pile.

"Well," said Johnny, "I never saw money made easier. You've got a fine trade, Doctor."

"It's cleverness does it," said the doctor, and slapped him on the back.

"Now a fool's content to stay in one place and do one thing, but the Fool-Killer never caught up with a good pitchman yet."

"Well, it's certainly lucky I met up with you," said Johnny, "and, if it's cleverness does it, I'll learn the trade or bust."

So he stayed with the doctor quite a while—in fact, till he could make up the remedy and do the card tricks almost as good as the doctor. And the doctor liked Johnny, for Johnny was a biddable boy. But one night they came into a town where things didn't go as they usually did. The crowd gathered as usual, and the doctor did his tricks. But, all the time, Johnny could see a sharp-faced little fellow going through the crowd and whispering to one man and another. Till, at last, right in the middle of the doctor's spiel, the sharp-faced fellow gave a shout of "That's him all right! I'd know them whiskers anywhere!" and, with that, the crowd growled once and began to tear slats out of the nearest fence. Well, the next thing Johnny knew, he and the doctor were being ridden out of town on a rail, with the doctor's long coattails flying at every jounce.

They didn't hurt Johnny particular—him only being a boy. But they warned 'em both never to show their faces in that town again, and then they heaved the doctor into a thistle patch and went their ways.

"Owoo!" said the doctor, "ouch!" as Johnny was helping him out of the thistle patch. "Go easy with those thistles! And why didn't you give me the office, you blame little fool?"

"Office?" said Johnny. "What office?"

"When that sharp-nosed man started snooping around," said the doctor. "I thought that infernal main street looked familiar—

I was through there two years ago, selling solid gold watches for a dollar apiece."

"But the works to a solid gold watch would be worth more than that," said Johnny.

"There weren't any works," said the doctor, with a groan, "but there was a nice lively beetle inside each case and it made the prettiest tick you ever heard."

"Well, that certainly was a clever idea," said Johnny. "I'd never have thought of that."

"Clever?" said the doctor. "Ouch—it was ruination! But who'd have thought the fools would bear a grudge for two years? And now we've lost the horse and buggy, too—not to speak of the bottles and the money. Well, there's lots more tricks to be played and we'll start again."

But, though he liked the doctor, Johnny began to feel dubious. For it occurred to him that, if all the doctor's cleverness got him was being ridden out of town on a rail, he couldn't be so far away from the Fool-Killer as he thought. And, sure enough, as he was going to sleep that night, he seemed to hear the Fool-Killer's footsteps coming after him—step, step, step. He pulled his jacket up over his ears, but he couldn't shut it out. So, when the doctor had got in the way of starting business over again, he and Johnny parted company. The doctor didn't bear any grudge; he shook hands with Johnny and told him to remember that cleverness was power. And Johnny went on with his running away.

He got to a town, and there was a store with a sign in the window, BOY WANTED, so he went in. There, sure enough, was the merchant, sitting at his desk, and a fine, important man he looked, in his black broadcloth suit.

Johnny tried to tell him about the Fool-Killer, but the merchant wasn't interested in that. He just looked Johnny over and saw that he looked biddable and strong for his age. "But, remember, no fooling around, boy!" said the merchant sternly, after he'd hired him.

"No fooling around?" said Johnny, with the light of hope in his eyes.

"No," said the merchant, meaningly. "We've no room for fools in this business, I can tell you! You work hard, and you'll rise.

But, if you've got any foolish notions, just knock them on the head and forget them."

Well, Johnny was glad enough to promise that, and he stayed with the merchant a year and a half. He swept out the store, and he put the shutters up on and took them down; he ran errands and wrapped up packages and learned to keep busy twelve hours a day. And, being a biddable boy and an honest one, he rose, just like the merchant had said. The merchant raised his wages and let him begin to wait on customers and learn accounts. And then, one night, Johnny woke up in the middle of the night. And it seemed to him he heard, far away but getting nearer, the steps of the Fool-Killer after him—tramping, tramping.

He went to the merchant next day and said, "Sir, I'm sorry to tell you this, but I'll have to be moving on."

"Well, I'm sorry to hear that, Johnny," said the merchant, "for you've been a good boy. And, if it's a question of salary—"

"It isn't that," said Johnny, "but tell me one thing, sir, if you don't mind my asking. Supposing I did stay with you—where would I end?"

The merchant smiled. "That's a hard question to answer," he said, "and I'm not much given to compliments. But I started, myself, as a boy, sweeping out the store. And you're a bright youngster with lots of go-ahead. I don't see why, if you stuck to it, you shouldn't make the same kind of success that I have."

"And what's that?" said Johnny.

The merchant began to look irritated, but he kept his smile.

"Well," he said, "I'm not a boastful man, but I'll tell you this. Ten years ago I was the richest man in town. Five years ago, I was the richest man in the county. And five years from now— well, I aim to be the richest man in the state."

His eyes kind of glittered as he said it, but Johnny was looking at his face. It was sallow-skinned and pouchy, with the jaw as hard as a rock. And it came upon Johnny that moment that, though he'd known the merchant a year and a half, he'd never really seen him enjoy himself except when he was driving a bargain.

"Sorry, sir," he said, "but, if it's like that, I'll certainly have to go. Because, you see, I'm running away from the Fool-Killer, and if I stayed here and got to be like you, he'd certainly catch up with me in no—"

"Why, you impertinent young cub!" roared the merchant, with his face gone red all of a sudden. "Get your money from the cashier!" and Johnny was on the road again before you could say "Jack Robinson." But, this time, he was used to it, and walked off whistling.

Well, after that, he hired out to quite a few different people, but I won't go into all of his adventures. He worked for an inventor for a while, and they split up because Johnny happened to ask him what would be the good of his patent, self-winding, perpetual-motion machine, once he did get it invented. And, while the inventor talked big about improving the human race and the beauties of science, it was plain he didn't know. So that night, Johnny heard the steps of the Fool-Killer, far off but coming closer, and, next morning, he went away. Then he stayed with a minister for a while, and he certainly hated to leave him, for the minister was a good man. But they got talking one evening and, as it chanced, Johnny asked him what happened to people who didn't believe in his particular religion. Well, the minister was broad-minded, but there's only one answer to that. He admitted they might be good folks—he even admitted they mightn't exactly go to hell—but he couldn't let them into heaven, no, not the best and the wisest of them, for there were the specifications laid down by creed and church, and, if you didn't fulfill them, you didn't.

So Johnny had to leave him, and, after that, he went with an old drunken fiddler for a while. He wasn't a good man, I guess, but he could play till the tears ran down your cheeks. And, when he was playing his best, it seemed to Johnny that the Fool-Killer was very far away. For, in spite of his faults and his weaknesses, while he played, there was might in the man. But he died drunk in a ditch, one night, with Johnny to hold his head, and, while he left Johnny his fiddle, it didn't do Johnny much good. For, while Johnny could play a tune, he couldn't play like the fiddler—it wasn't in his fingers.

Then it chanced that Johnny took up with a company of soldiers. He was still too young to enlist, but they made a kind of pet of him, and everything went swimmingly for a while. For

JOHNNY PYE AND THE FOOL-KILLER

the captain was the bravest man Johnny had ever seen, and he had an answer for everything, out of regulations and the Articles of War. But then they went West to fight Indians and the same old trouble cropped up again. For one night the captain said to him, "Johnny, we're going to fight the enemy tomorrow, but you'll stay in camp."

"Oh, I don't want to do that," said Johnny; "I want to be in on the fighting."

"It's an order," said the captain, grimly. Then he gave Johnny certain instructions and a letter to take to his wife.

"For the colonel's a copper-plated fool," he said, "and we're walking straight into an ambush."

"Why don't you tell him that?" said Johnny.

"I have," said the captain, "but he's the colonel."

"Colonel or no colonel," said Johnny, "if he's a fool, somebody ought to stop him."

"You can't do that, in an army," said the captain. "Orders are orders." But it turned out the captain was wrong about it, for, next day, before they could get moving, the Indians attacked and got badly licked. When it was all over, "Well, it was a good fight," said the captain, professionally. "All the same, if they'd waited and laid in ambush, they'd have had our hair. But, as it was, they didn't stand a chance."

"But why didn't they lay in ambush?" said Johnny.

"Well," said the captain, "I guess they had their orders too. And now, how would you like to be a soldier?"

"Well, it's a nice outdoors life, but I'd like to think it over," said Johnny. For he knew the captain was brave and he knew the Indians had been brave—you couldn't find two braver sets of people. But, all the same, when he thought the whole thing over, he seemed to hear steps in the sky. So he soldiered to the end of the campaign and then he left the army, though the captain told him he was making a mistake.

By now, of course, he wasn't a boy any longer; he was getting to be a young man with a young man's thoughts and feelings. And, half the time, nowadays, he'd forget about the Fool-Killer except as a dream he'd had when he was a boy. He could even laugh at it now and then, and think what a fool he'd been to believe there was such a man.

But, all the same, the desire in him wasn't satisfied, and something kept driving him on. He'd have called it ambitiousness, now, but it came to the same thing. And with every new trade he tried, sooner or later would come the dream—the dream of the big man in the checked shirt and corduroy pants, walking the ways of the world with his hickory stick in one hand. It made him angry to have that dream, now, but it had a singular power over him. Till, finally, when he was turned twenty or so, he got scared.

"Fool-Killer or no Fool-Killer," he said to himself. "I've got to ravel this matter out. For there must be some one thing a man could tie to, and be sure he wasn't a fool. I've tried cleverness and money and half a dozen other things, and they don't seem to be the answer. So now I'll try book learning and see what comes of that."

So he read all the books he could find, and whenever he'd seem to hear the steps of the Fool-Killer coming for the authors—and that was frequent—he'd try and shut his ears. But some books said one thing was best and some another, and he couldn't rightly decide.

"Well," he said to himself, when he'd read and read till his head felt as stuffed with book learning as a sausage with meat, "it's interesting, but it isn't exactly contemporaneous. So I think I'll go down to Washington and ask the wise men there. For it must take a lot of wisdom to run a country like the United States, and if there's people who can answer my questions, it's there they ought to be found."

So he packed his bag and off to Washington he went. He was modest for a youngster, and he didn't intend to try and see the President right away. He thought probably a congressman was about his size. So he saw a congressman, and the congressman told him the thing to be was an upstanding young American and vote the Republican ticket—which sounded all right to Johnny Pye, but not exactly what he was after.

Then he went to a senator, and the senator told him to be an upstanding young American and vote the Democratic ticket—which sounded all right, too, but not what he was after, either. And, somehow, though both men had been impressive and affable, right in the middle of their speeches he'd seemed to hear steps—you know.

But a man has to eat, whatever else he does, and Johnny found he'd better buckle down and get himself a job. It happened to be with the first congressman he struck, for that one came from Martinsville, which is why Johnny went to him in the first place. And, in a little while, he forgot his search entirely and the Fool-Killer, too, for the congressman's niece came East to visit him, and she was the Susie Marsh that Johnny had sat next in school. She'd been pretty then, but she was prettier now, and as soon as Johnny Pye saw her, his heart gave a jump and a thump.

"And don't think we don't remember you in Martinsville, Johnny Pye," she said, when her uncle had explained who his new clerk was. "Why, the whole town'll be excited when I write home. We've heard all about your killing Indians and inventing perpetual motion and traveling around the country with a famous doctor and making a fortune in dry goods and—oh, it's a wonderful story!"

"Well," said Johnny, and coughed, "some of that's just a little bit exaggerated. But it's nice of you to be interested. So they don't think I'm a fool any more, in Martinsville?"

"I never thought you were a fool," said Susie with a little smile, and Johnny felt his heart give another bump.

"And I always knew you were pretty, but never how pretty till now," said Johnny, and coughed again. "But, speaking of old times, how's the miller and his wife? For I did leave them right sudden, and while there were faults on both sides, I must have been a trial to them too."

"They've gone the way of all flesh," said Susie Marsh, "and there's a new miller now. But he isn't very well-liked, to tell the truth, and he's letting the mill run down."

"That's a pity," said Johnny, "for it was a likely mill." Then he began to ask her more questions and she began to remember things too. Well, you know how the time can go when two youngsters get talking like that.

Johnny Pye never worked so hard in his life as he did that winter. And it wasn't the Fool-Killer he thought about—it was Susie Marsh. First he thought she loved him and then he was sure she didn't, and then he was betwixt and between, and all perplexed and confused. But, finally, it turned out all right and he had her promise, and Johnny Pye knew he was the happiest man in the world. And that night, he waked up in the night and heard the Fool-Killer coming after him—step, step, step.

He didn't sleep much after that, and he came down to breakfast hollow-eyed. But his uncle-to-be didn't notice that—he was rubbing his hands and smiling.

"Put on your best necktie, Johnny!" he said, very cheerful, "for I've got an appointment with the President today, and, just to show I approve of my niece's fiancé, I'm taking you along."

"The President!" said Johnny, all dumbfounded.

"Yes," said Congressman Marsh, "you see, there's a little bill—well, we needn't go into that. But slick down your back hair, Johnny—we'll make Martinsville proud of us this day!"

Then a weight seemed to go from Johnny's shoulders and a load from his heart. He wrung Mr. Marsh's hand.

"Thank you, Uncle Eben!" he said. "I can't thank you enough." For, at last, he knew he was going to look upon a man that was bound to be safe from the Fool-Killer—and it seemed to him if he could just once do that, all his troubles and searchings would be ended.

Well, it doesn't signify which President it was—you can take it from me that he was President and a fine-looking man. He'd just been elected, too, so he was lively as a trout, and the saddle galls he'd get from Congress hadn't even begun to show. Anyhow, there he was, and Johnny feasted his eyes on him. For if there was anybody in the country the Fool-Killer couldn't bother, it must be a man like this.

The President and the congressman talked politics for a while, and then it was Johnny's turn.

"Well, young man," said the President, affably, "and what can I do for you—for you look to me like a fine, upstanding young American."

The congressman cut in quick before Johnny could open his mouth.

"Just a word of advice, Mr. President," he said. "Just a word in season. For my young friend's led an adventurous life, but

JOHNNY PYE AND THE FOOL-KILLER 163

now he's going to marry my niece and settle down. And what he needs most of all is a word of ripe wisdom from you."

"Well," said the President, looking at Johnny rather keenly, "if that's all he needs, a short horse is soon curried. I wish most of my callers wanted as little."

But, all the same, he drew Johnny out, as such men can, and before Johnny knew it, he was telling his life story.

"Well," said the President, at the end, "you certainly have been a rolling stone, young man. But there's nothing wrong in that. And, for one of your varied experience there's one obvious career. Politics!" he said, and slapped his fist in his hand.

"Well, said Johnny, scratching his head, "of course, since I've been in Washington, I've thought of that. But I don't know that I'm rightly fitted."

"You can write a speech," said Congressman Marsh, quite thoughtful, "for you've helped me with mine. You're a likeable fellow too. And you were born poor and worked up—and you've even got a war record—why, hell! Excuse me, Mr. President!—he's worth five hundred votes just as he stands!"

"I—I'm more than honored by you two gentlemen," said Johnny, abashed and flattered, "but supposing I did go into politics—where would I end up?"

The President looked sort of modest.

"The Presidency of the United States," said he, "is within the legitimate ambition of every American citizen. Provided he can get elected, of course."

"Oh," said Johnny, feeling dazzled, "I never thought of that. Well, that's a great thing. But it must be a great responsibility too."

"It is," said the President, looking just like his pictures on the campaign buttons.

"Why, it must be an awful responsibility!" said Johnny. "I can't hardly see how a mortal man can bear it. Tell me, Mr. President," he said, "may I ask you a question?"

"Certainly," said the President, looking prouder and more responsible and more and more like his picture on the campaign buttons every minute.

"Well," said Johnny, "it sounds like a fool question, but it's this: This is a great big country of ours, Mr. President, and it's got the most amazing lot of different people in it. How can any President satisfy all those people at one time? Can you yourself, Mr. President?"

The President looked a bit taken aback for a minute. But then he gave Johnny Pye a statesman's glance.

"With the help of God," he said, solemnly, "and in accordance with the principles of our great party, I intend . . ."

But Johnny didn't even hear the end of the sentence. For, even as the President was speaking, he heard a step outside in the corridor and he knew, somehow, it wasn't the step of a secretary or a guard. He was glad the President had said "with the help of God" for that sort of softened the step. And when the President finished, Johnny bowed.

"Thank you, Mr. President," he said; "that's what I wanted to know. And now I'll go back to Martinsville, I guess."

"Go back to Martinsville?" said the President, surprised.

"Yes, sir," said Johnny. "For I don't think I'm cut out for politics."

"And is that all you have to say to the President of the United States?" said his uncle-to-be, in a fume.

But the President had been thinking, meanwhile, and he was a bigger man than the congressman.

"Wait a minute, Congressman," he said. "This young man's honest, at least, and I like his looks. Moreover, of all the people who've come to see me in the last six months, he's the only one who hasn't wanted something—except the White House cat, and I guess she wanted something, too, because she meowed. You don't want to be President, young man—and, confidentially, I don't blame you. But how would you like to be postmaster at Martinsville?"

"Postmaster at Martinsville?" said Johnny. "But—"

"Oh, it's only a tenth-class post office," said the President, "but, for once in my life, I'll do something because I want to, and let Congress yell its head off. Come—is it yes or no?"

Johnny thought of all the places he'd been and all the trades he'd worked at. He thought, queerly enough, of the old drunk fiddler dead in the ditch, but he knew he couldn't be that. Mostly, though, he thought of Martinsville and Susie Marsh. And, though he'd just heard the Fool-Killer's step, he defied the Fool-Killer.

"Why, it's yes, of course, Mr. President," he said, "for then I can marry Susie."

"That's as good a reason as you'll find," said the President. "And now, I'll just write a note."

Well, he was as good as his word, and Johnny and his Susie were married and went back to live in Martinsville. And, as soon as Johnny learned the ways of postmastering, he found it as good a trade as most. There wasn't much mail in Martinsville, but, in between whiles, he ran the mill, and that was a good trade too. And all the time, he knew, at the back of his mind, that he hadn't quite settled accounts with the Fool-Killer. But he didn't much care about that, for he and Susie were happy. And after a while they had a child, and that was the most remarkable experience that had ever happened to any young couple, though the doctor said it was a perfectly normal baby.

One evening, when his son was about a year old, Johnny Pye took the river road, going home. It was a mite longer than the hill road, but it was the cool of the evening, and there's times when a man likes to walk by himself, fond as he may be of his wife and family.

He was thinking of the way things had turned out for him, and they seemed to him pretty astonishing and singular, as they do to most folks, when you think them over. In fact, he was thinking so hard that, before he knew it, he'd almost stumbled over an old scissors grinder who'd set up his grindstone and tools by the side of the road. The scissors grinder had his cart with him, but he'd turned the horse out to graze—and a lank, old, white horse it was, with every rib showing. And he was very busy, putting an edge on a scythe.

"Oh, sorry," said Johnny Pye. "I didn't know anybody was camping here. But you might come around to my house tomorrow—my wife's got some knives that need sharpening."

Then he stopped, for the old man gave him a long, keen look.

"Why, it's you, Johnny Pye," said the old man. "And how do you do, Johnny Pye! You've been a long time coming—in fact, now and then, I thought I'd have to fetch you. But you're here at last."

Johnny Pye was a grown man now, but he began to tremble.

"But it isn't you!" he said, wildly. "I mean you're not him! Why, I've known how he looks all my life! He's a big man, with a checked shirt, and he carries a hickory stick with a lump of lead in one end."

"Oh, no," said the scissors grinder, quite quiet. "You may have thought of me that way, but that's not the way I am." And Johnny Pye heard the scythe go whet-whet-whet on the stone. The old man ran some water on it and looked at the edge. Then he shook his head as if the edge didn't quite satisfy him. "Well, Johnny, are you ready?" he said, after a while.

"Ready?" said Johnny, in a hoarse voice. "Of course I'm not ready."

"That's what they all say," said the old man, nodding his head, and the scythe went whet-whet on the stone.

Johnny wiped his brow and started to argue it out.

"You see, if you'd found me earlier," he said, "or later. I don't want to be unreasonable, but I've got a wife and a child."

"Most has wives and many has children," said the old man, grimly, and the scythe went whet-whet on the stone as he pushed the treadle. And a shower of sparks flew, very clear and bright, for the night had begun to fall.

"Oh, stop that damn racket and let a man think for a minute!" said Johnny, desperate. "I can't go, I tell you. I won't. It isn't time. It's—"

The old man stopped the grindstone and pointed with the scythe at Johnny Pye.

"Tell me one good reason," he said. "There's men would be missed in the world, but are you one of them? A clever man might be missed, but are you a clever man?"

"No," said Johnny, thinking of the herb doctor. "I had a chance to be clever, but I gave it up."

"One," said the old man, ticking off on his fingers. "Well, a rich man might be missed—by some. But you aren't rich, I take it."

"No," said Johnny, thinking of the merchant, "nor wanted to be."

"Two," said the old man. "Cleverness—riches—they're done. But there's still martial bravery and being a hero. There might be an argument to make, if you were one of those."

Johnny Pye shuddered a little, remembering the way that battlefield had looked, out West, when the Indians were dead and the fight over.

"No," he said, "I've fought, but I'm not a hero."

"Well, then, there's religion," said the old man, sort of patient, "and science, and—but what's the use? We know what you did with those. I might feel a trifle of compunction if I had to deal with a President of the United States. But—"

"Oh, you know well enough I ain't President," said Johnny, with a groan. "Can't you get it over with and be done?"

"You're not putting up a very good case," said the old man, shaking his head. "I'm surprised at you, Johnny. Here you spend your youth running away from being a fool. And yet, what's the first thing you do, when you're man grown? Why, you marry a girl, settle down in your home town, and start raising children when you don't know how they'll turn out. You might have known I'd catch up with you, then—you just put yourself in my way."

"Fool I may be," said Johnny Pye in his agony, "and if you take it like that, I guess we're all fools. But Susie's my wife, and my child's my child. And, as for work in the world—well, somebody has to be postmaster, or folks wouldn't get the mail."

"Would it matter much if they didn't? said the old man, pointing his scythe.

"Well, no, I don't suppose it would, considering what's on the post cards," said Johnny Pye. "But while it's my business to sort it, I'll sort it as well as I can."

The old man whetted his scythe so hard that a long shower of sparks flew out on the grass.

"Well," he said, "I've got my job, too, and I do it likewise. But I'll tell you what I'll do. You're coming my way, no doubt of it, but, looking you over, you don't look quite ripe yet. So I'll let you off for a while. For that matter," said he, "if you'll answer one question of mine—how a man can be a human being and not be a fool—I'll let you off permanent. It'll be the first time in history," he said, "but you've got to do something on your own hook, once in a while. And now you can walk along, Johnny Pye."

With that he grounded the scythe till the sparks flew out like the tail of a comet and Johnny Pye walked along. The air of the meadow had never seemed so sweet to him before.

All the same, even with his relief, he didn't quite forget, and sometimes Susie had to tell the children not to disturb father because he was thinking. But time went ahead, as it does and pretty soon Johnny Pye found he was forty. He'd never expected to be forty, when he was young, and it kind of surprised him. But there it was, though he couldn't say he felt much different, except now and then when he stooped over. And he was a solid citizen of the town, well-liked and well-respected, with a growing family and a stake in the community, and when he thought those things over, they kind of surprised him too. But, pretty soon, it was as if things had always been that way.

It was after his eldest son had been drowned out fishing that Johnny Pye met the scissors grinder again. But this time he was bitter and distracted, and, if he could have got to the old man, he'd have done him a mortal harm. But, somehow or other, when he tried to come to grips with him, it was like reaching for air and mist. He could see the sparks fly from the ground scythe, but he couldn't even touch the wheel.

"You coward!" said Johnny Pye. "Stand up and fight like a man!" But the old man just nodded his head and the wheel kept grinding and grinding.

"Why couldn't you have taken me?" said Johnny Pye, as if those words had never been said before. "What's the sense in all this? Why can't you take me now?"

Then he tried to wrench the scythe from the old man's hands, but he couldn't touch it. And then he fell down and lay on the grass for a while.

"Time passes," said the old man, nodding his head. "Time passes."

"It will never cure the grief I have for my son," said Johnny Pye.

"It will not," said the old man, nodding his head. "But time passes. Would you leave your wife a widow and your other children fatherless for the sake of your grief?"

"No, God help me!" said Johnny Pye. "That wouldn't be right for a man."

JOHNNY PYE AND THE FOOL-KILLER

"Then go home to your house, Johnny Pye," said the old man. And Johnny Pye went, but there were lines in his face that hadn't been there before.

And time passed, like the flow of the river, and Johnny Pye's children married and had houses and children of their own. And Susie's hair grew white, and her back grew bent, and when Johnny Pye and his children followed her to her grave, folks said she'd died in the fullness of years, but that was hard for Johnny Pye to believe. Only folks didn't talk as plain as they used to, and the sun didn't heat as much, and sometimes, before dinner, he'd go to sleep in his chair.

And once, after Susie had died, the President of those days came through Martinsville and Johnny Pye shook hands with him and there was a piece in the paper about his shaking hands with two Presidents, fifty years apart. Johnny Pye cut out the clipping and kept it in his pocketbook. He liked this President all right, but, as he told people, he wasn't a patch on the other one fifty years ago. Well, you couldn't expect it—you didn't have Presidents these days, not to call them Presidents. All the same, he took a lot of satisfaction in the clipping.

He didn't get down to the river road much any more—it wasn't too long a walk, of course, but he just didn't often feel like it. But, one day, he slipped away from the granddaughter that was taking care of him, and went. It was kind of a steep road, really —he didn't remember its being so steep.

"Well," said the scissors grinder, "and good afternoon to you, Johnny Pye."

"You'll have to talk a little louder," said Johnny Pye. "My hearing's perfect, but folk don't speak as plain as they used to. Stranger in town?"

"Oh, so that's the way it is," said the scissors grinder.

"Yes, that's the way it is," said Johnny Pye. He knew he ought to be afraid of this fellow, now he'd put on his spectacles and got a good look at him, but for the life of him, he couldn't remember why.

"I know just who you are," he said, a little fretfully. "Never forgot a face in my life, and your name's right on the tip of my tongue—"

"Oh, don't bother about names," said the scissors grinder. "We're old acquaintances. And I asked you a question, years ago—do you remember that?"

"Yes," said Johnny Pye, "I remember." Then he began to laugh—a high, old man's laugh. "And of all the fool questions I ever was asked," he said, "that certainly took the cake."

"Oh?" said the scissors grinder.

"Uh-huh," said Johnny Pye. "For you asked me how a man could be a human being and yet not be a fool. And the answer is—when he's dead and gone and buried. Any fool would know that."

"That so?" said the scissors grinder.

"Of course," said Johnny Pye. "I ought to know. I'll be ninety-two next November, and I've shook hands with two Presidents. The first President I shook—"

"I'll be interested to hear about that," said the scissors grinder, "but we've got a little business, first. For, if all human beings are fools, how does the world get ahead?"

"Oh, there's lots of other things," said Johnny Pye, kind of impatient. "There's the brave and the wise and the clever—and they're apt to roll it ahead as much as an inch. But it's all mixed in together. For, Lord, it's only some fool kind of creature that would have crawled out of the sea to dry land in the first place —or got dropped from the Garden of Eden, if you like it better that way. You can't depend on the kind of folks people think they are—you've got to go by what they do. And I wouldn't give much for a man that some folks hadn't thought was a fool, in his time."

"Well," said the scissors grinder, "you've answered my question—at least as well as you could, which is all you can expect of a man. So I'll keep my part of the bargain."

"And what was that?" said Johnny. "For, while it's all straight in my head, I don't quite recollect the details."

"Why," said the scissors grinder, rather testy, "I'm to let you go, you old fool! You'll never see me again till the Last Judgment. There'll be trouble in the office about it," said he, "but you've got to do what you like, once in a while."

"Phew!" said Johnny Pye. "That needs thinking over!" And he scratched his head.

"Why?" said the scissors grinder, a bit affronted. "It ain't often I offer a man eternal life."

"Well," said Johnny Pye, "I take it very kind, but, you see, it's this way." He thought for a moment. "No," he said, "you wouldn't understand. You can't have touched seventy yet, by your looks, and no young man would."

"Try me," said the scissors grinder.

"Well," said Johnny Pye, "it's this way," and he scratched his head again. "I'm not saying—if you'd made the offer forty years ago, or even twenty. But, well, now, let's just take one detail. Let's say 'teeth.'"

"Well, of course," said the scissors grinder, "naturally—I mean you could hardly expect me to do anything about that."

"I thought so," said Johnny Pye. "Well, you see, these are good, bought teeth, but I'm sort of tired of hearing them click. And spectacles, I suppose, the same?"

"I'm afraid so," said the scissors grinder. "I can't interfere with time, you know—that's not my department. And, frankly, you couldn't expect, at a hundred and eighty, let's say, to be quite the man you were at ninety. But still, you'd be a wonder!"

"Maybe so," said Johnny Pye, "but you see—well, the truth is, I'm an old man now. You wouldn't think it to look at me, but it's so. And my friends—well, they're gone—and Susie and the boy—and somehow you don't get as close to the younger people, except the children. And to keep on just going and going till Judgment Day, with nobody around to talk to that had real horse sense—well, no, sir, it's a handsome offer but I just don't feel up to accepting it. It may not be patriotic of me, and I feel sorry for Martinsville. It'd do wonders for the climate and the chamber of commerce to have a leading citizen live till Judgment Day. But a man's got to do as he likes, at least once in his life." He stopped and looked at the scissors grinder. "I'll admit, I'd kind of like to beat out Ike Leavis," he said. "To hear him talk, you'd think nobody had ever pushed ninety before. But I suppose—"

"I'm afraid we can't issue a limited policy," said the scissors grinder.

"Well," said Johnny Pye, "I just thought of it. And Ike's all right." He waited a moment. "Tell me," he said, in a low voice. "Well, you know what I mean. Afterwards. I mean, if you're likely to see"—he coughed—"your friends again. I mean, if it's so —like some folks believe."

"I can't tell you that," said the scissors grinder. "I only go so far."

"Well, there's no harm in asking," said Johnny Pye, rather humbly. He peered into the darkness; a last shower of sparks flew from the scythe, then the whir of the wheel stopped.

"H'm," said Johnny Pye, testing the edge. "That's a well-ground scythe. But they used to grind 'em better in the old days." He listened and looked, for a moment, anxiously. "Oh. Lordy!" he said, "there's Helen coming to look for me. She'll take me back to the house."

"Not this time," said the scissor grinder. "Yes, there isn't bad steel in that scythe. Well, let's go, Johnny Pye."

THE DIE-HARD

There was a town called Shady, Georgia, and a time that's gone, and a boy named Jimmy Williams who was curious about things. Just a few years before the turn of the century it was, and that seems far away now. But Jimmy Williams was living in it, and it didn't seem far away to him.

It was a small town, Shady, and sleepy, though it had two trains a day and they were putting through a new spur to Vickery Junction.

They'd dedicated the War Memorial in the Square, but, on market days, you'd still see oxcarts on Main Street. And once, when Jimmy Williams was five, there'd been a light fall of snow and the whole town had dropped its business and gone out to see it. He could still remember the feel of the snow in his hands, for it was the only snow he'd ever touched or seen.

He was a bright boy—maybe a little too bright for his age. He'd think about a thing till it seemed real to him—and that's a dangerous gift. His father was the town doctor, and his father would try to show him the difference, but Doctor Williams was a right busy man. And the other Williams children were a good deal younger and his mother was busy with them. So Jimmy had more time to himself than most boys—and youth's a dreamy time.

I reckon it was that got him interested in Old Man Cappalow, in the first place. Every town has its legends and characters, and Old Man Cappalow was one of Shady's. He lived out of town, on the old Vincey place, all alone except for a light-colored Negro named Sam that he'd brought from Virginia with him; and the local Negroes wouldn't pass along that road at night. That was partly because of Sam, who was supposed to be a conjur, but mostly on account of Old Man Cappalow. He'd come in the troubled times, right after the end of the war, and ever since then he'd kept himself to himself. Except that once a month he went down to the bank and drew money that came in a letter from Virginia. But how he spent it, nobody knew. Except that he had a treasure—every boy in Shady knew that.

Now and then, a gang of them would get bold and they'd rattle sticks along the sides of his fence and yell, "Old Man Cappalow! Where's your money?" But then the light-colored Negro, Sam, would come out on the porch and look at them, and they'd run away. They didn't want to be conjured, and you couldn't be sure. But on the way home, they'd speculate and wonder about the treasure, and each time they speculated and wondered, it got bigger to them.

Some said it was the last treasure of the Confederacy, saved right up to the end to build a new *Alabama,* and that Old Man Cappalow had sneaked it out of Richmond when the city fell and kept it for himself; only now he didn't dare spend it, for the mark of Cain was on every piece. And some said it came from the sea islands, where the pirates had left it, protected by h'ants and devils, and Old Man Cappalow had had to fight devils for it six days and six nights before he could take it away. And if you looked inside his shirt, you could see the long white marks where the devils had clawed him. Well, sir, some said one thing and some said another. But they all agreed it was there, and it got to be a byword among the boys of the town.

It used to bother Jimmy Williams tremendously. Because he knew his father worked hard, and yet sometimes he'd only get fifty cents a visit, and often enough he'd get nothing. And he knew his mother worked hard, and that most folks in Shady weren't rich. And yet, all the time, there was that treasure, sitting out at Old Man Cappalow's. He didn't mean to steal it exactly. I don't know just what he did intend to do about it. But the idea of it bothered him and stayed at the back of his mind. Till, finally, one summer when he was turned thirteen, he started making expeditions to the Cappalow place.

He'd go in the cool of the morning or the cool of the afternoon, and sometimes he'd be fighting Indians and Yankees on the way, because he was still a boy, and sometimes he was thinking what he'd be when he grew up, for he was starting to be a man. But he never told the other boys what he was doing—and that was the mixture of both. He'd slip from the road, out of sight of the house, and go along by the fence. Then he'd lie down in the grass and the weeds, and look at the house.

It had been quite a fine place once, but now the porch was sagging and there were mended places in the roof and paper pasted over broken windowpanes. But that didn't mean much to Jimmy Williams; he was used to houses looking like that. There was a garden patch at the side, neat and well-kept, and sometimes he'd see the Negro, Sam, there, working. But what he looked at mostly was the side porch. For Old Man Cappalow would be sitting there.

He sat there, cool and icy-looking, in his white linen suit, on his cane chair, and now and then he'd have a leather-bound book in his hand, though he didn't often read it. He didn't move much, but he sat straight, his hands on his knees and his black eyes alive. There was something about his eyes that reminded Jimmy Williams of the windows of the house. They weren't blind, indeed they were bright, but there was something living behind them that wasn't usual. You didn't expect them to be so black, with his white hair. Jimmy Williams had seen a governor once, on Memorial Day, but the governor didn't look half as fine. This man was like a man made of ice—ice in the heat of the South. You could see he was old, but you couldn't tell how old, or whether he'd ever die.

Once in a great while he'd come out and shoot at a mark. The mark was a kind of metal shield, nailed up on a post, and it had been painted once, but the paint had worn away. He'd hold the pistol very steady, and the bullets would go "whang, whang" on the metal, very loud in the stillness. Jimmy Williams would watch him and wonder if that was the way he'd fought with his devils, and speculate about all kinds of things.

All the same, he was only a boy, and though it was fun and scary, to get so near Old Man Cappalow without being seen, and he'd have a grand tale to tell the others, if he ever decided to tell it, he didn't see any devils or any treasure. And probably he'd have given the whole business up in the end, boylike, if something hadn't happened.

He was lying in the weeds by the fence, one warm afternoon, and, boylike, he fell asleep. And he was just in the middle of a dream where Old Man Cappalow was promising him a million dollars if he'd go to the devil to get it, when he was wakened by a rustle in the weeds and a voice that said, "White boy."

Jimmy Williams rolled over and froze. For there, just half a dozen steps away from him, was the light-colored Negro. Sam, in his blue jeans, the way he worked in the garden patch, but looking like the butler at the club for all that.

I reckon if Jimmy Williams had been on his feet, he'd have run. But he wasn't on his feet. And he told himself he didn't mean to run, though his heart began to pound.

"White boy," said the light-colored Negro, "Marse John see you from up at the house. He send you his obleegances and say will you step that way." He spoke in a light, sweet voice, and there wasn't a thing in his manners you could have objected to. But just for a minute, Jimmy Williams wondered if he was being conjured. And then he didn't care. Because he was going to do what no boy in Shady had ever done. He was going to walk into Old Man Cappalow's house and not be scared. He wasn't going to be scared, though his heart kept pounding.

He scrambled to his feet and followed the line of the fence till he got to the driveway, the light-colored Negro just a little behind him. And when they got near the porch, Jimmy Williams stopped and took a leaf and wiped off his shoes, though he couldn't have told you why. The Negro stood watching while he did it, perfectly at ease. Jimmy Williams could see that the Negro thought better of him for wiping off his shoes, but not much. And that made him mad, and he wanted to say, "I'm no white trash. My father's a doctor," but he knew better than to say it. He just wiped his shoes and the Negro stood and waited. Then the Negro took him around to the side porch, and there was Old Man Cappalow, sitting in his cane chair.

"White boy here, Marse John," said the Negro in his low, sweet voice.

The old man lifted his head, and his black eyes looked at Jimmy Williams. It was a long stare and it went to Jimmy Williams' backbone.

"Sit down, boy," he said, at last, and his voice was friendly enough, but Jimmy Williams obeyed it. "You can go along, Sam," he said, and Jimmy Williams sat on the edge of a cane chair and tried to feel comfortable. He didn't do very well at it, but he tried.

"What's your name, boy?" said the old man, after a while.

"Jimmy Williams, sir," said Jimmy Williams. "I mean James Williams, Junior, sir."

"Williams," said the old man, and his black eyes glowed. "There was a Colonel Williams with the Sixty-fifth Virginia—or was it the Sixty-third? He came from Fairfax County and was quite of my opinion that we should have kept to primogeniture, in spite of Thomas Jefferson. But I doubt if you are kin."

"No, sir," said Jimmy Williams. "I mean, Father was with the Ninth Georgia. And he was a private. They were aiming to make him a corporal, he says, but they never got around to it. But he fit—he fought lots of Yankees. He fit tons of 'em. And I've seen his uniform. But now he's a doctor instead."

The old man seemed to look a little queer at that. "A doctor?" he said. "Well, some very reputable gentlemen have practiced medicine. There need be no loss of standing."

"Yes, sir," said Jimmy Williams. Then he couldn't keep it back any longer: "Please, sir, were you ever clawed by the devil?" he said.

"Ha-hrrm!" said the old man, looking startled. "You're a queer boy. And suppose I told you I had been?"

"I'd believe you," said Jimmy Williams, and the old man laughed. He did it as if he wasn't used to it, but he did it.

"Clawed by the devil!" he said. "Ha-hrrm! You're a bold boy. I didn't know they grew them nowadays. I'm surprised." But

THE DIE-HARD

he didn't look angry, as Jimmy Williams had expected him to.

"Well," said Jimmy Williams, "if you had been, I thought maybe you'd tell me about it. I'd be right interested. Or maybe let me see the clawmarks. I mean, if they're there."

"I can't show you those," said the old man, "though they're deep and wide." And he stared fiercely at Jimmy Williams. "But you weren't afraid to come here and you wiped your shoes when you came. So I'll show you something else." He rose and was tall. "Come into the house," he said.

So Jimmy Williams got up and went into the house with him. It was a big, cool, dim room they went into, and Jimmy Williams didn't see much at first. But then his eyes began to get used to the dimness.

Well, there were plenty of houses in Shady where the rooms were cool and dim and the sword hung over the mantelpiece and the furniture was worn and old. It wasn't that made the difference. But stepping into this house was somehow like stepping back into the past, though Jimmy Williams couldn't have put it that way. He just knew it was full of beautiful things and grand things that didn't quite fit it, and yet all belonged together. And they knew they were grand and stately, and yet there was dust in the air and a shadow on the wall. It was peaceful enough and handsome enough, yet it didn't make Jimmy Williams feel comfortable, though he couldn't have told you why.

"Well," said the old man, moving about among shadows, "how do you like it, Mr. Williams?"

"It's—I never saw anything like it," said Jimmy Williams.

The old man seemed pleased. "Touch the things, boy," he said. "Touch the things. They don't mind being touched."

So Jimmy Williams went around the room, staring at the miniatures and the pictures, and picking up one thing or another and putting it down. He was very careful and he didn't break anything. And there were some wonderful things. There was a game of chess on a table—carved-ivory pieces—a game that people had started, but hadn't finished. He didn't touch those, though he wanted to, because he felt the people might not like it when they came back to finish their game. And yet, at the same time, he felt that if they ever did come back, they'd be dead, and that made him feel queerer. There were silver-mounted pistols, long-barreled, on a desk by a big silver inkwell; there was a quill pen made of a heron's feather, and a silver sandbox beside it—there were all sorts of curious and interesting things. Finally Jimmy Williams stopped in front of a big, tall clock.

"I'm sorry, sir," he said, "but I don't think that's the right time."

"Oh, yes, it is," said the old man. "It's always the right time."

"Yes, sir," said Jimmy Williams, "but it isn't running."

"Of course not," said the old man. "They say you can't put the clock back, but you can. I've put it back and I mean to keep it back. The others can do as they please. I warned them—I warned them in 1850, when they accepted the Compromise. I warned them there could be no compromise. Well, they would not be warned."

"Was that bad of them, sir?" asked Jimmy Williams.

"It was misguided of them," said the old man. "Misguided of them all." He seemed to be talking more to himself than to Jimmy, but Jimmy Williams couldn't help listening. "There can be no compromise with one's class or one's breeding or once's sentiments," the old man said. "Afterwards—well, there were gentlemen I knew who went to Guatemala or elsewhere. I do not blame them for it. But mine is another course." He paused and glanced at the clock. Then he spoke in a different voice. "I beg your pardon," he said. "I fear I was growing heated. You will excuse me. I generally take some refreshment around this time in the afternoon. Perhaps you will join me, Mr. Williams?"

It didn't seem to Jimmy Williams as if the sliver hand bell in the old man's hand had even stopped ringing before the Negro, Sam, came in with a tray. He had a queer kind of old-fashioned long coat on now, and a queer old-fashioned cravat, but his pants were the pants of his blue jeans. Jimmy Williams noticed that, but Old Man Cappalow didn't seem to notice.

"Yes," he said, "there are many traitors. Men I held in the greatest esteem have betrayed their class and their system. They have accepted ruin and domination in the name of advancement. But we will not speak of them now." He took the frosted silver cup from the tray and motioned to Jimmy Williams that the small fluted glass was for him. "I shall ask you to rise, Mr. Wil-

THE DIE-HARD

liams," he said. "We shall drink a toast." He paused for a moment, standing straight. "To the Confederate States of America and damnation to all her enemies!" he said.

Jimmy Williams drank. He'd never drunk any wine before, except blackberry cordial, and this wine seemed to him powerfully thin and sour. But he felt grown up as he drank it, and that was a fine feeling.

"Every night of my life," said the old man, "I drink that toast. And usually I drink it alone. But I am glad of your company, Mr. Williams."

"Yes, sir," said Jimmy Williams, but all the same, he felt queer. For drinking the toast, somehow, had been very solemn, almost like being in church. But in church you didn't exactly pray for other people's damnation, though the preacher might get right excited over sin.

Well, then the two of them sat down again, and Old Man Cappalow began to talk of the great plantation days and the world as it used to be. Of course, Jimmy Williams had heard plenty of talk of that sort. But this was different. For the old man talked of those days as if they were still going on, not as if they were past. And as he talked, the whole room seemed to join in, with a thousand, sighing, small voices, stately and clear, till Jimmy Williams didn't know whether he was on his head or his heels and it seemed quite natural to him to look at the fresh, crisp Richmond newspaper on the desk and see it was dated "June 14, 1859" instead of "June 14, 1897." Well, maybe it was the wine, though he'd only had a thimbleful. But when Jimmy Williams went out into the sun again, he felt changed, and excited too. For he knew about Old Man Cappalow now, and he was just about the grandest person in the world.

The Negro went a little behind him, all the way to the gate, on soft feet. When they got there, the Negro opened the gate and spoke.

"Young marster," he said, "I don't know why Marse John took in his head to ask you up to the house. But we lives private, me and Marse John. We lives very private." There was a curious pleading in his voice.

"I don't tell tales," said Jimmy Williams, and kicked at the fence.

"Yes, sir," said the Negro, and he seemed relieved. "I knew you one of the right ones. I knew that. But we'se living very private till the big folks come back. We don't want no tales spread before. And then we'se going back to Otranto, the way we should."

"I know about Otranto. He told me," said Jimmy Williams, catching his breath.

"Otranto Marse John's plantation in Verginny," said the Negro, as if he hadn't heard. "He owns the river and the valley, the streams and the hills. We got four hundred field hands at Otranto and stables for sixty horses. But we can't go back there till the big folks come back. Marse John say so, and he always speak the truth. But they's goin' to come back, a-shootin' and pirootin', they pistols at they sides. And every day I irons his Richmond paper for him and he reads about the old times. We got boxes and boxes of papers down in the cellar." He paused. "And if he say the old days come back, it bound to be so," he said. Again his voice held that curious pleading, "You remember, young marster," he said. "You remember, white boy."

"I told you I didn't tell tales," said Jimmy Williams. But after that, things were different for him. Because there's one thing about a boy that age that most grown people forget. A boy that age can keep a secret in a way that's perfectly astonishing. And he can go through queer hells and heavens you'll never hear a word about, not even if you got him or bore him.

It was that way with Jimmy Williams; it mightn't have been for another boy. It began like a game, and then it stopped being a game. For, of course, he went back to Old Man Cappalow's. And the Negro, Sam, would show him up to the house and he'd sit in the dim room with the old man and drink the toast in the wine. And it wasn't Old Man Cappalow any more; it was Col. John Leonidas Cappalow, who'd raised and equipped his own regiment and never surrendered. Only, when the time was ripe, he was going back to Otranto, and the old days would bloom again, and Jimmy Williams would be part of them.

When he shut his eyes at night, he could see Otranto and its porches, above the rolling river, great and stately; he could hear the sixty horses stamping in their stalls. He could see the pretty girls, in their wide skirts, coming down the glassy, proud staircases; he could see the fine, handsome gentlemen who ruled the earth and the richness of it without a thought of care. It was all like a storybook to Jimmy Williams—a storybook come true. And more than anything he'd ever wanted in his life, he wanted to be part of it.

The only thing was, it was hard to fit the people he really knew into the story. Now and then Colonel Cappalow would ask him gravely if he knew anyone else in Shady who was worthy of being trusted with the secret. Well, there were plenty of boys like Bob Miller and Tommy Vine, but somehow you couldn't see them in the dim room. They'd fit in, all right, when the great days came back—they'd have to—but meanwhile—well, they might just take it for a tale. And then there was Carrie, the cook. She'd have to be a slave again, of course, and though Jimmy Williams didn't imagine that she'd mind, now and then he had just a suspicion that she might. He didn't ask her about it, but he had the suspicion.

It was even hard to fit Jimmy's father in, with his little black bag and his rumpled clothes and his laugh. Jimmy couldn't quite see his father going up the front steps of Otranto—not because he wasn't a gentleman or grand enough, but because it just didn't happen to be his kind of place. And then, his father didn't really hate anybody, as far as Jimmy knew. But you had to hate people a good deal, if you wanted to follow Colonel Cappalow. You had to shoot at the mark and feel you were really shooting the enemy's colors down. You had to believe that even people like General Lee had been wrong, because they hadn't held out in the mountains and fought till everybody died. Well, it was hard to believe a wrong thing of General Lee, and Jimmy Williams didn't quite manage it. He was willing to hate the Yankees and the Republicans—hate them hot and hard—but there weren't any of them in Shady. Well, come to think of it, there was Mr. Rosen, at the dry-goods store, and Mr. Ailey, at the mill. They didn't look very terrible and he was used to them, but he tried to hate them all he could. He got hold of the Rosen boy one day and rocked him home, but the Rosen boy cried, and Jimmy felt mean about it. But if he'd ever seen a real live Republican, with horns and a tail, he'd have done him a mortal injury—he felt sure he would.

And so the summer passed, and by the end of the summer Jimmy didn't feel quite sure which was real—the times now or the times Colonel Cappalow talked about. For he'd dream about Otranto at night and think of it during the day. He'd ride back there on a black horse, at Colonel Cappalow's left, and his saber would be long and shining. But if there was a change in him, there was a change in Colonel Cappalow too. He was a lot more excitable than he used to be, and when he talked to Jimmy sometimes, he'd call him by other names, and when he shot at the mark with the enemy's colors on it, his eyes would blaze. So by that, and by the news he read out of the old papers, Jimmy suddenly got to know that the time was near at hand. They had the treasure all waiting, and soon they'd be ready to rise. And Colonel Cappalow filled out Jimmy Williams' commission as captain in the army of the New Confederate States of America and presented it to him, with a speech. Jimmy Williams felt very proud of that commission, and hid it under a loose brick in his fireplace chimney, where it would be safe.

Well, then it came to the plans, and when Jimmy Williams first heard about them, he felt a little surprised. There were maps spread all over the big desk in the dim room now, and Colonel Cappalow moved pins and showed Jimmy strategy. And that was very exciting, and like a game. But first of all, they'd have to give a signal and strike a blow. You had to do that first, and then the country would rise. Well, Jimmy Williams could see the reason in that.

They were going into Shady and capture the post office first, and then the railroad station and, after that, they'd dynamite the railroad bridge to stop the trains, and Colonel Cappalow would read a proclamation from the steps of the courthouse. The only part Jimmy Williams didn't like about it was killing the postmaster and the station agent, in case they resisted. Jimmy Williams felt pretty sure they would resist, particularly the station agent, who was a mean customer. And, somehow, killing people you knew wasn't quite like killing Yankees and Republicans. The thought of it shook something in Jimmy's mind and made it waver. But after that they'd march on Washington, and everything would be all right.

All the same, he'd sworn his oath and he was a commissioned

THE DIE-HARD

officer in the army of the New Confederate States. So, when Colonel Cappalow gave him the pistol that morning, with the bullets and the powder, and explained how he was to keep watch at the door of the post office and shoot to kill if he had to, Jimmy said, "I shall execute the order, sir," the way he'd been taught. After that, they'd go for the station agent and he'd have a chance for a lot more shooting. And it was all going to be for noon the next day.

Somehow, Jimmy Williams couldn't quite believe it was going to be for noon the next day, even when he was loading the pistol in the woodshed of the Williams house, late that afternoon. And yet he saw, with a kind of horrible distinctness, that it was going to be. It might sound crazy to some, but not to him—Colonel Cappalow was a sure shot; he'd seen him shoot at the mark. He could see him shooting, now, and he wondered if a bullet went "whang" when it hit a man. And, just as he was fumbling with the bullets, the woodshed door opened suddenly and there was his father.

Well, naturally, Jimmy dropped the pistol and jumped. The pistol didn't explode, for he'd forgotten it needed a cap. But with that moment something seemed to break inside Jimmy Williams. For it was the first time he'd really been afraid and ashamed in front of his father, and now he was ashamed and afraid. And then it was like waking up out of an illness, for his father saw his white face and said, "What's the matter, son?" and the words began to come out of his mouth.

"Take it easy, son," said his father, but Jimmy couldn't take it easy. He told all about Otranto and Old Man Cappalow and hating the Yankees and killing the postmaster, all jumbled up and higgledy-piggledy. But Doctor Williams made sense of it. At first he smiled a little as he listened, but after a while he stopped smiling, and there was anger in his face. And when Jimmy was quite through, "Well, son," he said, "I reckon we've let you run wild. But I never thought . . ." He asked Jimmy a few quick questions, mostly about the dynamite, and he seemed relieved when Jimmy told him they were going to get it from the men who were blasting for the new spur track.

"And now, son," he said, "when did you say this massacre was going to start?"

"Twelve o'clock at the post office," said Jimmy. "But we weren't going to massacre. It was just the folks that resisted—"

Doctor Williams made a sound in his throat. "Well," he said, "you and I are going to take a ride in the country, Jimmy. No, we won't tell you mother, I think."

It was the last time Jimmy Williams went out to Old Man Cappalow's, and he remembered that. His father didn't say a word all the way, but once he felt in his back pocket for something he'd taken out of the drawer of his desk, and Jimmy remembered that too.

When they drove up in front of the house, his father gave the reins to Jimmy. "Stay in the buggy, Jimmy," he said. "I'll settle this."

Then he got out of the buggy, a little awkwardly, for he was a heavy man, and Jimmy heard his feet scrunch on the gravel. Jimmy knew again, as he saw him go up the steps, that he wouldn't have fitted in Otranto, and somehow he was glad.

The Negro, Sam, opened the door.

"Tell Colonel Cappalow Doctor Williams wishes to speak with him," said Jimmy's father, and Jimmy could see that his father's neck was red.

"Colonel Cappalow not receivin'," said Sam, in his light sweet voice, but Jimmy's father spoke again.

"Tell Colonel Cappalow," he said. He didn't raise his voice, but there was something in it that Jimmy had never heard in that voice before. Sam looked for a moment and went inside the house.

Then Colonel Cappalow came to the door himself. There was red from the evening sun on his white suit and his white hair, and he looked tall and proud. He looked first at Jimmy's father and then at Jimmy. And his voice said, quite coldly, and reasonably and clearly, "Traitor! All traitors!"

"You'll oblige me by leaving the boy out of it," said Jimmy's father heavily. "This is 1897, sir, not 1860," and for a moment there was something light and heady and dangerous in the air between them. Jimmy knew what his father had in his pocket then, and he sat stiff in the buggy and prayed for time to change and things to go away.

Then Colonel Cappalow put his hand to his forehead. "I beg

your pardon, sir," he said, in an altered voice. "You mentioned a date?"

"I said it was 1897," said Doctor Williams, standing square and stocky, "I said Marse Robert's dead—God bless him!—and Jefferson Davis too. And before he died, Marse Robert said we ought to be at peace. The ladies can keep up the war as long as they see fit—that's their privilege. But men ought to act like men."

He stared for a moment at the high-chinned, sculptural face.

"Why, damn your soul!" he said, and it was less an oath than a prayer. "I was with the Ninth Georgia; I went through three campaigns. We fought till the day of Appomattox and it was we-uns' fight." Something rough and from the past had slipped back into his speech—something, too, that Jimmy Williams had never heard in it before. "We didn't own niggers or plantations— the men I fought with. But when it was over, we reckoned it was over and we'd build up the land. Well, we've had a hard time to do it, but we're hoeing corn. We've got something better to do than fill up a boy with a lot of magnolious notions and aim to shoot up a postmaster because there's a Republican President. My God," he said, and again it was less an oath than a prayer, "it was bad enough getting licked when you thought you couldn't be—but when I look at you—well, hate stinks when it's kept too long in the barrel, no matter how you dress it up and talk fine about it. I'm warning you. You keep your hands off my boy. Now, that's enough."

"Traitors," said the old man vaguely, "all traitors." Then a change came over his face and he stumbled forward as if he had stumbled over a stone. The Negro and the white man both sprang to him, but it was the Negro who caught him and lowered him to the ground. Then Jimmy Williams heard his father calling for his black bag, and his limbs were able to move again.

Doctor Williams came out of the bedroom, drying his hands on a towel. His eyes fell upon Jimmy Williams, crouched in front of the chessboard.

"He's all right, son," he said. "At least—he's not all right. But he wasn't in pain."

Jimmy Williams shivered a little. "I heard him talking," he said difficultly. "I heard him calling people things."

"Yes," said his father. "Well, you mustn't think too much of that. You see, a man—" He stopped and began again, "Well, I've no doubt he was considerable of a man once. Only—well, there's a Frenchman calls it a fixed idea. You let it get a hold of you . . . and the way he was brought up. He got it in his head, you see —he couldn't stand it that he might have been wrong about anything. And the hate—well, it's not for a man. Not when it's like that. Now, where's that Nigra?"

Jimmy Williams shivered again; he did not want Sam back in the room. But when Sam came, he heard the Negro answer, politely.

"H'm," said Doctor Williams. "Twice before. He should have had medical attention."

"Marse John don't believe in doctors," said the low, sweet voice.

"He wouldn't," said Doctor Williams briefly. "Well, I'll take the boy home now. But I'll have to come back. I'm coroner for this county. You understand about that?"

"Yes, sir," said the low, sweet voice, "I understand about that." Then the Negro looked at the doctor. "Marse Williams," he said, "I wouldn't have let him do it. He thought he was bound to. But I wouldn't have let him do it."

"Well," said the doctor. He thought, and again said, "Well." Then he said, "Are there any relatives?"

"I take him back to Otranto," said the Negro. "It belongs to another gentleman now, but Marse John got a right to lie there. That's Verginny law, he told me."

"So it is," said the doctor. "I'd forgotten that."

"He don't want no relatives," said the Negro. "He got nephews and nieces and all sorts of kin. But they went against him and he cut them right out of his mind. He don't want no relatives." He paused. "He cut everything out of his mind but the old days," he said. "He start doing it right after the war. That's why we come here. He don't want no part nor portion of the present days. And they send him money from Verginny, but he only spend it the one way—except when we buy this place." He smiled as if at a secret.

"But how?" said the doctor, staring at furniture and pictures.

"Jus' one muleload from Otranto," said the Negro, softly. "And I'd like to see anybody cross Marse John in the old days." He coughed. "They's just one thing, Marse Williams," he said, in his suave voice. "I ain't skeered of sittin' up with Marse John. I always been with him. But it's the money."

"What money?" said Doctor Williams. "Well, that will go through the courts—"

"No, sir," said the Negro patiently. "I mean Marse John's special money that he spend the other money for. He got close to a millyum dollars in that blind closet under the stairs. And nobody dare come for it, as long as he's strong and spry. But now I don't know. I don't know."

"Well," said Doctor Williams, receiving the incredible fact, "I suppose we'd better see."

It was as the Negro had said—a blind closet under the stairs, opened by an elementary sliding catch.

"There's the millyum dollars," said the Negro as the door swung back. He held the cheap glass lamp high—the wide roomy closet was piled from floor to ceiling with stacks of printed paper.

"H'm," said Doctor Williams. "Yes, I thought so. . . . Have you ever seen a million dollars, son?"

"No sir," said Jimmy Williams.

"Well, take a look," said his father. He slipped a note from a packet, and held it under the lamp.

"It says 'One Thousand Dollars'" said Jimmy Williams. "Oh!"

"Yes," said his father gently. "And it also says 'Confederate States of America'. . . . You don't need to worry, Sam. The money's perfectly safe. Nobody will come for it. Except, maybe, museums."

"Yes, Marse Williams," said Sam unquestioningly, accepting the white man's word, now he had seen and judged the white man. He shut the closet.

On his way out, the doctor paused for a moment and looked at the Negro. He might have been thinking aloud—it seemed that way to Jimmy Williams.

"And why did you do it?" he said. "Well, that's something we'll never know. And what are you going to do, once you've taken him back to Otranto?"

"I got my arrangements, thank you, sir," said the Negro.

"I haven't a doubt of it," said Jimmy Williams' father. "But I wish I knew what they were."

"I got my arrangements, gentlemen," the Negro repeated, in his low, sweet voice. Then they left him, holding the lamp, with his tall shadow behind him.

"Maybe I oughtn't to have left him," said Jimmy Williams' father, after a while, as the buggy jogged along. "He's perfectly capable of setting fire to the place and burning it up as a sort of a funeral pyre. And maybe that wouldn't be a bad thing," he added, after a pause. Then he said, "Did you notice the chessmen? I wonder who played that game. It was stopped in the middle." Then, after a while, he said, "I remember the smell of the burning woods in the Wilderness. And I remember Reconstruction. But Marse Robert was right, all the same. You can't go back to the past. And hate's the most expensive commodity in the world. It's never been anything else, and I've seen a lot of it. We've got to realize that—got too much of it, still, as a nation."

But Jimmy Williams was hardly listening. He was thinking it was good to be alone with his father in a buggy at night and good they didn't have to live in Otranto after all.

GLAMOUR

I used to read quite a lot of books when I was younger, but now they just make me sore. Marian keeps on bringing them back from the lending library and, occasionally, I'll pick one up and read a few chapters, but sooner or later you're bound to strike something that makes you sick. I don't mean dirt or anything—just foolishness, and people acting the way they never act. Of course, the books she reads are mostly love stories. I suppose they're the worst kind.

But what I understand least is the money angle. It takes money to get drunk and it takes money to go around with a girl—at least that's been my experience. But the people in those books seem to have invented a special kind of money—it only gets spent on a party or a trip. The rest of the time they might as well be paying their bills with wampum, as far as you can figure it out.

Of course, often enough, the people in books are poor. But then they're so darn poor, it's crazy. And, often enough, just when everything's at its worst, some handy little legacy comes along and the new life opens out before them right away, like a great big tulip. Well, I only had one legacy in my life and I know what I did with that. It darn near ruined me.

Uncle Bannard died up in Vermont in 1924, and when his estate was settled, it came to $1237.62 apiece for Lou and me. Lou's husband put her share in Greater Los Angeles real estate —they live out on the Coast—and I guess they've done pretty well. But I took mine and quit the firm I was with, Rosenberg and Jenkins, mechanical toys and novelties, and went to Brooklyn to write a novel.

It sounds crazy, looking back on it. But I was a bug about reading and writing in those days, and I'd done some advertising copy for the firm that pulled. And that was the time when everybody was getting steamed up about "the new American writers," and it looked like a game without much overhead. I'd just missed the war—I was seventeen when it finished—and I'd missed college because of father's death. In fact, I hadn't done much of anything I really wanted since I had to quit high school —though the novelty business was all right as businesses go. So when I got a chance to cut loose, I cut.

I figured I could easily live a year on the twelve hundred, and, at first, I thought of France. But there'd be the nuisance of learning frog-talk and the passage there and back. Besides, I wanted to be near a big library. My novel was going to be about the American Revolution, if you can picture it. I'd read "Henry Esmond" over and over and I wanted to write a book like that.

I guess it must have been a bunch of my New England ancestors that picked Brooklyn for me. They were pioneers, all right —but, gosh, how they hated to take any chance but a big one! And I'm like that myself. I like to feel tidy in my mind when I'm taking a chance.

I figured I could be as solitary in Brooklyn as I could in Pisa, and a lot more comfortable. I knew how many words it took to make a novel—I'd counted some of them—so I bought enough paper and a second-hand typewriter and pencils and erasers. That about cleaned out my ready cash. I swore I wouldn't touch the legacy till I was really at work. But I felt like a million dollars —I swear I felt as if I were looking for treasure—when I got into the subway that shiny autumn day, and started across the river to look for a room.

It may have been my ancestors that sent me to Brooklyn, but I don't know what landed me at Mrs. Forge's. Old Wrestling Southgate, the one who was bothered with witches, would probably have called it a flowered snare of the fiend. And I'm not so sure, looking back, that he'd have been wrong.

Mrs. Forge opened the door herself—Serena was out. They'd talked about putting an ad in the paper but they'd just never got around to it; and, naturally, they wouldn't have put up a card. If it hadn't looked like the sort of house I'd wanted, I'd never having rung the bell. As it was, when she came to the door, I thought that I had made a mistake. So the first thing I did was beg her pardon.

She had on her black silk dress—the one with the white ruffles —just as if she were going out calling in the barouche. The minute she started to speak, I knew she was Southern. They all had that voice. I won't try to describe it. There's nothing worse than a whiny one—it beats the New England twang. But theirs didn't whine. They made you think of the sun and long afternoons and slow rivers—and time, time, time, just sliding along like a current, not going anywhere particular, but gay.

I think she liked my begging her pardon, for she took me in and gave me a slice of fruit cake and some lemonade. And I listened to her talk and felt, somehow, as if I'd been frozen for a long time and was just beginning to get warm. There was always a pitcher of lemonade in the ice-box, though the girls drank "coke," mostly. I've seen them come in from the snow, in the dead of winter, and drink it. They didn't think much of the cold, anyway, so they more or less pretended it didn't exist. They were that way.

The room was exactly what I wanted—big and sunny, with an outlook over a little backyard where there was the wreck of a forsythia bush and some spindly grass. I've forgotten to say the house was in one of those old-fashioned side-streets, not far from

Prospect Park. But it doesn't matter where it was. It must be gone, now.

You know, it took all my nerve to ask Mrs. Forge the price. She was very polite, but she made me feel like a guest. I don't know if you can understand that. And then she couldn't tell me.

"Well, now, Mr. Southgate," she said, in that soft, gentle, helpless voice that ran on as inexorably as water, "I wish my daughter Eva had been here to receive you. My daughter Eva has accepted a business position since we came here for my daughter Melissa's art training. And I said, only this morning, 'Eva, honey, suppose Serena's away and some young person comes here, askin' for that room. I'll be bound to say somethin' to them, sugar, and I'll feel right embarrassed.' But just then some little boys started shoutin' down the street and I never did rightly hear what she answered. So if you're in a hurry, Mr. Southgate, I don't just know what we can do."

"I could leave a desposit," I said. I'd noticed, by this time, that the black silk had a tear in it and that she was wearing a pair of run-down ball-slippers—incredibly small they were. But, all the same, she looked like a duchess.

"Why, I suppose you could, Mr. Southgate," she said, with an obvious lack of interest. "I suppose that would be businesslike. You gentlemen in the North are always so interested in business. I recollect Mr. Forge sayin' before he died, 'Call them d—— Yankees if you like, Milly, but we've all got to live in the same country and I've met some without horns.' Mr. Forge was always so humorous. So, you see, we're quite accustomed to Northerners. You don't happen to be kin to the Mobile Southgates, do you, Mr. Southgate? You'll excuse an old lady's askin'—but you seem to favor them a little, now your face is in the light."

I'm not trying to put down just the way she talked—she didn't say "ah" and "nah"—it was something lighter and suaver. But her talk went on like that. They all did it. It wasn't nervousness or trying to impress you. They found it as easy and restful to talk as most of us do to keep still; and, if the talk never got anywhere, they'd never expected it would. It was like a drug—it made life into a dream. And, of course, it isn't that.

Finally, I simply went for my stuff and moved in. I didn't know how much I was paying or what meals would be included in it, but I somehow felt that these things would be shown unto me when the time was ripe. That's what an hour and a half with Mrs. Forge did to me. But I did resolve to have a clear understanding with "my daughter, Eva," who seemed to be the business head of the family.

Serena let me in when I came back. I gave her fifty cents to get in her good graces and she took an instant dislike to me which never wavered. She was small and black and withered, with bright little sparks of eyes. I don't know how long she'd been with them, but I thought of her growing on the family, like mistletoe, from immemorial time.

Whenever I heard her singing in the kitchen, I felt as if she were putting a private curse on me. "Honey-bird—" she'd croon —"honey-bird, no one gwine tuh fly away wid mah honey-bird. Ole buzzard, he try his wings—he flap and he flap—man wid a gun he see him—hi, hi, hi—shoot ole buzzard wid a buckshot and never tetch mah honey-bird."

I knew who the old buzzard was, all right. And it may sound funny—but it wasn't. It was spooky. Eva wouldn't see it; they'd all treat Serena like a combination of unavoidable nuisance and troublesome child. I don't understand how they can treat servants that way. I mean friendly and grand at the same time. It isn't natural.

It sounds as if I were trying to keep from telling about Eva. I don't know why I'm doing that.

I got unpacked and pretty well settled. My room was on the third floor, back, but I could hear the girls coming home. There'd be the door and steps and a voice saying, "Honey, I'm so tired —I'm just plumb dragged out," and Mrs. Forge saying, "Now, honey, you rest yourself." There were three of those. I kind of wondered why they were all so tired. Later on, I found that was just something they said.

But then Mrs. Forge would begin to talk and they wouldn't be tired any more. They'd be quite excited and there'd be a good deal of laughter. I began to feel very uncomfortable. And then I got stubborn. After all, I'd rented the room.

So, when Eva finally knocked at the door, I just grunted, "Come in!" the way you would to a chamber-maid. She opened the door and stood in the dooryay, hesitant. I imagine Melissa had bet her she wouldn't have the nerve.

"Mr. Southgate, I believe?" she said, quite vaguely, as if I might be anything from a cloud to a chest of drawers.

"Dr. Livingstone, I presume?" I said. There was an old picture on the wall—the two Englishmen meeting formally in the middle of a paper jungle. But I'll hand her something—she saw I wasn't trying to be fresh.

"I reckon we have been making a lot of racket," she said. "But that's mostly Melissa. She never was rightly raised. Won't you give us the favor of your company downstairs, Mr. Southgate? We-all don't act crazy. We just sound like it."

She was dark, you know, and yet she had that white skin. There's a kind of flower called freesia—when the petals are very white, they have the color of her skin. And there's a strong sweetness to it—strong and ghostly at the same time. It smells like spring with the ghosts in it, between afternoon and dusk. And there's a word they call glamour. It was there.

She had small white teeth and red lips. There was one little freckle in the hollow of her throat—I don't know how she happened to have only one. Louisa was the beauty and Melissa the artist. They'd settled it that way. I couldn't have fallen in love with Louisa or Melissa. And yet, I liked to see them all together—the three sisters—I'd liked to have lived in a big, cool house by a river and spent my life seeing them all together. What fool thoughts you get, when you're young! I'd be the Northern cousin who managed the place. I used to send myself to sleep with it, every night, for months.

Mrs. Forge wasn't in it, or Serena. It was a big place—it went on for miles and miles. Most of the land wasn't good for much and the Negroes were bone-lazy, but I made them work. I'd get up in the first mist of morning and be in the saddle all day, overseeing and planning. But, always, I'd be coming back, on a tired horse, up that flowery avenue and they'd be waiting for me on the porch, the three white dresses bunched like a bouquet.

They'd be nice to me, because I was weary, and I'd go upstairs to the room looking over the river and change out of my hot clothes and wash. Then Eva would send me up a long drink with mint in it and I'd take it slowly. After supper, when I wasn't doing accounts, they'd sing or we'd all play some foolish sort of round game with ivory counters. I guess I got most of it out of books, but it was very real to me. That's one trouble with books —you get things out of them.

Often we got old, but it never seemed to change us much. Once in a while the other girls were married and, sometimes, I married Eva. But we never had any children and none of us ever moved away. I kept on working like a dog and they accepted it and I was content. We had quite a few neighbors, at first, but I got tired of that. So I made it a river island you could only reach by boat, and that was more satisfactory.

It wasn't a dream, you know, or anything sappy like that. I just made it up in my head. Toward the end of the year, I'd lie awake for hours, making it up, but it never seemed to tire me. I never really told Eva about it at all, not even when we were engaged. Maybe it would have made a difference, but I don't think so.

She wasn't the kind of person you'd tell any dreams to. She was in the dream. I don't mean she was noble or fatal or like a ghost. I've had her in my arms and she was warm and alive and you could have had children by her, because things are that way. But that wasn't the point—that wasn't the point at all.

She didn't even have much imagination. None of them had. They just lived, like trees. They didn't plan or foresee. I've spent hours trying to explain to Mrs. Forge that, if you had ten dollars, it wasn't just ten dollars, it was something you could put in a savings bank. She'd listen, very politely. But ten dollars, to her, was just something that went away. They thought it was fine if you had money, but they thought it was equally fine if you had a good-looking nose. Money was rather like rain to them—it fell or it didn't—and, they knew that there wasn't any way to make it rain.

I'm sure they'd never have come North at all, if it hadn't been for some obscure family dispute. They often seemed to wonder about it themselves. And I heard the dispute talked about dozens of times but I never really got the gist of it, except that it was connected with two things, the new spur-track to the turpentine plant, and Cousin Belle. "Cousin Belle, she just acted so mean—she gave up her manners," Mrs. Forge would say, placidly. "She left us no reco'se, Bannard—no reco'se at all." And then the girls would chime in. I suppose they got the money to come North from selling land to the turpentine plant, but even of that I am not sure.

Anyhow, they had golden visions, as they would have. Louisa was going to be a great actress and Melissa a great artist—and Eva—I don't know exactly what Eva expected, even now. But it was something. And it was all going to happen without any real work, it was going to fall from a cloud. Oh, yes, Melissa and Louisa went to classes and Eva had a job, but those, you felt, were stopgaps. They were passing the time till the cloud opened and the manna fell.

I'll say this for them—it didn't seem to hurt them to have their visions fail. The only person it really hurt was me.

Because I believed them, at first. How could I help it? The dream I had wasn't so wrong. They were living on an island—an island in the middle of Brooklyn—a piece of where they came from. People came to the house—art students and such—there were always plenty of young men. But, once inside the house, they submitted to the house. Serena would pass the cold ham, at supper, and you'd look out of the window and be surprised to find it snowing, for the window should have been open and the warm night coming through. I don't know what roomers they'd ever had before, but in my time there was only myself and Mr. Budd. He was a fat little clerk of fifty, very respectable, and he stayed because of the food, for Serena was a magnificent, wasteful cook.

Yes, I believed it, I believed in it all. It was like an enchantment. It was glamour. I believed in all they said and I saw them all going back to Chantry—the three famous sisters with their three distinguished husbands—like people in a fairy-tale.

We'd all have breakfast together, but the only person who talked much then was Mr. Budd. The Forges never were properly alive till later in the day. At breakfast, you saw them through a veil. Sometimes I'd feel my heart beat, staring at Eva, because she looked like one of those shut flowers in greenhouses—something shut and mysterious so you fairly held your breath, waiting for it to open. I suppose it was just because she took a long time to wake up.

Then Mr. Budd and the girls would go away, and, when my bed was made, I'd go up and work. I'm not saying much about the novel, but I worked hard on it. I'd made a little chart on cardboard with 365 squares and each day I'd ink one in.

I'd go out for lunch and take a walk afterwards. A man has to have regular exercise, and that's free. Then I'd work some more, until they started to come home. I couldn't work after that—not after the first months. But I'd make myself not listen for Eva's step.

The first time I kissed Eva was the New Year's party. One of Louisa's beaus had brought some red wine and we were singing and fooling around. Serena was off for the evening and Eva and I were out in the kitchen, looking for clean glasses. We were both feeling gay and it just seemed natural. I didn't even think of it again till the next afternoon, when we'd all gone to the movies. And then I suddenly began to shake all over, as if I had a chill, remembering, and she said, "What is it, honey?" and her hand slipped into my hand.

That was how it began. And that night I started inventing the river plantation. And I'm not a fool and I've been around. But I held hands with that girl through January, February, and most of March before I really kissed her again. I can't explain it at all. She wasn't being coy or mean or trying to fight me. It was as if we were floating downstream in a boat together, and it was so pleasant to look at her and be near her, you didn't need any more. The pain hadn't started, then.

And yet, all through that time, something in me was fighting, fighting, to get out of the boat, to get away from the river. It wasn't my river at all, you know. It never was. And part of me knew it. But, when you're in love, you haven't got common sense.

By the end of March, the novel was more than half finished. I'd allowed two months for revision and making contacts, which seemed sensible. And, one evening, it was cold, and Eva and I took a walk in the park. And when we came in, Mrs. Forge made us some hot cocoa—the other girls had gone to bed early, for once—and, while we were drinking it, Mrs. Forge fell asleep in her chair. And we put down our cups, as if it were a signal, and kissed—and the house was very quiet and we could hear her breathing, like sleep itself, through the long kiss.

Next morning, I woke up and the air felt warm and, when I looked out in the yard, there were leaves on the forsythia bush. Eva was just the same at breakfast, shut and mysterious, and I was just the same. But, when I went up to work, I shook my fist at old Wrestling Southgate, the fellow that was bothered with witches. Because I was going to marry Eva, and he could go to grass.

I tell you, they didn't plan or foresee. I told Mrs. Forge very straight just how I stood—finances and everything—and they treated it like a party. They were all as kind and excited as they could be, except Serena. She just refused to believe it and sang a lot more about buzzards. And, somehow or other, that made me feel queerer than ever. Because I knew Serena hated me but I knew she was a real person. I could understand her, she was close to the ground. And I loved the others but I didn't understand them, and sometimes I wouldn't be sure they were quite real. It was that way with Eva, even though we were in love.

I could kiss her but I couldn't be sure that she was always there when I kissed her. It wasn't coldness, it was merely another climate. I could talk for hours about what we were going to do when we were married and every time I stopped she'd say, "Go on, honey, it makes me feel so nice to hear you talk." But she'd have been as pleased if I'd sung it instead. God knows I didn't expect her to understand the novelty business, or even writing. But, sometimes, I'd honestly feel as if we didn't speak the same language. Which was foolish, because she wasn't foreign.

I remember getting angry with her one evening because I found out she was still writing to this boy friend, down South, and hadn't even told him about us. She opened her eyes very wide.

"Why, honey," she said, in the most reasonable of voices, "I couldn't stop writing Furfew right off like that. I've just always been sort of engaged to Furfew."

"Well, **now** you're engaged to me," I said.

"I know," she said. "That's why I can't stop writing him, honey. It would hurt Furfew something dreadful if he knew I had to stop writing him because I was engaged to you."

"Look here," I said, wondering which of us was crazy, "are we going to be married?"

"Of co'se, honey."

"Then what," I said, "has this Furfew got to do with it? Are you engaged to him or me?"

"Of co'se I'm engaged to you, honey, and we're going to get married. But Furfew, he's kind of like kin, and we been engaged a long time. It seems right mean and uncivil to break off with him short like that."

"I don't believe it," I said, "I don't believe there are any Furfews. It sounds like something you grow under glass. What's he like?"

She thought for a long time.

"He's right cute," she said finally. "But he's got a little doin's of a black moustache."

I managed to find out, however, that he owned the turpentine plant and was considered quite the John D. Rockefeller of Chantry. I was so used to no one in Chantry ever having any money that was worth anything, that this came as an unpleasing surprise. After that, Furfew used to try to come to the river plantation in a very shiny motor-launch with a red-and-white awning and I would warn him off with a shotgun.

But then the money business began. You like to give a girl presents when you're in love—you like to do things right. Well, Lord knows, Eva was no gold-digger—she was as likely to be pleased with a soda as a pair of imported gloves. On the other hand, she was as likely to be pleased with the gloves.

I kept on schedule with the work, but I couldn't with the money. Each week, I'd be just a little over the line. I tell you, the people in books don't know about money. The people who write them can tell what it's like to be broke. But they don't tell what it's like to go around with clothes enough to cover you and food enough to satisfy you, and still have your heart's desire depend on money you haven't got.

Sure, I could have gone back in the novelty business and Eva could have kept on working. That would have been right for nine people out of ten. But it wouldn't have been right for the way I felt about Eva. It can be like that.

I wanted to come to her—oh, like a rescuer, I suppose. Like a prince, like the Northern cousin that saved the plantation. I didn't want to make the best of things—I wanted it all. You can't compromise with glamour. Or that's the way I feel.

Besides, I'd put in eight months' work on that novel and it didn't seem sensible to throw it all away. It might be a ladder to climb out on. It might have been.

Eva never complained, but she never understood. She'd just say we could all go back and live in Chantry. Well, I'm not that kind of man. If it had only been the river plantation! But, by now, I knew Chantry as well as if I'd been born there, and there wasn't a thing for me to do. Except maybe a job in Furfew's turpentine plant. And wouldn't that have been pretty?

Then, gradually, I got to know that the Forges, too, were almost at the end of their string. I had to get it casually—they never talked about those things directly. But when you keep on spending what you've got, there comes a time when you don't have it any more. Only, it always surprised them. I wish I was built that way.

It was the middle of July by this time, and one Saturday afternoon Eva came home and said she'd been let off at her office. They were cutting down the staff. I'd just been going over my accounts, and when she told me that, I started laughing as if I couldn't stop.

She looked rather surprised at first, but then she laughed, too.

"Why, honey," she said, "you're the killin'est. You always take things so serious. And then, sometimes, you don't take them serious a bit."

"It's an old Northern custom," I said. "They call it 'Laugh, clown, laugh.' For God's sake, Eva, what are we going to do?"

"Why, honey," she said, "I suppose I could get me another position." She never told me it was up to me. She never would have. "But I just sort of despise those mean old offices. Do you think I ought to get me another position, honey?"

"Oh, darling, it doesn't matter," I said, still laughing. "Nothing matters but us."

"That's mighty sweet of you, honey," she said and she looked relieved. "That's just the way I feel. And, when we get married, we'll fix things up right nice for Melissa and Louisa, won't we? And mother, of co'se, because she just can't stand Cousin Belle."

"Sure," I said. "Sure. When we're married, we'll fix up everything." And we went out in the back yard to look at the forsythia bush. But that night, Furfew brought his launch inshore and landed on the lower end of the island. He pitched camp there, and I could see his fire at night, through a glass.

I can't describe the next two months very well. They were all mixed up, the reality and the dream. Melissa and Louisa had to give up their classes, so we were all home, and lots of people came to the house. Some of them were callers and some of them were bill-collectors but, whoever they were, they generally stayed to a meal. Serena never minded that, she liked company. I remember paying a grocery bill, with almost the last of my legacy, toward the end. There were eight hams on the bill and ten cases of "coke." It hadn't been paid for a long time.

Often, we'd all pile into an old Ford that belonged to one of the art students and go down to a public beach for the day. Eva didn't care so much about swimming but she loved to lie in the sand. And I'd lie beside her, painfully happy, and we'd hardly say anything at all. My God, but she was beautiful against those beach colors—the clear greens of the water and the hot white and tan of the sand. But then, she was just as beautiful, sitting in the plush rocker in the front parlor, under that green lamp.

They say the time between the Ordinance of Secession and the firing on Sumter was one of the gayest seasons Charleston ever had. I can understand that. They'd come to the brink of something, and fate was out of their hands. I got to feel that way.

Everything mixed, I tell you, everything mixed. I'd be sitting on the beach with Eva and, at the same time, I'd be riding around the river plantation, getting reports from my foreman and planning years ahead. I got to love that place. Even toward the end, it was safe, it didn't change. Of course, we kept having more and more trouble with Furfew; he kept extending his lines from the lower end of the island, but it never came to actual warfare—just fights between our men.

Meanwhile, I finished the novel and started revising it. And sometimes Eva would say why didn't we get married, anyway, and I knew we couldn't. You can't get married without some future ahead of you. So we started having arguments, and that was bad.

Why didn't I just seduce her like the big, brave heroes in books? Well, there were times when I thought it might be the answer for both of us. But it never happened. It wasn't shame or good principles. It just isn't so awfully easy to seduce a dream.

I knew they were writing letters but I didn't want to know any more. I knew the legacy was gone and my savings account was going, but I didn't care. I just wanted things to go on.

Finally, I heard that Furfew was coming North. I was going around like a sleepwalker most of the time, then, so it didn't hit me, at first. And then it did hit me.

Eva and I were out in the back yard. We'd fixed up an old swing seat there and it was dusky. Serena was humming in the kitchen. "Ole buzzard he fly away now—buzzard he fly away." I can't sing, but I can remember the way she sang it. It's funny how things stick in your head.

Eva had her head on my shoulder and my arms were around her. But we were as far away as Brooklyn and New York with the bridges down. Somebody was making love, but it wasn't us.

"When's he coming?" I said, finally.

"He's drivin' up in his car," she said. "He started yesterday."

"Young Lochinvar complete with windshield," I said. "He ought to be careful of those roads. Has he got a good car?"

"Yes," she said. "He's got a right pretty car."

"Oh, Eva, Eva," I said. "Doesn't it break your heart?"

"Why, honey," she said. "Come here to me."

We held each other a long time. She was very gentle. I'll remember that.

I stayed up most of that night, finishing revision on the novel. And, before I went to sleep, Furfew came to the house on the river plantation and walked in. I was standing in the hall and I couldn't lift a hand to him. So then I knew how it was going to be.

He came in the flesh, next afternoon. Yes, it was a good car. But he didn't look like Benedict Arnold. He was tall and black-haired and soft-voiced and he had on the sort of clothes they wear. He wasn't so old, either, not much older than I was. But the minute I saw him beside Eva, I knew it was all up. You only had to look at them. They were the same kind.

Oh, sure, he was a good business man. I got that in a minute. But, underneath all the externals, they were the same kind. It hadn't anything to do with the faithfulness or meanness. They were just the same breed of cats. If you're a dog and you fall in love with a cat, that's just your hard luck.

He'd brought up some corn with him and he and I sat up late, drinking it. We were awfully polite and noble in our conversation but we got things settled just the same. The funny thing is, I liked him. He was Young Lochinvar, he was little Mr. Fix-it, he was death and destruction to me, but I couldn't help liking him. He could have come to the island when Eva and I were married. He'd have been a great help. I'd have built him a house by the cove. And that's queer.

Next day, they all went out in the car for a picnic, and I stayed home, reading my novel. I read it all through—and there was nothing there. I'd tried to make the heroine like Eva, but even that hadn't worked. Sometimes you get a novelty like that—it looks like a world-beater till you get it into production. And then, you know you've just got to cut your losses. Well, this was the same proposition.

So I took it down to the furnace and watched it burn. It takes quite a while to burn four hundred sheets of paper in a cold furnace. You'd be surprised.

On my way back, I passed through the kitchen where Serena was. We looked at each other and she put her hand on the bread-knife.

"I'll like to see you burning in hell, Serena," I said. I'd always wanted to say that. Then I went upstairs, feeling her eyes on my back like the point of the bread-knife.

When I lay down on the bed, I knew that something was finished. It wasn't only Eva or the novel. I guess it was what you call youth. Well, we've all got to lose it, but generally it just fades out.

I lay there a long time, not sleeping, not thinking. And I heard them coming back and, after a while, the door opened gently and I knew it was Eva. But my eyes were shut and I didn't make a move. So, after another while, she went away.

There isn't much else to tell. Furfew settled everything up—don't tell me Southerners can't move fast when they want to—and the packers came and four days later they all started back for Chantry in the car. I guess he wasn't taking any chances, but he needn't have worried. I knew it was up. Even hearing Cousin Belle had "come around" didn't excite me. I was past that.

Eva kissed me good-by—they all did, for that matter—the mother and the three sisters. They were sort of gay and excited, thinking of the motor-trip and getting back. To look at them, you wouldn't have said they'd ever seen a bill-collector. Well, that was the way they were.

"Don't write," I said to Eva. "Don't write, Mrs. Lochinvar."

She puckered her brows as she did when she was really puzzled.

"Why, honey, of co'se I'll write," she said. "Why wouldn't I write you, honey?"

I am sure she did, too. I can see the shape of the letters. But I never got them because I never left an address.

The person who was utterly dumbfounded was Mr. Budd. We camped in the house for a week, getting our own meals and sleeping under overcoats—the lease wasn't up till the first and Furfew had made an arrangement with the owner. And Mr. Budd couldn't get over it.

"I always knew they were crazy," he said. "But I'll never get such cooking again." I could see him looking into a future of boarding-houses. "You're young," he said. "You can eat anything. But when a man gets my age—"

He was wrong, though. I wasn't young. If I had been, I wouldn't have spent that week figuring out three novelties. Two of them were duds, but the third was Jiggety Jane. You've seen her—the little dancing doll that went all over the country when people were doing the Charleston. I made the face like Serena's at first, but it looked too lifelike, so we changed the face. The other people made most of the money, but I didn't care. I never liked the darn thing anyway. And it gave me a chance to start on my own.

They couldn't stop me after that. You're harder to stop, once you get rid of your youth. No, I don't think it was ironic or any of those things. You don't, outside of a book. There wasn't any connection between the two matters.

That fall I met Marian and we got married a year later. She's got a lot of sense, that girl, and it's worked out fine. Maybe we did have the children a little quick, but she'd always wanted children. When you've got children and a home, you've got something to keep you steady. And, if she gets a kick out of reading love stories, let her. So I don't have to.

In a book, I'd have run across Eva, or seen Furfew's name in a paper. But that's never happened and I suppose it never will. I imagine they're all still in Chantry, and Chantry's one of those places that never gets in the news. The only thing I can't imagine is any of them being dead.

I wouldn't mind seeing Furfew again, for that matter. As I say, I liked the man. The only thing I hold against him is his moving them back, that way, before the lease was up. It was all right and he had his reasons. But they had two weeks left—two weeks till the first. And that would just have finished the year.

And when I get to sleep nowadays, Marian's there in the next bed, so that's all right, too. I've only tried to go back to the river plantation once, after a convention in Chicago when I was pretty well lit. And then, I couldn't do it. I was standing on the other side of the river and I could see the house across the water. Just the way it always was, but it didn't look lived in. At least nobody came to the window—nobody came out.

THE PRODIGAL CHILDREN

They had been together a great many times, on a great many beaches, in a great many restaurants, looking out over the water. The restaurants had been called by various names in various languages; they had had orchestras and dance bands and juke boxes and a little man who played a guitar and a girl who played an accordion. They had been full of sailors in berets and Futurist painters, also in berets, and women in evening dress and women

THE PRODIGAL CHILDREN 205

with monocles and women in slacks, and men in tail coats and women also in tail coats, and men with their bare feet stuck in *espadrilles*. This one was called Mrs. Sims' Clam House and, except for two tanned children solemnly eating strawberry ice cream at the counter, it was entirely empty when they came in.

They moved to the small corner table overlooking the water and sat down. The table was supposed to seat four, but they pulled up the clean hard chairs and made it do for seven. They never minded things like that; they had done them many times. They were not particularly demanding; they merely wanted the best, and the new place was always the best. After a while, it got spoiled and they left and found another place. They left while the crowds were still coming and before the receivers came. But only the local people and a few summer colonists yet came to Mrs. Sims' Clam House. It was as new a place as that.

"It's frantic," said Jinny Crick, taking off her sunglasses and slipping them into the special compartment in the special handbag. "Look at the boats. It's heavenly. Isn't it frantic?"

"It's a nice little place," said Beth Blake, in her rich voice. "We think it's a nice little place." She looked at the waitress. "Good evening, Pearl," she said pleasantly. "Fish chowder, crab buns and the salad for all of us." She smiled. "I won't let them have anything else," she said, "even if they cry and scream for it. They mustn't have another thing."

"Well, that's all right, I guess, Mrs. Blake," said the waitress in a small, indomitable voice. "Tea, coffee or milk?"

"Black coffee, very hot, in very thick china cups," said the small man unexpectedly and deeply. His name was Harry Crandall and, though he had flown from the Coast two days before, the noise of the airplane was not quite out of his head. "But they must be thick china—dinner china," he added anxiously, peering at the waitress.

"I guess we got them thick enough, if that's what you want," said the waitress.

"Splendid," said Harry Crandall. "And that is just what I want." He looked around the small new place. "Thank God, there aren't any curtains," he said. "I was afraid of red-checked ones. And matches that look like little sailors. But it isn't. No offense meant to the Navy," he added to the blond young man in ensign's uniform on the other side of Jinny Crick, "but I just don't happen to like matches that look like little sailors."

"You want some matches?" said the waitress.

"No, thank you," said Harry Crandall abstractedly, "I want no matches. I match no want ads. I just keep rolling along." He smiled secretly.

"How was the Coast?" said Jinny Crick. "Did you see Jimmy and Mike?"

"No," said Harry Crandall. "Jimmy's in the Signal Corps. And Mike was out at Palm Springs, rewriting the story line for Little Dorrit. It's going to be Colossal's new contribution to Anglo-American friendship. They've changed it a little, of course. Little Dorrit is a waif brought up in the Romney Marsh and she takes a fishing trawler over to Dunkirk. If you can believe Mike over the telephone. As a matter of fact, it will probably turn out to be a good picture. Mike has a knack."

"A knack and a promise," said Beth Blake. "A knack in his engine. How's the newest bride?"

"She's the best society of Cedarhurst," said Harry Crandall. "But I like Mike. I always did."

"We all love Mike," said Jinny Crick. "It's just the brides and the clothes that get us down. The last time I saw him he had on a shirt with pores in it. But I suppose that's the Coast."

The ensign, who had been trying to follow these remarks, turning his head politely toward each speaker in turn, now addressed Harry Crandall.

"Were you out there making a picture yourself, sir?" he said respectfully.

"No," said Harry Crandall. "This was a radio show. Propaganda." He bit off the word.

"It must have been very good stuff, sir," said the ensign, again respectfully, and attacked his chowder. The red-haired girl sitting opposite him tried to smile at him, but could not catch his eye. Poor Tom—it was all her fault and she had let him in for it. But his train went at 9:38 and there wouldn't be much longer now. All the same, she was glad that he had seen these people, and seen them as they were. It would make things so much easier to explain later on. Though older people were always hard to explain.

She sat in a little pool of silence, quite contented to be opposite Tom, while around her the swift talk flowed—the casual conversation, full of names and jokes, jumping gaps to the next new thing—the patter and the lingo. She had been brought up on it, she had been brought up on them all. It went back to French sands and the rocking sleep on trains and liners, and all the wonderful people coming in through the garden for cocktails, sitting out on the terrace and talking, coming up the stairs to the studio and making a pleasant noise—Aunt Beth and Uncle Charlie and the nice man they all called Monkey and all the others. At one time, many years ago—nearly five years ago, when she was only fifteen—she had thought them the most wonderful people in the world. Then Mummy and Daddy had finally broken up and, since then, she had been away a great deal at schools and camps and colleges. So since then she hadn't really seen very much of them, though she had dutifully read their books and seen their plays and their paintings and their pictures in magazines—even boasted of them, now and then, at new schools, when you had to boast of something. And they had remembered birthdays and graduations and vacations—remembered then with thoughtful and difficult presents and telegrams from California and offers of trips and week ends that she'd stopped accepting, once she began to build her life for herself. And all of that had been genuine, and she granted it. But it wasn't her kind of life any more at all.

She glanced around the table, seeing them with the hard clear eyes of youth. It was hard to grow up and see them as they were, and yet it had to be done. Aunt Beth and Uncle Charlie; Sid Vining, the stage designer; Harry Crandall, the writer; Jinny Crick, who was always there because she was always there. They looked harmless enough and she had been fond of them all. But they were the generation that had made the trouble, and you couldn't forget about that. They had got the world in a mess, and it was her generation and Tom's that would have to straighten it out. They had got the world in a mess—they and wonderful people like them. They had shouted for peace and disarmament, they had shouted of the horrors of war, then they had turned around and shouted for war. They drank too much, they divorced too easily, they lived by a code of their own; there was no health in them. So they ought to behave as if there were no health in them. And yet, even now, they didn't behave that way—and that was the irritating fact. They were eating, instead, with the serious and absorbed attention they always gave to good food.

"Don't tell me that's saffron," said Sid Vining, "because I wouldn't believe you. But it is."

"They get it from a little shop in Weymouth. All the way from Weymouth," said Beth Blake.

"It could be a mint, you know," said Sid Vining earnestly, "with the food as good as this. Remember the place at St. Tropez?"

"They didn't ration gas at St. Tropez," said Jinny Crick. . . . "That's a song title, isn't it, ensign?"

"I guess it really is," said Tom Finlay, smiling pleasantly.

The red-haired girl felt a sudden desire to touch him, to reassure herself of his solid reality. For Sid Vining was talking now of the things that could be done with Mrs. Sims' Clam House and, as the others threw in their quick, light comments, the little place changed and grew. Quietly but inexorably it grew, and the large cars slid up to the dock and the chattering people flooded in—the tanned men in white dinner jackets, the pleasantly scented women who threw their little fur wraps over the backs of the hard bare chairs and sat on stools at the bar and thought it was quaint and darling. It grew, as places always grew when the wonderful people came and until they left.

She wanted to pound on the table and say, "Stop it! Stop it!"

But Harry Crandall caught her eye and smiled. "What's the matter?" he said. "It isn't going to happen, you know. It couldn't any more."

"You wouldn't understand," she said. "The boats out there are real boats and they catch real fish. It isn't just a—a stage set for—"

"For people like us?" he said. "No, the point is well taken. It isn't a stage set any more."

"I guess I'm being rude," said the girl. "I guess maybe I am.

But what was the Hotel du Cap like, at Antibes, the last time you saw it?"

"They were quartering Senegalese there," said Harry Crandall, and shrugged. "Well, they had to—I wish they'd quartered more. But it was nice out on the rocks—you must remember."

"I remember all right," said the girl. "I remember those fine old days and the screaming parties and the Russian woman who jumped out of the window. I wasn't particularly old, but I remember."

"You're lucky," said Harry Crandall, "even with that. I didn't get over till I was in the Army."

"If you want the child's point of view—well, it wasn't much fun," said the girl. "We all wanted ice-cream sodas and American clothes and movies that weren't months late. We wanted the funnies and games like the ones we read about, and not to be foreign."

"That's interesting," said Harry Crandall. "Yes, I see how that could be."

The girl stared at him. That was another thing about them that she had forgotten—they were always so open-minded. They'd attack you for a taste, demolish you for a judgment, but not for an opinion, particularly when it was critical of them.

"I suppose that's why I used to be an isolationist," she said. "It hurt Mummy and Daddy. They couldn't understand it."

"Perfectly natural reaction," said Harry Crandall.

"But how can you say that?" said the girl. "Ever since the war first broke out, you—"

He looked at her, and his face was empty and sad. "After the last war," he said, "the one thing I swore I'd never write was propaganda. But this one is for our skins, and the chips are down." He smiled at her. "So no explanations or apologies," he said. "Have some coffee. It's good."

She tried to read the pleasant, lined, empty face. There could be nothing there of importance to her; she knew that when she looked at Tom. And yet the eyes were as alive as a prodigal child's. But the prodigal children were finished.

"And speaking of blackouts, Beth," said Charles Blake, "as we weren't."

"Yes, we should," said Beth Blake, and again, like migratory birds, they collected themselves and began to make gestures of departure. It took a little time, but it was efficient and smooth. They said goodbye, carefully and politely, to Pearl, to Mrs. Sims, to the man at the counter. They looked into the kitchen for a moment, they walked out on the dock and looked at the sunset. It was obvious to the red-haired girl that they should lower their voices on the dock and be less themselves than they were, but they did nothing of the sort. It was obvious that the other people on the dock should hate them, but that did not seem to happen either.

When, at last, she and Tom were in the small car together, the girl gave a sigh of relief.

"Let's drive back by the Point, Tom," she said. "It's only half a mile farther and we needn't be back right away."

"Well, they're very interesting people," said Tom a little later. "They certainly give you something to think about." He laughed a little nervously. "Was I all right, darling?" he said.

"You were fine," said the girl. "Just fine. And you don't have to be polite."

"Well, they were polite to me," said Tom, and she saw the stubborn line of his jaw.

"They always are while you're with them," said the girl. "Oh, don't let's quarrel," she said.

"I wasn't quarreling, beautiful," said Tom, and they both stared out over the darkening water. He was there and solid and the way she wanted him to be. And they should be talking a great deal and they were not talking at all. The wonderful people had spoiled it.

"Oh, damn them!" she said with sudden violence. "Damn them from hell to breakfast! Damn them all!"

"Why, honey," he said. "Why, honey, what's the matter?" Then his arms were around her and she should have felt safe and secure. But there was neither safety nor security anywhere any more. The wonderful people had seen to that long ago, when they first set a match to the world.

"Oh, it's all right," she said. "It's all right, Tom. But we've got to get to your train."

When she returned to the house the blackout shades were already drawn and the highball tray was waiting. Beth Blake was explaining about the blackout shades.

"It's just dim-out, really," she was saying, "but we thought we'd do it rather thoroughly, since we had to." She gestured at the gay, bright flower patterns on the inside of the shades. "Jimmy Bender thought they ought to be much more Dali," she said. "He said he'd do them over, but I don't think Dali's very cozy for a blackout. I'd hate to look at eyes and watches while I was being bombed. So we just made them pretty-pretty, and now Charlie says it's like living inside a seed catalogue." Her rich laugh rang. She turned to the red-haired girl. "I hope your young man got a seat on the train," she said. "They're so tiresomely crowded now, especially on week ends."

"Oh, he got one all right," said the red-haired girl. . . . "No, thanks, Uncle Charlie, not a drink right now; I just want to powder my nose."

And there goes a very nice youngster who's just seen a ghost, thought Harry Crandall, watching her stride from the room. *But the young are so hard to reach. Were we as hard to reach as that? Well, yes, I suppose we were.*

He removed himself unobstrusively from the group and sat quietly in a corner, listening to the phonograph, his highball on one knee. Charlie Blake was playing a new calypso—he always found them, somehow.

"Telling you about the Battle of Midway when those Japanese ships went down," went the strange, effective voice. "Telling you about the Battle of Midway when the U. S. Navy fleet went to town—"

Harry Crandall listened, glad for the fact of noise. He'd talk, if he had to, in a minute, but right now he didn't want to talk, even to Charlie or Beth. And Charlie and Beth wouldn't mind; they had been together long enough.

He tried to remember when he had first met the Blakes— '21? '22? But it was hard to remember when you were tired. He'd met them with Steve Searle, who was dead of a heart attack, and Mimi Post, who wouldn't get out of her sanitarium now, and a lot of the old crowd. But it had been a new crowd then—quite new and shiny. In the days of the Dôme and the Rotonde and Marta's down in the Village and the start of many things; the days of the fierce bursts of work and the quick trips on liners; the days when Paris was Mecca and there wouldn't be any more wars. Yes, a new crowd—quite new and shiny. And everybody had been poor at the start, except the Blakes. But nobody minded the Blakes' not being poor.

Well, he thought, *we've had a good run for it, money or no money. We've had what won't be again—the food and the talk and the wine. But France fell, dammit—France fell. She couldn't fall, but she did. And that handsome youngster probably thinks it happened because they liked good food and things in proportion. But that's part of what you want to preserve. Not all, but part.*

He looked around the room at the good faces—the faces of his friends. They had been together so often and so long and through so many happenings. The work was a different thing, that, in time, could be assessed. Not such bad work either, on the whole, though no doubt it could have been better. But he was thinking of the people, not the work. For nobody was going to be able to put in a book what Charlie Blake was like twenty years ago or why Jinny Crick, for all her mannered folly, had both charm and heart. It couldn't be put in a book or explained to the young. *But these are my friends, my colleagues, my generation— the people I have chosen to live and die beside. And we went on a queer adventure—very queer when you come to think of it, for it brought us back precisely, and in twenty years, to the things we had left behind, and now we must fight for those, if anything good is to live. And after that, we'll be old. But we've seen some things.*

He noticed that the red-haired girl was back in the room again, on a sofa beside Sid Vining. *Well, here goes for a rescue,* he thought. *She won't get on with Sid—not in whatever mood she's in, and Sid's pretty much on edge himself.*

He approached them amiably. "Nice drinks? Nice picture post cards, gentleman and lady?" he said. "Nice guide for the conducted tour?"

"Don't give her a drink," said Sid Vining sourly. "She thinks it's the Demon Rum." He rose and bowed. "I have been rebuked by infants," he said. "I shall go get myself stinking in comparative peace." He stalked away.

"Well," said Harry Crandall, and sat down.

The girl said nothing.

"He won't, you know," said Harry Crandall. "In case you wanted information."

"Who cares if he does?" said the girl in a low fierce voice.

Harry Crandall considered this. "Oh, some of us, in a way," he said. "It isn't particularly good for his work. And he's about the best scene designer we've got. But he's been mostly on the wagon for quite a while now."

"Then why doesn't he do something," said the girl, "instead of talking about putting little bars in restaurants? Why doesn't he do camouflage?"

He stared at her and laughed. "Poor Sid," he said. "He's got a trick knee. And bad eyes. The Army's turned him down twice. Now he thinks they may take him, but he isn't sure. So he's a little touchy."

"Oh," said the girl.

"Yes," said Harry Crandall. "And now I'd really better get you a drink. You've had a white face all evening, and I don't like girls with white faces. Also, I need one myself. You get tired on planes; it's the monotony, I guess."

He mixed two drinks expertly, thinking, *Harry Crandall, the rescuer, Harry Crandall, the lifeguard. Aren't you proud of yourself, Mr. Harry Fix-it Crandall? But Howdy and Ella Martinson were friends of yours, and swell people, so the least you can do is to get their daughter a drink at a party. That will help so much.*

When he brought them back, the girl looked at hers doubtfully. "I don't really like it," she said.

"I am not attempting to inebriate you," said Harry Crandall patiently; "I am recommending for shock. And don't tell me you haven't had one."

"I haven't," said the girl, but she sipped at the very light highball.

"Of course not," said Harry Crandall. "Your generation doesn't.

You drink milk and cokes and grow to be six-foot-three. Which is perfectly fine, and I'm for it. But nobody's shock-proof these days. Nobody at all."

"It wasn't anything at all," said the girl, but the color began to come back to her white face.

"Of course it wasn't anything," said Harry Crandall.

"It was just driving back through the blackout," said the girl. "I mean, it takes quite a long time. I—I didn't realize it would take so long. It was spooky," she said, with hurt.

"That so?" said Harry Crandall. "Yes, that must make tough driving." He did not say, *In the last war I remember the first time we moved with lights, after the Armistice. I remember that because it hit you right in the face; it scared you for a minute. And I remember how London looked at the start of this one.* He did not say any of those things.

"And then I came back," said the girl, "and I'd just seen Tom off, and Aunt Beth was talking about blackout shades and being silly, and I went upstairs to powder my nose in her bedroom, and she's got a very bright tin pail full of very white sand, and I guess it matches the bedroom, and—oh!"

"Nobody will notice it if you cry," said Harry Crandall. "Or we could go out in the kitchen. People often do."

"I'm not going to cry!" said the girl. "But it suddenly got rather horrible. And Aunt Jinny—Mrs. Crick—was in the bedroom. She was sitting there in a chair and she was crying. But she wasn't making any sound—just the tears coming out of her eyes. And I stood there like a fool and didn't know what to do!" Her voice rose sharply.

"That's quite all right," said Harry Crandall carefully. "You see, Jinny has a boy in the coastal patrol. You played with him once, but you probably wouldn't remember him—his name's Sam Langley and he's even taller than you are. Red hair too," he said reflectively. "Well, you see how that might worry her. And then Toby Crick's in London for lend-lease, and she's rather fond of Toby."

"If you're trying to make me feel like even more of a heel, you're succeeding very nicely," said the girl.

"Oh, no," said Harry Crandall. "No. I'm not claiming the higher maternal virtues for Jinny—in fact, I'd hate to be mothered by her myself. But I'd hate not to have her around, with her silly square make-up box, making up her silly face and worrying about it. You get to be that way about people after a while. And it's been a long while." He sighed for a moment. "So you fought with your young man," he said.

"I didn't fight with him," said the girl. "It was just—it was going to be wonderful—and then, suddenly, it didn't mean anything."

"You can't go entirely by one week end," said Harry Crandall, remarking that the girl's color had now returned to normal. *And, Old Mother Hubbard, how did you pull that well-worn advice right out of the hat?* he thought.

"You don't understand," said the girl. "You couldn't possibly! It's got to be right for me—after Mummy and Daddy and the way they broke up! It's got to be safe and secure! Something's got to be! And I thought Tom was, and I was counting on that. I thought not even Aunt Beth and the rest of you could spoil him. And then—"

"And then," said Harry Crandall, "we exerted our well-known wiles?"

"Oh, it isn't what you did," said the girl. "You never do. But you made him look dull and ordinary, and he was respectful to you—so horribly respectful."

"In other words," said Harry Crandall, "he was polite." He cleared his throat. *I wish I could remember more about that young man,* he thought. *He was perfectly all right and I liked him, but I never could pick him out in a parade.* "And as for his being dull," he said guardedly, "I thought he had some pretty solid ideas."

"Yes, that's Tom," said the girl eagerly. She pulled her handkerchief from her handbag and firmly blew her nose. "And they're real ideas too. He thinks there are going to be a lot of changes after the war and we'll all have to be more responsible."

"That's an interesting point of view," said Harry Crandall. *All the same, she'd better meet young Sam Langley,* he thought. *This Tom may be all she thinks, but he ought to have more competition. And the first time you fall in love you're always so sure it's for keeps.* He cocked his ear to what the girl was saying now.

"But I can't get over being so scared," she said like a child. "Why was I?"

"There's a war on," said Harry Crandall, "and a big one. And you can forget for a while, just the way you can almost go to sleep on a march. But now and then it comes over you, like a wave. It isn't a question of courage and it doesn't affect your doing things. You drove the car back all right, didn't you? You didn't drive it into a ditch? Well, that's all you have to know."

"Yes, that's so," she said gratefully. "I didn't drive it into the ditch."

"Remember that," said Harry Crandall. "Because there was a big car and it got in the ditch. And now we've got to get it out. Not just your generation or mine," he said carefully, "but all of us. That's the difference. Do you hate us all very much? You might, you know. After all, we did have the parties."

"I don't know," said the girl. "I don't know."

"As for me, I'm entirely vulnerable," said Harry Crandall. "This is Charle's last leave and Beth's going to shut the house. But I'm everything you think. I'm a nasty little civilian propagandist, and will the new crowd make hay of that, in ten years' time, when it's all over! Remember the fearsome tripe the established names—or most of them—wrote about the last one, and how it retched the bowels of my generation? Well, they'll retch at me just the same way. But somebody had to do it." He spoke without heat or pride.

"I don't understand you," said the girl. "I don't understand any of you. I don't know that I want to."

"It doesn't matter a bit," said Harry Crandall. "Only maybe you'd better. If you're going to make a new world—and I gather you are." He looked at her, glad to see her so stiff and uncompromising. "Well, we were, too," he said. "And it wasn't a bad one. It had freedom and pleasure and good food and truthful art. But we had to make our own rules and we couldn't see around the next curve. So that's that, and what happened happened." He stared at his drink. "And you'll do it very differently," he said.

"I should hope so," said the girl.

"That's all right," said Harry Crandall, "but remember that

freedom means freedom, not bossing other people—and your friends in the end, are your friends. With which profound remark," he said, "your cracker-barrel philosopher will now sign off." He finished his drink and stood up. "Let's go outside for a minute," he said. "Charlie's got a perfectly devilish blackout arrangement on the terrace door, but I think I know my way through it."

When they were outside in the cool darkness, the girl took a deep breath.

"It smells nice," she said. "It smells good. Even in wars."

"Yes," said Harry Crandall gently. "You'll sleep, of course?" he said.

"Why, of course I'll sleep," said the girl. "Why shouldn't I?"

He chuckled faintly to himself. "No reason," he said. *But you're over your jitters,* he thought, *and you won't have the same kind again. You'll sleep like a baby and wake, and tomorrow you'll write to Tom, or he'll write to you. And you'll marry him or somebody, but it won't be me, thank goodness, for I've chosen the friends I must live and die beside. And we're getting on, every one of us, but we've got about one more kick in us, and those that are left are tough. No, we won't be easy in your Zion. But we'll try to behave. We're trying.*

"Born and bred in the brier patch, Br'er Fox," he said, half to himself. "Born and bred in the brier patch, and now we're back there again. But we did take life with both hands; we weren't cautious about it. And that's still something to do."

But the girl was still standing there, breathing in the night, a tall, confident figure beneath the calm sky that sometime might hold the planes. He smiled, nodded his head and went back to the house and his friends.

SCHOONER FAIRCHILD'S CLASS

When he said good night to his son and Tom Drury and the rest of them, Lane Parrington walked down the steps of the Leaf Club and stood, for a moment, breathing in the night air. He had made the speech they'd asked him to make, and taken pains with it, too—but now he was wondering whether it wasn't the same old graduate's speech after all. He hadn't meant it to be so, but you ran into a lingo, once you started putting thoughts on paper—you began to view with alarm and talk about imperiled bulwarks and the American way of life.

And yet he'd been genuinely pleased when the invitation came—and they'd asked him three months ahead. That meant something, even to the Lane Parrington of United Investments—it was curious how old bonds held. He had been decorated by two foreign governments and had declined a ministry—there was the place in Virginia, the place on Long Island, the farm in Vermont and the big apartment on the river. There were the statements issued when sailing for Europe and the photographs and articles in news-weeklies and magazines. And yet he had been pleased when they asked him to speak at the annual dinner of an undergraduate club in his own college. Of course, the Leaf was a little different, as all Leaf members knew. When he had been a new member, as his son was now, the speech had been made by a Secretary of State.

Well, he'd done well enough, he supposed—at least Ted had come up, afterward, a little shyly, and said, "Well, Dad, you're quite an orator." But, once or twice, in the course of the speech, he had caught Ted fiddling with his coffee spoon. They were almost always too long—those speeches by graduates—he had tried to remember that. But he couldn't help running a little overtime—not after he'd got up and seen them waiting there. They were only boys, of course, but boys who would soon be men with men's responsibilities—he had even made a point of that.

On of the things about the Leaf—you got a chance of hearing what—well, what really important men thought of the state of the world and the state of the nation. They could get a lot from professors but hardly that. So, when a sensible fellow got up to explain what sensible men really thought about this business at Washington—why, damn it, nobody was going to ring a gong on him! And they'd clapped him well, at the end, and Ted's face had looked relieved. They always clapped well, at the end.

Afterward, he had rather hoped to meet Ted's friends and get in a little closer touch with them than he did at the place in Virginia or the place on Long Island or the apartment in New York. He saw them there, of course—they got in cars and out of cars, they dressed and went to dances, they played on the tennis courts and swam in the pool. They were a good crowd—a typical Leaf crowd, well-exercised and well-mannered. They were polite to Cora and polite to him. He offered them cigars now and then; during the last two years he offered them whisky and soda. They listened to what he had to say and, if he told a good story, they usually laughed at it. They played tennis with him, occasionally, and said, "Good shot, sir!"—afterward, they played harder tennis. One of them was Ted, his son, well-mannered, well-exercised, a member of the Leaf. He could talk to Ted about college athletics, the college curriculum, his allowance, the weather, the virtues of capitalism and whether to get a new beach wagon this summer. Now, to these subjects was added the Leaf and the virtues of the Leaf. He could talk to Ted about any number of things.

Nevertheless, sometimes when the annual dinner was over, there would be a little group at the Leaf around this graduate or that. He remembered one such group his senior year, around a sharp-tongued old man with hooded eyes. The ex-senator was old and broken, but they'd stayed up till two while his caustic voice made hay of accepted catchwords. Well, he had met Ted's friends and remembered most of their names. They had congratulated him on his speech and he had drunk a highball with them. It had all been in accord with the best traditions of the Leaf but it hadn't lasted very long.

For a moment, indeed, he had almost gotten into an argument with one of them—the pink-faced, incredibly youthful one with the glasses who was head of the Student Union—they hadn't had student unions in his time. He had been answering a couple of questions quite informally, using slang, and the pink-faced youth had broken in with, "But, look here, sir—I mean, that was a good speech you made from the conservative point of view and all that—but when you talk about labor's being made responsible, just what do you mean and how far do you go? Do you mean you want to scrap the Wagner Act or amend it or what?"

But then the rest of them had said, "Oh, don't mind Stu—he's our communist. Skip it, Stu—how's dialectic materialism today?" and it had passed off in kidding. Lane Parrington felt a little sorry about that—he would have enjoyed a good argument with an intelligent youngster—he was certainly broad-minded enough for that. But, instead, he'd declined another highball and said, well, he supposed he ought to be getting back to the inn. It had all been very well-mannered and in accord with the best traditions of the Leaf. He wondered how the old ex-senator had got them to talk.

Ted had offered to walk along with him, of course, and, equally, of course, he had declined. Now he stood for a moment on the sidewalk, wondering whether he ought to look in at class headquarters before going back to the inn. He ought to, he supposed—after all, it was his thirtieth reunion. It would be full of cigar smoke and voices and there would be a drunk from another class—there was always, somehow or other, a drunk from another class who insisted on leading cheers. And Schooner Fairchild, the class funny man, would be telling stories—the one about the Kickapoo chief, the one about President Dodge and the telephone. As it was in the beginning, is now and ever shall be. He didn't dislike Schooner Fairchild any more—you couldn't dislike a man who had wasted his life. But Schooner, somehow, had never seemed conscious of that.

Yes, he'd go to class headquarters—he'd go, if for no other reason than to prove that he did not dislike Schooner Fairchild. He started walking down Club Row. There were twelve of the clubhouses now—there had been only eight in his time. They all looked very much alike, even the new ones—it took an initiated eye to detect the slight enormous differences—to know that Wampum, in spite of its pretentious lanterns, was second-rate and would always be second-rate, while Abbey, small and dingy, ranked with Momus and the Leaf. Parrington stood still, reliving the moment of more than thirty years ago when he'd gotten the bid from Wampum and thought he would have to accept it. It hadn't been necessary—the Leaf messenger had knocked on his door at just three minutes to nine. But whenever he passed the Wampum house he remembered. For almost an hour, it had seemed as if the destined career of Lane Parrington wasn't going to turn out right after all.

The small agonies of youth—they were unimportant, of course, but they left a mark. And he'd had to succeed—he'd had to have the Leaf, just as later on, he'd had to have money—he wasn't a Schooner Fairchild, to take things as they came. You were geared like that or you weren't—if you weren't, you might as well stay in Emmetsburg and end up as a harried high school principal with sick headaches and a fine Spencerian handwriting, as his father had. But he had wanted to get out of Emmetsburg the moment he had realized there were other places to go.

He remembered a look through a microscope and a lashing, tailed thing that swam. There were only two classes of people, the wigglers and the ones who stood still—he should have made his speech on that—it would have been a better speech. And the ones who stood still didn't like the wigglers—that, too, he knew, from experience. If they saw a wiggler coming, they closed ranks and opposed their large, well-mannered inertia to the brusque, ill-mannered life. Later on, of course, they gave in gracefully, but without real liking. He had made the Leaf on his record—and a very good record it had had to be. He had even spent three painful seasons with the track squad, just to demonstrate that desirable all-aroundness that was one of the talking points. And even so, they had smelled it—they had known, instinctively, that he wasn't quite their kind. Tom Drury, for instance, had always been pleasant enough—but Tom Drury had always made him feel that he was talking a little too much and a little too loud. Tom Drury, who, even then, had looked like a magnificent sheep. But he had also been class president, and the heir to Drury and Son. And yet, they all liked Schooner Fairchild—they liked him still.

And here was the end of Club Row, and the Momus House. He stopped and took out a cigar. It was silly to fight old battles, especially when they were won. If they asked the Drurys to dinner now, the Drurys came—he'd been offered and declined a partnership in Drury and Son. But he had helped Tom out with some of their affiliates and Tom had needed help—Tom would always be impressive, of course, but it took more than impressiveness to handle certain things. And now Ted was coming along —and Ted was sound as a bell. So sound he might marry one of the Drury daughters, if he wanted—though that was Ted's business. He wondered if he wanted Ted to marry young. He had done so himself—on the whole, it had been a mistake.

Funny, how things mixed in your mind. As always, when he remembered Dorothy, there was the sharp, sweet smell of her perfume; then the stubborn, competent look of her hands on the wheel of a car. They had been too much alike to have married—lucky they'd found it out in time. She had let him keep the child—of course he would have fought for it anyway—but it was considered very modern in those days. Then the war had washed over and obliterated a great deal—afterward, he had married Cora. And that had worked out as it should—Ted was fond of her and she treated him with just the right shade of companionableness. Most things worked out in the end. He wondered if Dorothy had gotten what she wanted at last—he supposed she had, with her Texan. But she'd died in a hospital at Galveston, ten years ago, trying to have the Texan's child, so he couldn't ask her now. They had warned her about having more children—but, as soon as you warned Dorothy about anything, that was what she wanted to do. He could have told them. But the Texan was one of those handsome, chivalrous men.

Strange, that out of their two warring ambitions should have come the sound, reliable, healthy Ted. But, no, it wasn't strange—he had planned it as carefully as one could, and Cora had helped a great deal. Cora never got out of her depth and she had a fine social sense. And the very best nurses and schools from the very first—and there you were! You did it as you ran a business—picked the right people and gave them authority. He had hardly ever had to interfere himself.

There would be a great deal of money—but that could be taken care of—there were ways. There were trust funds and foundations and clever secretaries. And Ted need never realize it. There was no reason he should—no reason in the least. Ted could think he was doing it all.

He pulled hard on his cigar and started to walk away. For the door of the Momus Club had suddenly swung open, emitting a gush of light and a small, chubby, gray-haired figure with a turned-up nose and a jack-o'-lantern grin. It stood on the steps for a moment, saying good night a dozen times and laughing. Lane Parrington walked fast—but it was no use. He heard pattering footsteps behind him—a voice cried, "Ought-Eight!" with conviction, then, "Lane Parrington, b'gosh!" He stopped and turned.

"Oh, hello, Schooner," he said, unenthusiastically. "Your dinner over, too?"

"Oh, the boys'll keep it up till three," said Schooner Fairchild, mopping his pink brow. "But, after an hour and a half, I told them it was time they got some other poor devil at the piano. I'm not as young as I was." He panted, comically, and linked arms with Lane Parrington. "Class headquarters?" he said. "I shouldn't go—Minnie will scalp me. But I will."

"Well," said Lane Parrington uncomfortably—he hated having his arm held, "I suppose we ought to look in."

"Duty, Mr. Easy, always duty," said Schooner Fairchild and chuckled. "Hey, don't walk so fast—an old man can't keep up with you." He stopped and mopped his brow again. "By the way," he said, "that's a fine boy of yours, Lane."

"Oh," said Lane Parrington awkwardly. "Thanks. But I didn't know—"

"Saw something of him last summer," said Schooner Fairchild cheerfully. "Sylvia brought him around to the house. He could have a rather nice baritone, if he wanted."

"Baritone?" said Lane Parrington. "Sylvia?"

"Eldest daughter and pride of the Fairchild château," said Schooner Fairchild, slurring his words by a tiny fraction. "She collects 'em—not always—always with Father's approval. But your boy's a nice boy. Serious, of course." He chuckled again, it seemed to Lane Parrington maddeningly. "Oh, the sailor said to the admiral, and the admiral said he—" he chanted. "Remember that one, Lane?"

"No," said Lane Parrington.

"That's right," said Schooner Fairchild, amiably. "Stupid of me. I thought for a minute, you'd been in the quartet. But that was dear old Pozzy Banks. Poor Pozzy—he never could sing 'The Last Rose of Summer' properly till he was as drunk as an owl. A man of great talents. I hoped he'd be here this time but he couldn't make it. He wanted to come," he hummed, "but he didn't have the fare . . ."

"That's too bad," said Lane Parrington, seriously. "And yet, with business picking up . . ."

Schooner Fairchild looked at him queerly, for an instant. "Oh, bless you!" he said. "Pozzy never had a nickel. But he was fun." He tugged at Lane Parrington's arm, as they turned a corner and saw an electric sign—1908—above the door. "Well, here we go!" he said.

An hour later, Lane Parrington decided that it was just as he had expected. True, the drunk from the unidentified class had gone home. But others, from other classes, had arrived. And Schooner Fairchild was sitting at the piano.

He himself was wedged uncomfortably at the back of the room between Ed Runner and a man whose name, he thought, was either Ferguson or Whitelaw, but who, in any case, addressed him as "Lane, old boy." This made conversation difficult, for it was hard to call his neighbor either "Fergy" or "Whitey" without being sure of his name. On the other hand, conversation with Ed Runner was equally difficult, for that gentleman had embarked upon an interminable reminiscence whose point turned upon the exact location of Bill Webley's room Sophomore year. As Lane Parrington had never been in any of Bill Webley's rooms, he had very little to add to the discussion. He was also drinking beer, which never agreed with him, and the cigar smoke stung his eyes. And around the singer and the piano boiled and seethed a motley crew of graduates of all classes—the Roman togas of 1913, the convict stripes of 1935, the shorts and explorers' helmets of 1928. For the news had somehow gone around, through the various class headquarters, that Schooner Fairchild was doing his stuff—and, here and there, among the crowd, were undergraduates, who had heard from brothers and uncles about Schooner Fairchild, but had never seen him before in the flesh.

He had told the story of the Kickapoo chief, he had given the imitation of President Dodge and the telephone. Both these and other efforts, Lane Parrington noted wonderingly, had been received with tumultuous cheers. Now he played a few chords and swung around on the piano stool.

"I shall now," he said, with his cherubic face very solemn, "emit my positively last and final number—an imitation of dear old Pozzy Banks, attempting to sing 'The Last Rose of Summer' while under the influence of wine. Not all of you have been privileged to know dear old Pozzy—a man of the most varied and diverse talents—it is our great regret that he is not with us tonight. But for those of you who were not privileged to know Pozzy, may I state as an introduction that dear old Pozzy is built something on the lines of a truck, and that, when under the influence of wine, it was his custom to sing directly into his hat, which he held out before him like a card tray. We will now begin." He whirled round, struck a few lugubrious notes and began to sing.

It was, as even Lane Parrington had to admit, extremely funny. He heard himself joining in the wild, deep roar of laughter that greeted the end of the first verse—he was annoyed at himself but he could not help it. By some magic, by some trick of gesture and voice, the chubby, bald-headed figure had suddenly become a large and lugubrious young man—a young man slightly under the influence of wine but still with the very best intentions, singing sentimentally and lugubriously into his hat. It was a trick and an act and a sleight of hand not worth learning—but it did not fail in its effect. Lane Parrington found himself laughing till he ached—beside him, the man named either Ferguson or Whitelaw was whooping and gasping for breath.

"And now," said Schooner Fairchild, while they were still laughing, "let somebody play who *can* play!" And, magically crooking his finger, he summoned a dark-haired undergraduate from the crowd, pushed him down on the piano stool, and, somehow or other, slipped through the press and vanished, while they were still calling his name.

Lane Parrington, a little later, found himself strolling up and down the dejected back yard of class headquarters. They had put up a tent, some iron tables and a number of paper lanterns, but, at this hour, the effect was not particularly gay. It must be very late and he ought to go to bed. But he did not look at his watch. He was trying to think about certain things in his life and get them into a proportion. It should be a simple thing to do, as simple as making money, but it was not.

Ted—Dorothy—the Leaf—Emmetsburg—Schooner Fairchild—Tom Drury—the place in Virginia and the mean house at Emmetsburg—United Investments and a sleight-of-hand trick at a tiny piano. He shuffled the factors of the equation about; they should add up to a whole. And, if they did, he would be willing to admit it; he told himself that. Yes, even if the final sum proved him wrong for years—that had always been one of the factors of his own success, his knowing just when to cut a loss.

A shaky voice hummed behind him:

> "Oh, the ship's cat said to the cabin boy,
> To the cabin boy said she . . ."

He turned—it was Schooner Fairchild and, he thought at first, Schooner Fairchild was very drunk. Then he saw the man's lips were gray, caught him and helped him into one of the iron chairs.

"Sorry," wheezed Schooner Fairchild. "Must have run too fast, getting away from the gang. Damn' silly—left my medicine at the inn."

"Here—wait—" said Lane Parrington, remembering the flask of brandy in his pocket. He uncorked it and held it to the other man's lips. "Can you swallow?" he said solicitously.

An elfish, undefeated smile lit Schooner Fairchild's face. "Always could, from a child," he gasped. "Never ask a Fairchild twice." He drank and said, incredibly, it seemed to Lane Parrington, "Napoleon . . . isn't it? Sir, you spoil me." His color began to come back. "Better," he said.

"Just stay there," said Lane Parrington. He dashed back into club headquarters—deserted now, he noticed, except for the gloomy caretaker and the man called Ferguson or Whitelaw, who was ungracefully asleep on a leather couch. Efficiently, he found glasses, ice, soda, plain water and ginger ale, and returned, his hands full of these trophies, to find Schooner Fairchild sitting up in his chair and attempting to get a cigarette from the pocket of his coat.

His eyes twinkled as he saw Lane Parrington's collection of glassware. "My!" he said. "We *are* going to make a night of it. Great shock to me—never thought it of you, Lane."

"Hadn't I better get a doctor?" said Lane Parrington. "There's a telephone—"

"Not a chance," said Schooner Fairchild. "It would worry Minnie sick. She made me promise before I came up to take care. It's just the old pump—misses a little sometimes. But I'll be all right, now—right as a trivet, whatever a trivet is. Just give me another shot of Napoleon."

"Of course," said Lane Parrington, "but—"

"Brandy on beer, never fear," said Schooner Fairchild. "Fairchild's Medical Maxims, Number One. And a cigarette . . . thanks." He breathed deeply. "And there we are," he said, with a smile. "Just catches you in the short ribs, now and then. But, when it's over, it's over. You ought to try a little yourself, Lane —damn' silly performance of mine and you look tired."

"Thanks," said Lane Parrington, "I will." He made himself, neatly, an efficient brandy and soda and raised the glass to his lips. "Well—er—here's luck," he said, a little stiffly.

"Luck!" nodded Schooner Fairchild. They both drank. Lane Parrington looked at the pleasant, undefeated face.

"Listen, Schooner," said Lane Parrington, suddenly and harshly, "if you had the whole works to shoot over again—" He stopped.

"That's the hell of a question to ask a man at three o'clock in the morning," said Schooner equably. "Why?"

"Oh, I don't know," said Lane Parrington. "But that stuff at the piano you did—well, how did you do it?" His voice was oddly ingenious, for Lane Parrington.

"Genius, my boy, sheer, untrammeled genius," said Schooner Fairchild. He chuckled and sobered. "Well, somebody has to," he said reasonably. "And you wouldn't expect Tom Drury to do it, would you?—poor old Tom!"

"No," said Lane Parrington, breathing. "I wouldn't expect Tom Drury to do it."

"Oh, Tom's all right," said Schooner Fairchild. "He was just born with an ingrowing Drury and never had it operated on. But he's a fine guy, all the same. Lord," he said, "it must be a curse —to have to be a Drury, whether you like it or not. I never could have stood it—I never could have played the game. Of course," he added hastily, "I suppose it's different, if you do it all yourself, the way you have. That must be a lot of fun."

"I wouldn't exactly call it fun," said Lane Parrington earnestly. "You see, after all, Schooner, there are quite a good many things that enter into . . ." He paused, and laughed hopelessly. "Was I always a stuffed shirt?" he said. "I suppose I was."

"Oh, I wouldn't call you a stuffed shirt," said Schooner, a little quickly. "You just had to succeed—and you've done it. Gosh, we all knew you were going to, right from the first—there couldn't be any mistake about that. It must be a swell feeling." He looked at Lane Parrington and his voice trailed off. He began again. "You see, it was different with me," he said. "I couldn't help it. Why, just take a look at me—I've even got a comedy face. Well, I never wanted anything very much except—oh, to have a good time and know other people were having a good time. Oh, I tried taking the other things seriously—I tried when I was a broker, but I couldn't, it was just no go. I made money enough —everybody was making money—but every now and then, in the middle of a million-share day, I'd just think how damn silly it was for everybody to be watching the board and getting all excited over things called ATT and UGI. And that's no way for a broker to act—you've got to believe those silly initials mean something, if you want to be a broker.

"Well, I've tried a good many things since. And now and then I've been lucky, and we've gotten along. And I've spent most of Minnie's money, but she says it was worth it—and we've got the five girls and they're wonders—and I'll probably die playing the piano at some fool party, for you can't keep it up forever, but I only hope it happens before somebody says, 'There goes poor old Schooner. He used to be pretty amusing, in his time!' But, you see, I couldn't help it," he ended diffidently. "And, you know, I've tried. I've tried hard. But then I'd start laughing, and it always got in the way."

Lane Parrington looked at the man who had spent his wife's money and his own for a sleight-of-hand trick, five daughters, and the sound of friendly laughter. He looked at him without understanding, and yet with a curious longing.

"But, Schooner—" he said, "with all you can do—you ought to—"

"Oh," said Schooner, a trifle wearily, "one has one's dreams. Sure, I'd like to be Victor Boucher—he's a beautiful comedian. Or Bill Fields, for instance. Who wouldn't? But I don't kid myself. It's a parlor talent—it doesn't go over the footlights. But, Lord, what fun I've had with it! And the funny things people keep doing, forever and ever, amen. And the decent—the very decent things they keep doing, too. Well, I always thought it would be a good life, while you had it." He paused, and Lane Parrington saw the fatigue on his face. "Well, it's been a good party," he said. "I wish old Pozzy could have been here. But I guess we ought to go to bed."

"I'll phone for a cab," said Lane Parrington. "Nope—you're riding."

Lane Parrington shut the door of Schooner Fairchild's room behind him and stood, for a moment, with his hand on the knob. He had seen Schooner safely to bed—he had even insisted on the latter's taking his medicine, though Schooner had been a little petulant about it. Now, however, he still wondered about calling a doctor—if Schooner should be worse in the morning, he would have Anstey come up by plane. It was nothing to do, though not everybody could do it, and Anstey was much the best man. In any case, he would insist on Schooner's seeing Anstey this week. Then he wondered just how he was going to insist.

The old elevator just across the corridor came to a wheezing stop. Its door opened and a dark-haired girl in evening dress came out. Lane Parrington dropped his hand from the doorknob and turned away. But the girl took three quick steps after him.

"I'm sorry," she said, a little breathlessly, "but I'm Sylvia Fairchild. Is Father ill? The elevator boy said something—and I saw you coming out of his room."

"He's all right," said Lane Parrington. "It was just the slightest sort of—"

"Oh!" said the girl, "do you mind coming back for a minute? You're Ted's father, aren't you? My room's next door, but I've got a key for his, too—Mother told me to be sure—" She seemed very self-possessed. Lane Parrington waited uncomfortably in the corridor for what seemed to him a long time, while she went into her father's room. When she came out again, she seemed relieved.

"It's all right," she said, in a low voice. "He's asleep, and his color's good. And he's . . ." She paused. "Oh, damn!" she said. "We can't talk out here. Come into my room for a minute—we can leave the door open—after all, you *are* Ted's father. I'll have to tell Mother, you see—and Father will just say it wasn't anything."

She opened the door and led the way into the room. "Here,"

she said. "Just throw those stockings off the chair—I'll sit on the bed. Well?"

"Well, I asked him if he wanted a doctor . . ." said Lane Parrington humbly.

When he had finished a concise, efficient report, the girl nodded, and he saw for the first time that she was pretty, with her dark, neat head and her clever, stubborn chin.

"Thank you," she said. "I mean, really. Father's a perfect lamb —but he doesn't like to worry Mother, and it worries her a lot more not to know. And sometimes it's rather difficult, getting the truth out of Father's friends. Not you," she was pleased to add. "You've been perfectly truthful. And the brandy was quite all right."

"I'm glad," said Lane Parrington. "I wish your father would see Anstey," he added, a trifle awkwardly. "I could—er—make arrangements."

"He has," said the girl. Her mouth twitched. "Oh," she said. "I shouldn't have gone to the dance. I couldn't help the Momus Club, but he might have come back afterward, if I'd been here. Only, I don't know."

"I wouldn't reproach myself," said Lane Parrington. "After all—"

"Oh, I know," said the girl. "After all! If you don't all manage to kill him, between you! Friends!" she sniffed. Then, suddenly, her face broke into lines of amusement. "I sound just like Aunt Emma," she said. "And that's pretty silly of me. Aunt Emma's almost pure poison. Of course it isn't your fault and I really do thank you. Very much. Do you know, I never expected you'd be a friend of Father's."

"After all," said Lane Parrington stiffly, "we were in the same class."

"Oh, I know," said the girl. "Father's talked about you, of course." Her mouth twitched again, but this time, it seemed to Lane Parrington, with a secret merriment. "And so has Ted, naturally," she added politely.

"I'm glad he happened to mention me," said Lane Parrington, and she grinned, frankly.

"I deserved that," she said, while Lane Parrington averted his eyes from what seemed to be a remarkably flimsy garment hung over the bottom of the bed. "But Ted has, really. He admires you quite a lot, you know, though, of course, you're different generations."

"Tell me—" said Lane Parrington. "No, I won't ask you."

"Oh, you know Ted," said the girl, rather impatiently. "It's awfully hard to get him to say things—and he will spend such a lot of time thinking he ought to be noble, poor lamb. But he's losing just a little of that, thank goodness—when he first came to Widgeon Point, he was trying so hard to be exactly like that terrible Drury boy. You see—" she said, suddenly and gravely, "he could lose quite a lot of it and still have more than most people."

Lane Parrington cleared his throat. There seemed nothing for him to say. Then he thought of something.

"His mother was—er—a remarkable person," he said. "We were not at all happy together. But she had remarkable qualities."

"Yes," said the girl. "Ted's told me. He remembers her." They looked at each other for a moment—he noted the stubborn chin, the swift and admirable hands. Then a clock on the mantel struck and the girl jumped.

"Good heavens!" she said. "It's four o'clock! Well—good night. And I do thank you, Mr. Parrington."

"It wasn't anything," said Lane Parrington. "But remember me to your father. But I'll see you in the morning, of course."

The following afternoon, Lane Parrington found himself waiting for his car in the lobby of the inn. There had been a little trouble with the garage and it was late. But he did not care, particularly, though he felt glad to be going back to New York. He had said good-by to Ted an hour before—Ted was going on to a house party at the Chiltons'—they'd eventually meet on Long Island, he supposed. Meanwhile, he had had a pleasant morning, attended the commencement exercises, and had lunch with Ted and the Fairchilds at the inn. Schooner had been a little subdued and both Ted and the girl frankly sleepy, but he had enjoyed the occasion nevertheless. And somehow the fact that the president's baccalaureate address had also viewed with alarm and talked about imperiled bulwarks and the American way of life— had, in fact, repeated with solemn precision a good many of the points in his own speech—did not irk Lane Parrington as it might have the day before. After all, the boys were young and could stand it. They had stood a good deal of nonsense, even in his own time.

Now he thought once more of the equation he had tried too earnestly to solve, in the back yard of commencement headquarters—and, for a moment, almost grinned. It was, of course, insoluble—life was not as neat as that. You did what you could, as it was given you to do—very often you did the wrong things. And if you did the wrong things, you could hardly remedy them by a sudden repentance—or, at least, he could not. There were still the wigglers and the ones who stood still—and each had his own virtues. And because he was a wiggler, he had thoughtfully and zealously done his best to make his son into the image of one of the magnificent sheep—the image of Tom Drury, who was neither hungry nor gay. He could not remedy that, but he thought he knew somebody who could remedy it, remembering the Fairchild girl's stubborn chin. And, in that case at least, the grandchildren ought to be worth watching.

"Your car, Mr. Parrington," said a bellboy. He moved toward the door. It was hard to keep from being a stuffed shirt, if you had the instinct in you, but one could try. A good deal might be done, with trying.

As he stepped out upon the steps of the inn, he noticed a figure, saluting—old Negro Mose, the campus character who remembered everybody's name.

"Hello, Mose!" said Lane Parrington. "Remember me?"

"Remember you—sho', Mr. Parrington," said Mose. He regarded Lane Parrington with beady eyes. "Let's see—you was 1906."

"Nineteen hundred and eight," said Lane Parrington, but without rancor.

Mose gave a professional chuckle. "Sho'!" he said. "I was forgettin'! Let's see—you hasn't been back fo' years, Mister Parrington—but you was in Tom Drury's class—an' Schooner Fairchild's class—"

"No," said Lane Parrington and gave the expected dollar, "not Tom Drury's class. Schooner Fairchild's class."

DOC MELLHORN AND THE
PEARLY GATES

Doc Mellhorn had never expected to go anywhere at all when he died. So, when he found himself on the road again, it surprised him. But perhaps I'd better explain a little about Doc Mellhorn first. He was seventy-odd when he left our town; but when he came, he was as young as Bates or Filsinger or any of the boys at the hospital. Only there wasn't any hospital when he came. He came with a young man's beard and a brand-new bag and a lot of newfangled ideas about medicine that we didn't take to much. And he left, forty-odd years later, with a first-class county health record and a lot of people alive that wouldn't have been alive if he hadn't been there. Yes, a country doctor. And nobody ever called him a man in white or a death grappler that I know of, though they did think of giving him a degree at Pewauket College once. But then the board met again and decided they needed a new gymnasium, so they gave the degree to J. Prentiss Parmalee instead.

They say he was a thin young man when he first came, a thin young man with an Eastern accent who'd wanted to study in Vienna. But most of us remember him chunky and solid, with white hair and a little bald spot that always got burned bright red in the first hot weather. He had about four card tricks that he'd do for you, if you were a youngster—they were always the same ones—and now and then, if he felt like it, he'd take a silver half dollar out of the back of your neck. And that worked as well with the youngsters who were going to build rocket ships as it had with the youngsters who were going to be railway engineers. It always worked. I guess it was Doc Mellhorn more than the trick.

But there wasn't anything unusual about him, except maybe the card tricks. Or, anyway, he didn't think so. He was just a good doctor and he knew us inside out. I've heard people call him a pigheaded, obstinate old mule—that was in the fight about the water supply. And I've heard a weepy old lady call him a saint. I took the tale to him once, and he looked at me over his glasses and said, "Well, I've always respected a mule. Got ten times the sense of a—horse." Then he took a silver half dollar out of my ear.

Well, how do you describe a man like that? You don't—you call him up at three in the morning. And when he sends in his bill, you think it's a little steep.

All the same, when it came to it, there were people who drove a hundred and fifty miles to the funeral. And the Masons came down from Bluff City, and the Poles came from across the tracks, with a wreath the size of a house, and you saw cars in town that you didn't often see there. But it was after the funeral that the queer things began for Doc Mellhorn.

The last thing he remembered, he'd been lying in bed, feeling pretty sick, on the whole, but glad for the rest. And now he was driving his Model T down a long straight road between rolling, misty prairies that seemed to go from nowhere to nowhere.

It didn't seem funny to him to be driving the Model T again. That was the car he'd learned on, and he kept to it till his family made him change. And it didn't seem funny to him not to be sick any more. He hadn't had much time to be sick in his life—the patients usually attended to that. He looked around for his bag, first thing, but it was there on the seat beside him. It was the old bag, not the presentation one they'd given him at the hospital, but that was all right too. It meant he was out on a call and, if he couldn't quite recollect at the moment just where the call was, it was certain to come to him. He'd wakened up often enough in his buggy, in the old days, and found the horse was taking him home, without his doing much about it. A doctor gets used to things like that.

All the same, when he'd driven and driven for some time without raising so much as a traffic light, just the same rolling prairies on either hand, he began to get a little suspicious. He thought, for a while, of stopping the car and getting out, just to take a look around, but he'd always hated to lose time on a call. Then he noticed something else. He was driving without his glasses. And yet he hadn't driven without his glasses in fifteen years.

"H'm," said Doc Mellhorn. "I'm crazy as a June bug. Or else— Well, it might be so, I suppose."

But this time he did stop the car. He opened his bag and looked inside it, but everything seemed to be in order. He opened his wallet and looked at that, but there were his own initials, half rubbed away, and he recognized them. He took his pulse, but it felt perfectly steady.

"H'm," said Doc Mellhorn. "Well."

Then, just to prove that everything was perfectly normal, he took a silver half dollar out of the steering wheel of the car.

"Never did it smoother," said Doc Mellhorn. "Well, all the same, if this is the new highway, it's longer than I remember it."

But just then a motorcycle came roaring down the road and stopped with a flourish, the way motor cops do.

"Any trouble?" said the motor cop. Doc Mellhorn couldn't see his face for his goggles, but the goggles looked normal.

"I am a physician," said Doc Mellhorn, as he'd said a thousand times before to all sorts of people, "on my way to an urgent case." He passed his hand across his forehead. "Is this the right road?" he said.

"Straight ahead to the traffic light," said the cop. "They're expecting you, Doctor Mellhorn. Shall I give you an escort?"

"No; thanks all the same," said Doc Mellhorn, and the motor cop roared away. The Model T ground as Doc Mellhorn gassed her. "Well, they've got a new breed of traffic cop," said Doc Mellhorn, "or else—"

But when he got to the light, it was just like any light at a crossroads. He waited till it changed and the officer waved him on. There seemed to be a good deal of traffic going the other way, but he didn't get a chance to notice it much, because Lizzie bucked a little, as she usually did when you kept her waiting. Still, the sight of traffic relieved him, though he hadn't passed anybody on his own road yet.

Pretty soon he noticed the look of the country had changed. It was parkway now and very nicely landscaped. There was dogwood in bloom on the little hills, white and pink against the green; though, as Doc Mellhorn remembered it, it had been August when he left his house. And every now and then there'd be a nice little white-painted sign that said TO THE GATES.

"H'm," said Doc Mellhorn. "New State Parkway, I guess. Well, they've fixed it up pretty. But I wonder where they got the dogwood. Haven't seen it bloom like that since I was East."

Then he drove along in a sort of dream for a while, for the dogwood reminded him of the days when he was a young man in an Eastern college. He remembered the look of that college and the girls who'd come to dances, the girls who wore white gloves and had rolls of hair. They were pretty girls, too, and he wondered what had become of them. "Had babies, I guess," thought Doc Mellhorn. "Or some of them, anyway." But he liked to think of them as the way they had been when they were just pretty, and excited at being at a dance.

He remembered other things too—the hacked desks in the lecture rooms, and the trees on the campus, and the first pipe he'd ever broken in, and a fellow called Paisley Grew that he hadn't thought of in years—a rawboned fellow with a gift for tall stories and playing the jew's-harp.

"Ought to have looked up Paisley," he said. "Yes, I ought. Didn't amount to a hill of beans, I guess, but I always liked him. I wonder if he still plays the jew's-harp. Pshaw, I know he's been dead twenty years."

He was passing other cars now and other cars were passing him, but he didn't pay much attention, except when he happened to notice a license you didn't often see in the state, like Rhode Island or Mississippi. He was too full of his own thoughts. There were foot passengers, too, plenty of them—and once he passed a man driving a load of hay. He wondered what the man would do with the hay when he got to the Gates. But probably there were arrangements for that.

"Not that I believe a word of it," he said, "but it'll surprise Father Kelly. Or maybe it won't. I used to have some handsome arguments with that man, but I always knew I could count on him, in spite of me being a heretic."

Then he saw the Wall and the Gates, right across the valley. He saw them, and they reached to the top of the sky. He rubbed his eyes for a while, but they kept on being there.

"Quite a sight," said Doc Mellhorn.

No one told him just where to go or how to act, but it seemed to him that he knew. If he'd thought about it, he'd have said that

DOC MELLHORN AND THE PEARLY GATES

you waited in line, but there wasn't any waiting in line. He just went where he was expected to go and the reception clerk knew his name right away.

"Yes, Doctor Mellhorn," he said. "And now, what would you like to do first?"

"I think I'd like to sit down," said Doc Mellhorn. So he sat, and it was a comfortable chair. He even bounced the springs of it once or twice, till he caught the reception clerk's eye on him.

"Is there anything I can get you?" said the reception clerk. He was young and brisk and neat as a pin, and you could see he aimed to give service and studied about it. Doc Mellhorn thought, "He's the kind that wipes off your windshield no matter how clean it is."

"No," said Doc Mellhorn. "You see, I don't believe this. I don't believe any of it. I'm sorry if that sounds cranky, but I don't."

"That's quite all right, sir," said the reception clerk. "It often takes a while." And he smiled as if Doc Mellhorn had done him a favor.

"Young man, I'm a physician," said Doc Mellhorn, "and do you mean to tell me—"

Then he stopped, for he suddenly saw there was no use arguing. He was either there or he wasn't. And it felt as if he were there.

"Well," said Doc Mellhorn, with a sigh, "how do I begin?"

"That's entirely at your own volition, sir," said the reception clerk briskly. "Any meetings with relatives, of course. Or if you would prefer to get yourself settled first. Or take a tour, alone or conducted. Perhaps these will offer suggestions," and he started to hand over a handful of leaflets. But Doc Mellhorn put them aside.

"Wait a minute," he said. "I want to think. Well, naturally, there's Mother and Dad. But I couldn't see them just yet. I wouldn't believe it. And Grandma—well, now, if I saw Grandma —and me older than she is—was—used to be—well, I don't know what it would do to me. You've got to let me get my breath. Well, of course, there's Uncle Frank—he'd be easier." He paused. "Is he here?" he said.

The reception clerk looked in a file. "I am happy to say that

Mr. Francis V. Mellhorn arrived July 12, 1907," he said. He smiled winningly.

"Well!" said Doc Mellhorn. "Uncle Frank! Well, I'll be—well! But it must have been a great consolation to Mother. We heard —well, never mind what we heard—I guess it wasn't so. . . . No, don't reach for that phone just yet, or whatever it is. I'm still thinking."

"We sometimes find," said the reception clerk eagerly, "that a person not a relative may be the best introduction. Even a stranger sometimes—a distinguished stranger connected with one's own profession—"

"Well, now, that's an idea," said Doc Mellhorn heartily, trying to keep his mind off how much he disliked the reception clerk. He couldn't just say why he disliked him, but he knew he did.

It reminded him of the time he'd had to have his gall bladder out in the city hospital and the young, brisk interns had come to see him and called him "Doctor" every other word.

"Yes, that's an idea," he said. He reflected. "Well, of course, I'd like to see Koch," he said. "And Semmelweiss. Not to speak of Walter Reed. But, shucks, they'd be busy men. But there is one fellow—only he lived pretty far back—"

"Hippocrates, please," said the reception clerk into the telephone or whatever it was. "*H* for horse—"

"No!" said Doc Mellhorn quite violently. "Excuse me, but you just wait a minute. I mean if you can wait. I mean, if Hippocrates wants to come, I've no objection. But I never took much of a fancy to him, in spite of his oath. It's Aesculapius I'm thinking about. George W. Oh, glory!" he said. "But he won't talk English. I forgot."

"I shall be happy to act as interpreter," said the reception clerk, smiling brilliantly.

"I haven't a doubt," said Doc Mellhorn. "But just wait a shake." In a minute, by the way the clerk was acting, he was going to be talking to Aesculapius. "And what in time am I going to say to the man?" he thought. "It's too much." He gazed wildly around the neat reception room—distempered, as he noticed, in a warm shade of golden tan. Then his eyes fell on the worn black bag at his feet and a sudden warm wave of relief flooded over him.

"Wait a minute," he said, and his voice gathered forced and authority. "Where's my patient?"

"Patient?" said the reception clerk, looking puzzled for the first time.

"Patient," said Doc Mellhorn. "*P* for phlebitis." He tapped his bag.

"I'm afraid you don't quite understand, sir," said the reception clerk.

"I understand this," said Doc Mellhorn. "I was called here. And if I wasn't called professionally, why have I got my bag?"

"But, my dear Doctor Mellhorn—" said the reception clerk.

"I'm not your dear doctor," said Doc Mellhorn. "I was called here, I tell you. I'm sorry not to give you the patient's name, but the call must have come in my absence and the girl doesn't spell very well. But in any well-regulated hospital—"

"But I tell you," said the reception clerk, and his hair wasn't slick any more, "nobody's ill here. Nobody can be ill. If they could, it wouldn't be He—"

"Humph," said Doc Mellhorn. He thought it over, and felt worse. "Then what does a fellow like Koch do?" he said. "Or Pasteur?" He raised a hand. "Oh, don't tell me," he said. "I can see they'd be busy. Yes, I guess it'd be all right for a research man. But I never was . . . Oh, well, shucks, I've published a few papers. And there's that clamp of mine—always meant to do something about it. But they've got better ones now. Mean to say there isn't so much as a case of mumps in the whole place?"

"I assure you," said the reception clerk, in a weary voice. "And now, once you see Doctor Aesculapius—"

"Funny," said Doc Mellhorn. "Lord knows there's plenty of times you'd be glad to be quit of the whole thing. And don't talk to me about the healer's art or grateful patients. Well, I've known a few . . . a few. But I've known others. All the same, it's different, being told there isn't any need for what you can do."

"*A* for Ararát," said the reception clerk into his instrument. "*E* for Eden."

"Should think you'd have a dial," said Doc Mellhorn desperately. "We've got 'em down below." He thought hard and frantically. "Wait a shake. It's coming back to me," he said. "Got anybody named Grew here? Paisley Grew?"

"S for serpent . . ." said the reception clerk. "What was that?"

"Fellow that called me," said Doc Mellhorn. "G-r-e-w. First name, Paisley."

"I will consult the index," said the reception clerk.

He did so, and Doc Mellhorn waited, hoping against hope.

"We have 94,183 Grews, including 83 Prescotts and one Penobscot," the reception clerk said at last. "But I fail to find Paisley Grew. Are you quite sure of the name?"

"Of course," said Mellhorn briskly. "Paisley Grew. Chronic indigestion. Might be appendix—can't say—have to see. But anyhow, he's called." He picked up his bag. "Well, thanks for the information," he said, liking the reception clerk better than he had yet. "Not your fault, anyway."

"But—but where are you going?" said the reception clerk.

"Well, there's another establishment, isn't there?" said Doc Mellhorn. "Always heard there was. Call probably came from there. Crossed wires, I expect."

"But you can't go there!" said the reception clerk. "I mean—"

"Can't go?" said Doc Mellhorn. "I'm a physician. A patient's called me."

"But if you'll only wait and see Aesculapius!" said the reception clerk, running his hands wildly through his hair. "He'll be here almost any moment."

"Please give him my apologies," said Doc Mellhorn. "He's a doctor. He'll understand. And if any messages come for me, just stick them on the spike. Do I need a road map? Noticed the road I came was all one way."

"There is, I believe, a back road in rather bad repair," said the reception clerk icily. "I can call Information if you wish."

"Oh, don't bother," said Doc Mellhorn. "I'll find it. And I never saw a road beat Lizzie yet." He took a silver half dollar from the doorknob of the door. "See that?" he said. 'Slick as a whistle. Well, good-by, young man."

But it wasn't till he'd cranked up Lizzie and was on his way that Doc Mellhorn really felt safe. He found the back road and it was all the reception clerk had said it was and more. But he didn't mind—in fact, after one particularly bad rut, he grinned.

"I suppose I ought to have seen the folks," he said. "Yes, I know I ought. But—not so much as a case of mumps in the whole abiding dominion! Well, it's lucky I took a chance on Paisley Grew."

After another mile or so, he grinned again.

"And I'd like to see old Aesculapius' face. Probably rang him in the middle of dinner—they always do. But shucks, it's happened to all of us."

Well, the road got worse and worse and the sky above it darker and darker, and what with one thing and another, Doc Mellhorn was glad enough when he got to the other gates. They were pretty impressive gates, too, though of course in a different way, and reminded Doc Mellhorn a little of the furnaces outside Steeltown, where he'd practiced for a year when he was young.

This time Doc Mellhorn wasn't going to take any advice from reception clerks and he had his story all ready. All the same, he wasn't either registered or expected, so there was a little fuss. Finally they tried to scare him by saying he came at his own risk and that there were some pretty tough characters about. But Doc Mellhorn remarked that he'd practiced in Steeltown. So, after he'd told them what seemed to him a million times that he was a physician on a case, they finally let him in and directed him to Paisley Grew. Paisley was on Level 346 in Pit 68,953, and Doc Mellhorn recognized him the minute he saw him. He even had the jew's-harp, stuck in the back of his overalls.

"Well, Doc," said Paisley finally, when the first greetings were over, "you certainly are a sight for sore eyes! Though, of course, I'm sorry to see you here," and he grinned.

"Well, I can't see that it's so different from a lot of places," said Doc Mellhorn, wiping his forehead. "Warmish, though."

"It's the humidity, really," said Paisley Grew. "That's what it really is."

"Yes, I know, said Doc Mellhorn. "And now tell me, Paisley; how's that indigestion of yours?"

"Well, I'll tell you, Doc," said Paisley. "When I first came here, I thought the climate was doing it good. I did for a fact. But now I'm not so sure. I've tried all sorts of things for it—I've even tried being transferred to the boiling asphalt lakes. But it just seems to hang on, and every now and then, when I least expect it, it catches me. Take last night. I didn't have a thing to eat that I don't generally eat—well, maybe I did have one little snort of hot sulphur, but it wasn't the sulphur that did it. All the same, I woke up at four, and it was just like a knife. Now . . ."

He went on from there and it took him some time. And Doc Mellhorn listened, happy as a clam. He never thought he'd be glad to listen to a hypochondriac, but he was. And when Paisley was all through, he examined him and prescribed for him. It was just a little soda bicarb and pepsin, but Paisley said it took hold something wonderful. And they had a fine time that evening, talking over the old days.

Finally, of course, the talk got around to how Paisley liked it where he was. And Paisley was honest enough about that.

"Well, Doc," he said, "of course this isn't the place for you, and I can see you're just visiting. But I haven't many real complaints. It's hot, to be sure, and they work you, and some of the boys here are rough. But they've had some pretty interesting experiences, too, when you get them talking—yes, sir. And anyhow, it isn't Peabodyville, New Jersey," he said with vehemence. "I spent five years in Peabodyville, trying to work up in the leather business. After that I bust out, and I guess that's what landed me here. But it's an improvement on Peabodyville." He looked at Doc Mellhorn sidewise. "Say, Doc," he said, "I know this is a vacation for you, but all the same there's a couple of the boys—nothing really wrong with them of course—but—well, if you could just look them over—"

"I was thinking the office hours would be nine to one," said Doc Mellhorn.

So Paisley took him around and they found a nice little place for an office in one of the abandoned mine galleries, and Doc Mellhorn hung out his shingle. And right away patients started coming around. They didn't get many doctors there, in the first place, and the ones they did get weren't exactly the cream of the profession, so Doc Mellhorn had it all to himself. It was mostly sprains, fractures, bruises and dislocations, of course, with occaional burns and scalds—and, on the whole, it reminded Doc Mellhorn a good deal of his practice in Steeltown, especially when it came to foreign bodies in the eye. Now and then Doc Mellhorn ran into a more unusual case—for instance, there was one of the guards that got part of himself pretty badly damaged in a rock slide. Well, Doc Mellhorn had never set a tail before, but he managed it all right, and got a beautiful primary union, too, in spite of the fact that he had no X-ray facilities. He thought of writing up the case for the State Medical Journal, but then he couldn't figure out any way to send it to them, so he had to let it slide. And then there was an advanced carcinoma of the liver —a Greek named Papadoupolous or Prometheus or something. Doc Mellhorn couldn't do much for him, considering the circumstances, but he did what he could, and he and the Greek used to have long conversations. The rest was just everyday practice— run of the mine—but he enjoyed it.

Now and then it would cross his mind that he ought to get out Lizzie and run back to the other place for a visit with the folks. But that was just like going back East had been on earth— he'd think he had everything pretty well cleared up, and then a new flock of patients would come in. And it wasn't that he didn't miss his wife and children and grandchildren—he did. But there wasn't any way to get back to them, and he knew it. And there was the work in front of him and the office crowded every day. So he just went along, hardly noticng the time.

Now and then, to be sure, he'd get a suspicion that he wasn't too popular with the authorities of the place. But he was used to not being popular with authorities and he didn't pay much attention. But finally they sent an inspector around. The minute Doc Mellhorn saw him, he knew there was going to be trouble.

Not that the inspector was uncivil. In fact, he was a pretty high-up official—you could tell by his antlers. And Doc Mellhorn was just as polite, showing him around. He showed him the free dispensary and the clinic and the nurse—Scotch girl named Smith, she was—and the dental chair he'd rigged up with the help of a fellow named Ferguson, who used to be an engineer before he was sentenced. And the inspector looked them all over, and finally he came back to Doc Mellhorn's office. The girl named Smith had put up curtains in the office, and with that and a couple of potted gas plants it looked more homelike than it had. The inspector looked around it and sighed.

"I'm sorry, Doctor Mellhorn," he said at last, "but you can see for yourself, it won't do."

"What won't do?" said Doc Mellhorn, stoutly. But, all the same, he felt afraid.

"Any of it," said the inspector. "We could overlook the alleviation of minor suffering—I'd be inclined to do so myself—though these people are here to suffer, and there's no changing that. But you're playing merry Hades with the whole system."

"I'm a physician in practice," said Doc Mellhorn.

"Yes," said the inspector. "That's just the trouble. Now, take these reports you've been sending," and he took out a sheaf of papers. "What have you to say about that?"

"Well, seeing as there's no county health officer, or at least I couldn't find one—" said Doc Mellhorn.

"Precisely," said the inspector. "And what have you done? You've condemned fourteen levels of this pit as unsanitary nuisances. You've recommended 2136 lost souls for special diet, remedial exercise, hospitalization—Well—I won't go through the list."

"I'll stand back of every one of those recommendations," said Doc Mellhorn. "And now we've got the chair working, we can handle most of the dental work on the spot. Only Ferguson needs more amalgam."

"I know," said the inspector patiently, "but the money has to come from somewhere—you must realize that. We're not a rich community, in spite of what people think. And these unauthorized requests—oh, we fill them, of course, but—"

"Ferguson needs more amalgam," said Doc Mellhorn. "And that last batch wasn't standard. I wouldn't use it on a dog."

"He's always needing more amalgam!" said the inspector bitterly, making a note. "Is he going to fill every tooth in Hades? By the way, my wife tells me I need a little work done myself—but we won't go into that. We'll take just one thing—your entirely unauthorized employment of Miss Smith. Miss Smith has no business working for you. She's supposed to be gnawed by a never-dying worm every Monday, Wednesday and Friday."

"Sounds silly to me," said Doc Mellhorn.

"I don't care how silly it sounds," said the inspector. "It's regulations. And, besides, she isn't even a registered nurse."

"She's a practical one," said Doc Mellhorn. "Of course, back on earth a lot of her patients died. But that was because when

DOC MELLHORN AND THE PEARLY GATES 245

she didn't like a patient, she poisoned him. Well, she can't poison anybody here and I've kind of got her out of the notion of it anyway. She's been doing A-1 work for me and I'd like to recommend her for—"

"Please!" said the inspector. "Please! And as if that wasn't enough, you've even been meddling with the staff. I've a note here on young Asmodeus—Asmodeus XIV—"

"Oh, you mean Mickey!" said Doc Mellhorn, with a chuckle. "Short for Mickey Mouse. We call him that in the clinic. And he's a young imp if I ever saw one."

"The original Asmodeus is one of our most prominent citizens," said the inspector severely. "How do you suppose he felt when we got your report that his fourteenth great-grandson had rickets?"

"Well," said Doc Mellhorn, "I know rickets. And he had 'em. And you're going to have rickets in these youngsters as long as you keep feeding 'em low-grade coke. I put Mickey on the best Pennsylvania anthracite, and look at him now!"

"I admit the success of your treatment," said the inspector, "but, naturally—well, since then we've been deluged with demands for anthracite from as far south as Sheol. We'll have to float a new bond issue. And what will the taxpayers say?"

"He was just cutting his first horns when he came to us," said Doc Mellhorn reminiscently, "and they were coming in crooked. Now, I ask you, did you ever see a straighter pair? Of course, if I'd had cod liver oil—My gracious, you ought to have somebody here that can fill a prescription; I can't do it all."

The inspector shut his papers together with a snap. "I'm sorry, Doctor Mellhorn," he said, "but this is final. You have no right here, in the first place; no local license to practice in the second—"

"Yes, that's a little irregular," said Doc Mellhorn, "but I'm a registered member of four different medical associations—you might take that into account. And I'll take any examination that's required."

"No," said the inspector violently. "No, no, no! You can't stay here! You've got to go away! It isn't possible!"

Doc Mellhorn drew a long breath. "Well," he said, "there wasn't any work for me at the other place. And here you won't let me practice. So what's a man to do?"

The inspector was silent.

"Tell me," said Doc Mellhorn presently. "Suppose you do throw me out? What happens to Miss Smith and Paisley and the rest of them?"

"Oh, what's done is done," said the inspector impatiently, "here as well as anywhere else. We'll have to keep on with the anthracite and the rest of it. And Hades only knows what'll happen in the future. If it's any satisfaction to you, you've started something."

"Well, I guess Smith and Ferguson between them can handle the practice," said Doc Mellhorn. "But that's got to be a promise."

"It's a promise," said the inspector.

"Then there's Mickey—I mean Asmodeus," said Doc Mellhorn. "He's a smart youngster—smart as a whip—if he is a hellion. Well, you know how a youngster gets. Well, it seems he wants to be a doctor. But I don't know what sort of training he'd get—"

"He'll get it," said the inspector feverishly. "We'll found the finest medical college you ever saw, right here in West Baal. Well build a hospital that'll knock your eye out. You'll be satisfied. But now, if you don't mind—"

"All right," said Doc Mellhorn, and rose.

The inspector looked surprised. "But don't you want to—" he said. "I mean my instructions are we're to give you a banquet, if necessary—after all, the community appreciates—"

"Thanks," said Doc Mellhorn, with a shudder, "but if I've got to go, I'd rather get out of town. You hang around and announce your retirement, and pretty soon folks start thinking they ought to give you a testimonial. And I never did like testimonials."

All the same, before he left he took a silver half dollar out of Mickey Asmodeus' chin.

When he was back on the road again and the lights of the gates had faded into a low ruddy glow behind him, Doc Mellhorn felt alone for the first time. He'd been lonely at times during his life, but he'd never felt alone like this before. Because, as far as he could see, there was only him and Lizzie now.

"Now, maybe if I'd talked to Aesculapius—" he said. "But pshaw, I always was pigheaded."

He didn't pay much attention to the way he was driving and it seemed to him that the road wasn't quite the same. But he felt tired for a wonder—bone-tired and beaten—and he didn't much care about the road. He hadn't felt tired since he left earth, but now the loneliness tired him.

"Active—always been active," he said to himself. "I can't just lay down on the job. But what's a man to do?"

"What's a man to do?" he said. "I'm a doctor. I can't work miracles."

Then the black fit came over him and he remembered all the times he'd been wrong and all the people he couldn't do anything for. "Never was much of a doctor, I guess," he said. "Maybe, if I'd gone to Vienna. Well, the right kind of man would have gone. And about that Bigelow kid," he said. "How was I to know he'd hemorrhage? But I should have known.

"I've diagnosed walking typhoid as appendicitis. Just the once, but that's enough. And I still don't know what held me back when I was all ready to operate. I used to wake up in a sweat, six months afterward, thinking I had.

"I could have saved those premature twins, if I'd known as much then as I do now. I guess that guy Dafoe would have done it anyway—look at what he had to work with. But I didn't. And that finished the Gorham's having children. That's a dandy doctor, isn't it? Makes you feel fine.

"I could have pulled Old Man Halsey through. And Edna Biggs. And the little Lauriat girl. No, I couldn't have done it with her. That was before insulin. I couldn't have cured Ted Allen. No, I'm clear on that. But I've never been satisfied about the Collins woman. Bates is all right—good as they come. But I knew her, inside and out—ought to, too—she was the biggest nuisance that ever came into the office. And if I hadn't been down with the flue . . .

"Then there's the flu epidemic. I didn't take my clothes off, four days and nights. But what's the good of that, when you lose them? Oh, sure, the statistics looked good. You can have the statistics.

"Should have started raising hell about the water supply two years before I did.

"Oh, yes, it makes you feel fine, pulling babies into the world. Makes you feel you're doing something. And just fine when you see a few of them, twenty-thirty years later, not worth two toots on a cow's horn. Can't say I ever delivered a Dillinger. But there's one or two in state's prison. And more that ought to be. Don't mind even that so much as a few of the fools. Makes you wonder.

"And then, there's incurable cancer. That's a daisy. What can you do about it, Doctor? Well, Doctor, we can alleviate the pain in the last stages. Some. Ever been in a cancer ward, Doctor? Yes, Doctor, I have.

"What do you do for the common cold, Doctor? Two dozen clean linen handkerchiefs. Yes, it's a good joke—I'll laugh. And what do you do for a boy when you know he's dying, Doctor? Take a silver half dollar out of his ear. But it kept the Lane kid quiet and his fever went down that night. I took the credit, but I don't know why it went down.

"I've only got one brain. And one pair of hands.

"I could have saved. I could have done. I could have.

"Guess it's just as well you can't live forever. You make fewer mistakes. And sometimes I'd see Bates looking at me as if he wondered why I ever thought I could practice.

"Pigheaded, opinionated, ineffective old imbecile! And yet, Lord, Lord, I'd do it all over again."

He lifted his eyes from the pattern of the road in front of him. There were white markers on it now and Lizzie seemed to be bouncing down a residential street. There were trees in the street and it reminded him of town. He rubbed his eyes for a second, and Lizzie rolled on by herself—she often did. It didn't seem strange to him to stop at the right house.

"Well, Mother," he said rather gruffly to the group on the lawn. "Well, Dad. . . . Well, Uncle Frank." He beheld a small, stern figure advancing, hands outstretched. "Well, Grandma," he said meekly.

Later on he was walking up and down in the grape arbor with Uncle Frank. Now and then he picked a grape and ate it. They'd always been good grapes, those Catawbas, as he remembered them.

"What beats me," he said, not for the first time, "is why I didn't notice the Gates. The second time, I mean."

"Oh, that Gate," said Uncle Frank, with the easy, unctuous roll in his voice that Doc Mellhorn so well remembered. He smoothed his handle-bar moustaches. "That Gate, my dear Edward—well, of course it has to be there in the first place. Literature you know. And then, it's a choice," he said richly.

"I'll draw cards," said Doc Mellhorn. He ate another grape.

"Fact is," said Uncle Frank, "that Gate's for one kind of person. You pass it and then you can rest for all eternity. Just fold your hands. It suits some."

"I can see that it would," said Doc Mellhorn.

"Yes," said Uncle Frank, "but it wouldn't suit a Mellhorn. I'm happy to say that very few of our family remain permanently on that side. I spent some time there myself." He said, rather self-consciously, "Well, my last years had been somewhat stormy. So few people cared for refined impersonations of our feathered songsters, including lightning sketches. I felt that I'd earned a rest. But after a while—well, I got tired of being at liberty."

"And what happens when you get tired?" said Doc Mellhorn.

"You find out what you want to do," said Uncle Frank.

"My kind of work?" said Doc Mellhorn.

"Your kind of work," said his uncle. "Been busy, haven't you?"

"Well," said Doc Mellhorn. "But here. If there isn't so much as a case of mumps in—"

"Would it have to be mumps?" said his uncle. "Of course, if you're aching for mumps, I guess it could be arranged. But how many new souls do you suppose we get here a day?"

"Sizable lot, I expect."

"And how many of them get here in first-class condition?" said Uncle Frank triumphantly. "Why, I've seen Doctor Rush—Benjamin Rush—come back so tired from a day's round he could hardly flap one pinion against the other. Oh, if it's work you want—And then, of course, there's the earth."

"Hold on," said Doc Mellhorn. "I'm not going to appear to any young intern in wings and a harp. Not at my time of life. And anyway, he'd laugh himself sick."

"'Tain't that," said Uncle Frank. "Look here. You've left children and grandchildren behind you, haven't you? And they're going on?"

"Yes," said Doc Mellhorn.

"Same with what you did," said Uncle Frank. "I mean the inside part of it—that stays. I don't mean any funny business—voices in your ear and all that. But haven't you ever got clean tuckered out, and been able to draw on something you didn't know was there?"

"Pshaw, any man's done that," said Doc Mellhorn. "But you take the adrenal—"

"Take anything you like," said Uncle Frank placidly. "I'm not going to argue with you. Not my department. But you'll find it isn't all adrenalin. Like it here?" he said abruptly. "Feel satisfied?"

"Why, yes," said Doc Mellhorn surprisedly, "I do." He looked around the grape arbor and suddenly realized that he felt happy.

"No, they wouldn't all arrive in first-class shape," he said to himself. "So there'd be a place." He turned to Uncle Frank. "By the way," he said diffidently, "I mean, I got back so quick—there wouldn't be a chance of my visiting the other establishment now and then? Where I just came from? Smith and Ferguson are all right, but I'd like to keep in touch."

"Well," said Uncle Frank, "you can take that up with the delegation." He arranged the handkerchief in his breast pocket. "They ought to be along any minute now," he said. "Sister's been in a stew about it all day. She says there won't be enough chairs, but she always says that."

"Delegation?" said Doc Mellhorn. "But—"

"You don't realize," said Uncle Frank, with his rich chuckle. "You're a famous man. You've broken pretty near every regulation except the fire laws, and refused the Gate first crack. They've got to do something about it."

"But—" said Doc Mellhorn, looking wildly around for a place of escape.

"Sh-h!" hissed Uncle Frank. "Hold up your head and look as though money were bid for you. It won't take long—just a welcome." He shaded his eyes with his hand. "My," he said with frank admiration, "you've certainly brought them out. There's Rush, by the way."

"Where?" said Doc Mellhorn.

"Second from the left, third row, in a wig," said Uncle Frank. "And there's—"

Then he stopped, and stepped aside. A tall grave figure was advancing down the grape arbor—a bearded man with a wise, majestic face who wore robes as if they belonged to him, not as

Doc Mellhorn had seen them worn in college commencements. There was a small fillet of gold about his head and in his left hand, Doc Mellhorn noticed without astonishment, was a winged staff entwined with two fangless serpents. Behind him were many others. Doc Mellhorn stood straighter.

The bearded figure stopped in front of Doc Mellhorn. "Welcome, Brother," said Aesculapius.

"It's an honor to meet you, Doctor," said Doc Mellhorn. He shook the outstretched hand. Then he took a silver half dollar from the mouth of the left-hand snake.

TWO

Far From Here and Now

THE BAREFOOT SAINT

At Chezeray, in the fertile, high-lying tableland between the Seine and the Eure, the whole town smells like a cider-press, in the Fall. They make good *calvados* in that neighborhood, they know how to cook and eat. They know the tricks of the rose, the horse, and the spaniel, but they are not voluble people and it takes a magician to cheat them in a bargain. They know how to keep their money warm and they are hard to change. The priest rides a bicycle, with his black skirts tucked up to his knees; the radio at the *Café des Sports* gets the programs from the Eiffel Tower every night; but the striped fields beyond the town are the fields of generations of infinitely patient farmers and the old mortar is still as hard as iron in the ruins of the old walls.

It is only a score of miles to the Deauville road, but Paris is another country for all of that. This is France, or a stubborn part of it—the snail on the wall has his own house, the trees are knotted with bearing but they continue to bear. The crypt of the little chapel goes back to Rome and in the chapel itself you will find the statue of a saint who is not in any calendar—a small saint, carved from grey stone. Her smile is decided and courteous, her hand extended to bless, but she has no name and her feet have never worn shoes. Nevertheless, there is always a candle before her. They can pray to St. Thérèse at Lisieux, or to St.

Jeanne at Rouen, if they like and as much as they like. Chezeray has a saint of its own.

And for how this barefoot and nameless saint first came to her town of Chezeray, the tale tells this, in black-letter, written with a monk's pen.

When the Great Fear of the Year 1000 had passed from Christendom and a man could go to sleep at night without hearing the knock of the Last Judgment in every beat of his heart, many learned doctors looked for a new earth, taught its lesson by shame and terror, turning away from Satan as the burnt child turns from the fire. Alas, it was not to be so. Never had the Devil and his angels been more active, never were the black arts more highly regarded or practised with such appalling craft. In every nation, sorcerers and magicians flourished; burn one at the stake and a whole coven sprang up from the ashes; cast one in the river and the waters themselves were attaint. It was a time of prodigies and searchings and tribulations. In France, after many years, this evil matter came to a head at last in Gilles de Rais, that notable wizard, and was ended. But long before Gilles had said his first prayer backward at his familiar's knee, there were men in our country fully as evil as he. There was, for example, the man called Gui Bastide.

His true name was Ormastes and he was a magician from Persia. Why he came from Persia the tale does not tell—perhaps even the earth of that hot, corruptible country of enchanters sickened of him at last. But come he did, and he travelled into France as a rat slips down the cable of some ship just come into port, bringing the plague in its coat. And with all France open before him, the Devil brought him to settle in our own village of Chezeray. They say that the Devil loves a thriving town. But after Gui Bastide had been with us some few months, the town ceased to thrive.

He said that he was a retired merchant and that his mother had been Simone Bastide, a poor widow of Chezeray. He must have thrown some sort of spell over the older folk—for when he spoke, they remembered him, a little boy, picking up sticks in the forest and playing boys' games. He was a good fellow, always ready to pay for the wine. He gave greatly to the church—it was, doubtless, permitted him by his allies, for the sake of the terrible things he was to bring to pass.

The first sign of his power and intentions was the death of Angelique Ourcq. She was not more than fourteen and as good as bread. He had given her a ribbon once, on Market Day, because he said it suited her pretty hair, and would talk to her now and then on grave, instructive subjects. One morning she arose and went into the middle of the market-place and began to scream in a loud voice, cursing God and all His angels. They tried to restrain her, but she foamed at the lips and fought, and one of the women she scratched with her fingers died in two days. Nor would she leave off blaspheming the whole company of Heaven—even when they gagged her, she made signs with her hands. So Chezeray knew that the Devil had come to Chezeray and entered into her. She was tried and condemned and burnt in the public square.

There had never been such sorrow in the town since the Great Fear. Through a crowd of which not even the most pious reviled her, she was led to her fire. At the last, they say, she was like the good girl she had always been—for the ribbon had been taken from her when they dressed her in her shift for execution—and only cried pitifully and uncomprehendingly, like a beaten child. After that, there was a smoked place in the square, and people passed by it sickly, making the sign of the cross, while each man looked from the corner of his eyes at his neighbor, afraid to think.

There were long, hot rains all summer. No one could remember such rains—and the crops that were not rotted, ripened too early, a grain full of bad, small ears. Fat, silly Jean Doumic killed Pierre Quervel with a cleaver in a squabble about nothing at all. They hanged him over the East Gate; and after that, the children were afraid to play games there. Two charcoal burners were eaten by wolves—not in the forest, but in the cleared fields, as they were bringing their load to town. And to cap things, the great bell of the chapel, Anne, the bell with the voice of a young boy, cracked into two pieces one day as the sexton was ringing her and so crippled him that he had to walk with two sticks the rest of his life.

A cloud lay on the countryside—a cloud that did not lift. The Bishop came down in his mitre to drive the invisible evil away, with relics and a saint's thighbone. But, after he had left, things were worse than before. And Gui Bastide walked about in a Turkey gown and was foremost in pious suggestions for exorcising the trouble, for, unlike most demons, he could pronounce the name of God without burning pains.

After the birth of a child with horns who prophesied unceasingly for three days in its cradle and then vanished, leaving a heap of dried leaves where it had lain, the town was like a colony of ghosts or lepers. No man would speak to another except by signs—and, when they were not in the chapel, the families were shut up in their houses, hardly daring even to eat or drink for fear the meat on the plate might become alive. The winter came on early, whetting a knife, and men began to draw in their belts about their stomachs, there was so little grain. As for the poor—who were few—they died like Mayflies, for a rumor had got about that some vagabond from another town was responsible for these terrors, and no one would feed them.

The priest prayed for hours to every saint in Heaven—but Ormastes, the magician, knew every saint by name, and, as soon as a prayer would rise as high as the chimney-pots, he would send his familiars to take from it the name to which it was addressed so that it wandered like a senseless thing to the gates of Paradise and could not ask admittance. To God also the priest prayed, and fervently—but there were three wars in Christendom then, besides the constant trouble of the Turks, and the Grand Seigneur cannot always attend to all his million petitions in person, at times like those. These things are sometimes permitted—that we may learn what cup was drunk by the saints.

So the priest only wearied his knees till the bone began to rub through them—and still no succor came. I have said that he implored every saint in Paradise—that is not so. He did not call on the Saint with the Bare Feet—the Saint Who Has No Name. And this was because, in the first place, he did not know that she existed, and, in the second, if he had, he would not have known how to address her respectfully—for he was a rather literal man. And how she came to be nameless fell about thus.

She was French, but she had been stolen when she was two years old, when a raid of barbarians came over the Rhine. This was in the wrecked time before Charlemagne. The barbarians brought her up as a scullion among the camp followers and she could not remember the name that had been given her—it was not a Christian name. As for her new masters—all they ever called her was "Here, you!" or "You there with the stubby nose!" She accepted this fact as a condition of her servitude, and by the grace in her that God grants to the defenceless she remained a clean virgin in her life among those heathen.

Now, when she was about sixteen, St. Avennel of Lorraine came seeking martyrdom among the pagans of Germany. And, after escaping many deaths, he arrived at the camp of her army and preached to the soldiers—after which he broke their idol, which was a wooden goat, into three pieces with a stone. So they bound him and made preparations by bending down the tops of two strong saplings that grew at some distance from each other, intending, in the morning, to tie one of his arms to one sapling and one to the other, and then release the saplings. But this girl had seen St. Avennel and taken pity on him, and in the night, when the camp was asleep, she crept between the sentries to bring him a cup of water. And St. Avennel blessed her and, finding her ready and eager for the knowledge of God, in the three hours before dawn he explained God and all His mysteries to her and baptized her in the water she had brought him, naming her Claire, in the name of the Father and the Son and the Holy Ghost. Next morning she informed the heathen of these matters, and, after St. Avennel had died, they bent down two other saplings, and she perished so, praising God.

When she arrived in Heaven at the heels of St. Avennel, she was very warmly received, you may be sure. As you know, though, martyrdoms were rather more common in those days than they are now. So, while she was given much praise for the directness and consistency of her actions, it was hardly to be expected that she should enjoy such an ovation as St. Genevieve, for instance, received on the occasion of her entrance—for, though she had done her uttermost, she had not the incessant years of mortification and service on earth behind her of such saints as St. Hilary or St. Bridget or St. Simon Stylites. Still, she was treated, she thought, very much beyond her deserts for all that, and instantly given a fitting place in the heavenly hierarchy with all its rights, powers, immunities, and privileges.

THE BAREFOOT SAINT

But then the terrible question of her name came up.

"What is this child's name?" said St. Peter, in his capacity as interlocutor, with a kindly glance at the barefoot saint's head, as yet unaccustomed to its halo. She was too embarrassed to answer. Besides, she had had her name for such a short while.

"Claire is her name," St. Avennel answered rather proudly. "For it was nearly my last act on earth to baptize her Claire."

At this, both St. Claire of Auxerre and St. Claire of Amphipolis arose.

"There are already two St. Claires in Heaven," remarked the first, looking coldly at her neighbor, and St. Eustace muttered "Three is for the Holy Trinity, to whom be all praise and laud—but three St. Claires in Heaven like the two we have already, and I, for one, should be inclined to ask for my caldron of boiling lead again."

"If she is to be St. Claire as well as myself and my sister," put in St. Claire of Amphipolis, with a side glance at St. Claire of Auxerre that had more woman than saint in it—for even in Heaven the blessed know their own minds—"It is necessary to find out where she comes from—for it is evident that she cannot be merely St. Claire."

"That is true," said St. Peter. "Child, what is the name of the place where you were martyred?"

The barefoot saint felt more embarrassed than ever.

"I don't know," she said, timidly, after a long time, "If you please—I don't think it has any name."

This created a slight commotion in Heaven.

St. Peter turned to St. Avennel. Heaven's gatekeeper was beginning to feel worried, but he dealt with the matter tactfully.

"Do you know the name of the place, St. Avennel?" he queried.

"Certainly not," said St. Avennel crisply. "All I know is that I christened this child Claire and that she is St. Claire."

"She cannot be simply St. Claire," said St. Claire of Auxerre, and for the first time since the two had met in Heaven, St. Claire of Amphipolis agreed with her.

"She is St. Claire," said St. Avennel, annoyed, and it almost seemed as if a personal dispute were about to develop between himself and the two St. Claires who were already St. Claires.

"I will send a cherub to make inquiries," said St. Peter, soothingly. "The place undoubtedly has a name—all places have."

When the council was reconvened, the cherub made his report. He seemed rather tired.

As far as could be ascertained, by methods human and divine, the place of the two saints' martyrdom was a large, waste campfield which had no name in any language.

"Well, call her St. Claire of the Barbarians!" said St. Claire of Amphipolis, with a rustle of her garments, "that will do very well for the present."

"She shall not on any account be called St. Claire of the Barbarians!" said St. Avennel, passing a reminiscent hand over his principal scars. And St. Avennel's services had been so recent and so spectacular that no one dared contradict him.

"St. Claire of the Bare Feet is a pretty name," broke in St. Peter, hurriedly. "Well now—St. Claire of the Bare Feet—"

"Is childish, ridiculous, and derogatory to the dignity of Heaven," pronounced St. Paul, weightily. "I must enter my voice in protest against any such scheme."

There was a painful silence in Heaven for several minutes. St. Avennel looked intensely displeased with the whole affair.

Now the barefoot saint raised her head again. She looked St. Peter squarely in the beard.

"If you please," she said, modestly but with some firmness, "I don't want any name, really. I wouldn't know what to do with a name if I had it."

"*What?*" said St. Avennel.

"You see, I never had a name in my life except for six hours," said the barefoot saint, "and it takes a good deal longer than that to get used to such things."

"It was a very nice name I gave you," said St. Avennel, aggrievedly.

"It is," said his disciple, "but here two people have it already."

"That makes no difference at all," said St. Avennel, glaring at the other St. Claires.

"It makes all the difference in the world," said his godchild, "for I would not offend either of these ladies for my seat in Heaven. In fact, I will not have a name."

"But, my dear child," argued St. Peter, "the prayers—the

petitions—how will people on earth know how to find you up here if you insist on having no name?"

"They will know," said the barefoot saint.

So it was settled. And, in the angelic countries, time passes like a minute and is scarcely perceived at all, so that it was several centuries before the barefoot saint had reason or opportunity to regret her decision.

But, one morning, St. Claire of Amphipolis passed her on the golden streets. "Have you had many petitions today, sister?" she said, her eyes glinting sharply under her aureole.

"Why, no," said the barefoot saint, quite truthfully—then later, a little sadly, "not one."

"That seems curious," chattered St. Claire of Amphipolis, "for today I have given sight to two blind beggars and healed a goitre and saved a whole shipful of sailors who cried to me out of the middle of the blackest storm on the Atlantic. Their praises go up to God the father like the smoke of sanctified candles—and I feel sure He must be very pleased with me, though He does say so little. But you must excuse me, my dear, for these are busy days—and I have to chastise a king and scare four heretics out of their wits with a rain of frogs before four o'clock this afternoon, mortal time—*Good*-bye—" and she swept away, in a great flurry of holiness, and left the barefoot saint wondering why alone of all the saints of heaven she had no human petitioners—for she had always been a dutiful girl.

And one evening—or it may have been fifty years later—St. Claire of Auxerre passed her near the jasper walls, where she was watching the younger seraphs play at quoits with their halos, flinging them from comet to tasselled comet.

"Good evening, sister!" said St. Claire of Auxerre—and she seemed to be in a great hurry, for she had tucked up her nimbus about her knees—"And how goes the task of aiding the distressed on earth? Have a score appealed to you today or only a dozen—for you look tired and seem to be taking a much-needed rest?"

"Neither a score nor a dozen," answered the barefoot saint, very sorrowfully this time, but as truthfully as ever, "not one."

"Well, well, well, times are changed to be sure!" said St. Claire of Auxerre, sardonically, "for these new saints that come into Heaven and do nothing but enjoy themselves! And when I was a girl! But I really must hurry along, dear, for I have so many affairs on hand that I hardly know where to turn. There were eleven requests for happy delivery in childbirth only this morning—and I have to stop a little war, and appear to a pagan philosopher in the form of a cross of white roses before I can call myself really settled for the night. Still, live and learn, my dear, live and learn, and when you're a little older and a great deal wiser, people may—" but St. Claire's last words were cut off as if a hand had snatched them out of her mouth, for she rushed away so fast that she looked like a meteor, and then she was a sparkling speck, and then nothing whatever.

But the barefoot saint hid herself in a cloud and wept, for it seemed to her that she had missed her vocation and was of no use in Heaven.

Then, because it is never permitted to be quite unhappy in Heaven, God blew the cloud beyond the shining gates, and she looked down and saw the earth. And it happened that the very first land she saw was her own land, France, and in it Chezeray, and the very bad state of Chezeray.

After a short while, she dried her eyes and looked upon Chezeray more intently. She began to smile.

"There seems to be something for me to do after all," she said. "Yes, there seems to be something that I can do rather well."

She had faults enough, no doubt, but false modesty was not among them.

"It is hard," said a quiet voice in her ear. "It is very hard, St. Barefoot."

"I don't care how hard it is," said the barefoot saint, with a chuckle. "When the pot's dirty, it takes hot water to clean it."

Then she straightened her robe, smoothed back her hair, and descended to the earth with rapid invisibility.

It was a rigid December evening, howling with wind, and Ormastes sat alone in his room, smiling at himself and his triumph. After a while, he hid that smile with his hand, for even he did not like to see it reflected in the tall yellow mirror in front of him. Outside, the flurries of the snow fought like pallid lions, tearing at each other and at the fronts of the houses and even at the windows of Ormastes, their master. He had brought the storm.

After a while, he roused himself and began a minor incantation. But he had hardly said the Lord's Prayer backward twice and the chalk marks inside the red circle at his feet had not yet begun to glow like foxfire, when he heard a sound at his door that was neither wind nor snow, a sound like human speech and a weak hand tapping for entrance. It broke his mood for a moment, and the room, that had been heavy with magic, cleared. Then he shook himself and began again, but, before his sorceries took hold of the air once more, the sound was repeated.

"What the devil can that be?" said Ormastes aloud, and as he said it a shudder went through him as if he had been touched with hot iron, for if those who have sold their souls to evil will not wince at the name of God they must at that of their Master. That is the bargain.

Again he began—and again there was the sound. This time it was impatient. And yet, no mortal but him could live within that storm.

He hid his apparatus, he put his skeleton and his crocodile in their cupboard, and turned the yellow mirror with its face to the wall. Then he went to the door and opened it.

Crouched up on the sill like a frozen squirrel was a girl about sixteen years old. She was dressed in one poor garment that the wind tugged away from her and her feet were as bare as shells and blue with the cold.

"Fire," she said, faintly. "Help," and Ormastes lifted her in. He dried her feet and ankles with his own napkins. He put her before the fire and gave her wine.

Then he smiled again, and this time his smile was gray as ashes and deadly as yewberries, for he could tell by his arts that she was Christian and a clean virgin—and it was of such that he stood in great need at this time.

The girl revived with the wine and the heat. She began to stir a little and moan. Ormastes put a full cloak about her and, taking a little rosy vial from his breast, gave her three drops of the clear liquid within it. Then she seemed to come to herself and sat up dazedly.

"I am lost," she said, "I was dying. And who are you?"

"I am Gui Bastide, well known in Chezeray, a solid citizen," he answered. "And you, my child?"

"I am Claire Nupieds and mother keeps the wine-shop by the East Gate," she answered innocently. "Only nobody ever comes there any more because of the trouble and we must have bread. So I went out to beg some from Simon the baker, we are so hungry. But I did not know the storm was so fierce, and when the cold had caught me, I lost my way. The last thing I can remember is falling against someone's door—"

She was telling lies as fast as an ass can trot—but nearly anything is permitted in a good cause.

"It was my door," said Ormastes, "and you are a lucky child and your mother a lucky woman, for though I am not Simon the baker, my heart is as soft as cheese when it comes to helping the necessitous—and I can give you all the bread you want and to spare."

Well, then there were thanks to be sure, and between the gratitude of the saint and Ormastes's expostulations that it was nothing at all for an honest fellow to do for his neighbors, they took up quite a quarter of an hour between them.

But, finally, "I am very tired," said the saint, drooping her head, "and if you will give me a sack to cover me, I will lie down here till morning when I must get back to mother, for she will be nearly mad thinking I have been frozen in the storm."

"In a little while I will give you a whole room to yourself and the best bed in Chezeray," Ormastes answered, "but meanwhile—I have some little tricks I would like to show you— things that amuse my nephews and nieces when we are," and he coughed, "at home, around the fire. Just something to interest the children, but rather neat in their way. Would you like to see them, little Claire?"

"Oh yes, yes, yes!" said the saint, sitting bolt upright and trying to look as stupid as she possibly could.

Then Ormastes cracked his fingers together behind his back till his great rings hurt him for he felt that the game and the soul of the child before him were delivered into his hands.

He began mildly. There was nothing he showed at first that would have disquieted a nervous boy. He had shadows dance on the wall and pictures come in the fire, and brought out a box of wonderfully carved wooden toys from a red chest and struck them with a wand, and made them jig and play with each other like tadpoles. Of course, each new pastime that he presented was a trifle odder than the last, and that with a strained and indefinably unpleasant oddity. Not one of the wooden kings and queens, for instance, had five whole fingers to a hand. But the saint played her part and gaped like a servant on fair-day. She laughed and clapped her hands and asked for more.

Then Ormastes redrew his circle and turned the mirror towards it. He proceeded admirably in the path of his sorceries—never had the spirits been so eager to come. Soon there were three large murmuring skulls with eyes like phosphorus in the centre of the circle and a crowd of twisted devilkins hopped about them, going through such mimicries as made the saint wish herself safely back on her cloud. All the bones in the skeleton shook as if he were bitter cold and the mirror was full of vague and deadly shapes. Ormastes watched the child as a cat watches a mousehole—for this was a strong and subtle destruction that he had prepared, and his body and mind were all one starving lust for her soul. But the saint plucked up heart, and said, with an evident yawn, that it was strange how the days kept drawing in. She picked up one of the skulls as a bowler picks up a ball and threw it idly at a devilkin. It caught him square and he yelped for it hurt him very badly. And with that the whole phantasmagoria blew away like foggy weather—the fire died out of the floor—the mirror shuddered back into peace again—the circle was broken in three places.

"That was very funny indeed. Do it again, please," said the saint, approvingly. Ormastes looked at her as if he could not believe in sight.

Still, he knew in the caverns of his heart that he was the most skilled magician in all Persia, and, while he had been beaten once, he thought that it had been by a mortal innocence, and he had arts unexercised that could corrupt the egg in the nest and the seed under the ground. This time he made his preparations with almost excessive care.

He filled a crystal bowl with new blood—explaining to the saint that it was wine—crucified a lizard on the small portable altar that accompanied him in all his travels, and arranged seven black candles so that they formed the Unspeakable Figure. He filled the room with narcotic incense till he could hardly breathe in it, brought out his crocodile, and began to bound up and down the length of the chamber, gashing himself with a curved knife and uttering short, blasphemous cries. The crocodile moved, its eyes opened, it placed its head in the saint's white lap. And then the whole room seemed to coagulate into a single drop of cold, venomous oil, and through the weaving of the smoke and the ravings of Ormastes, a voice and a form took shape. The form was princely to look upon and the first notes of the voice had a singular sweetness. But if they and Death both beckoned a man, a man would run to Death and hide under his ragged cloak.

The voice spoke. "I am here," it said, "and who calls me from Hell?" Then Ormastes fell on his face like a dead body, for he had seen His Master. And, lying there in such abominable shock and terror of soul as he had never known, he heard only one sound, a sound that followed the whirlwind of that Voice and broke it to pieces, an unbelievable sound, the clear, pleased laughter of the saint.

When he opened his eyes again and knew that he was still alive, there was neither incense nor Presence in the room. The crocodile had rolled over on its back, a stuffed, pitiful figure—the yellow mirror was abolished as if it had been beaten on an anvil—the sacrilegious pentacles of Ormastes were gone with the crystal bowl, and lizard and candles were a pool of black wax. Also the floor was carpeted with a fine grey ash like the dust of ground bones. These things he did not seem to mind.

He staggered to his feet. The saint stood facing him, and, as he looked at her, he saw that she shone.

"I repent!" he croaked hoarsely. "I submit. I ask pardon of God."

She smiled and stretched out her hand. Within it were half a dozen flakes of white snow that lay there, unmelting. They seemed to Ormastes, gazing at them, the coolest and most peaceful things he had ever seen.

"Is there still time?" he asked, and now his voice was that of a man who has been tortured beyond the last extremity of the flesh.

For answer, the saint laid the flakes of snow upon his parched mouth. And, suddenly, there was no more Ormastes—only a small boy child about five years old, weeping and naked except for a Turkey gown that was much too big for it.

The saint smiled, modestly, yet with a touch of pardonable pride. Then she knitted her brows. The boy was well enough—but she had forgotten to provide him with a family. Still, it only needed another miracle for that, and she was in the vein.

She picked up the child in her arms and comforted him.

"You are little Gui Bastide, son of Simone Bastide, the widow," she told him, "and it's high time I took you home, for your people will be wondering where you are."

"Yes," said the child, "that is right," and he curled up in her arms and slept as if he had not been to sleep for twenty years.

So they left the house of Ormastes the magician. The town was brilliant with frost and clean with bright, biting air. People stirred in the streets and the market-place. Already they were talking and disputing like neighbors. The Terror had passed.

She carried the child to a poor house. There was a smell of hot cabbage soup from the door. When the child sniffed it, he woke and sprawled out of the saint's embrace like a starfish, all arms and legs and hunger. He ran to the door and beat upon it.

"Mother!" he piped impatiently. "Mother! Is breakfast ready? I'm here, but I don't know what I've done with my clothes!"

The door opened. A woman's face looked out.

"Ready and boiling and waiting!' she answered impatiently. Then she saw that her son stood before her stark naked and her mouth fell open and hung like a gate ajar.

"Great merciful Lord on High!" she said in a whisper and, grabbing hold of Ormastes the magician by the scruff of his neck, ran him into the house. The door slammed. From within, a little later, came the sound of slaps.

THE BISHOP'S BEGGAR

It seems that in the old days there was a bishop of Remo, and he was a heedless and proud young man, though of good intentions. Now, that was possible in those days, when the fire and light of the new learning had spread through Italy, and men drank, as if intoxicated, at a new spring. There were bishops who cared less for the Word of God than for their own splendor, and cardinals who were rather men of the world—and of no good world—than sons of the Church. I do not say that our bishop was as idle and self-seeking as some of these; I do say that he was a child of his time. He would have liked to be a lord, but his eldest brother was the lord; he would have liked to be a soldier, but his second brother was the soldier. So he went into the Church, for there, too, a man who bore a great name could rise. He was clever, he was ambitious, he had great connections. Now and then, to be sure, he asked a disquieting question, but the Baldis had always been original. The path that is rugged for many was made smooth for him from the first. When he was made bishop of Remo at an early age, the fact did not surprise him. Since he was to be neither lord nor soldier, he found that pleasant enough.

All went well for him, at first. They were glad to have a young and handsome bishop at Remo, for the bishop before him had been old and ill-favored. It was a pleasure to no one to kiss his ring, and he frightened the children with his peering eyes. With the coming of our bishop all this was changed. There was a great to-do and refurbishing of the bishop's palace; the smells of good cooking drifted again from the bishop's kitchens; when the bishop drove through the city, men threw their caps in the air. There were fine new frescoes in the cathedral, a new way of chanting in the choir. As for sin and suffering—well, they are always with us. The people of Remo liked to sin pleasantly and be reminded of it as little as possible.

Nevertheless, at times, a grayness would come over our bishop's spirit. He could not understand why it came. His life was both full and busy. He was a friend to art, a host to the gay and the learned, a ruler of men. He did not meddle in things which did not concern him; he felt in his heart that there was no prize in the Church which might not be within his grasp. And yet, at times, there was a grayness within him. It was singular.

He could not show that grayness before the world, he could not show it to his secretary or the witty company that gathered at his table. He could wrestle with it in prayer, and so he did.

But he found it no easy task. Had the Devil appeared before him with horns and a tail, he would have known what to do. But a grayness of spirit—a cool little voice in the mind which said to him now and then, "What do you in these robes, at this place, Gianfrancesco Baldi?"—that was another matter.

He came to find by experience that motion in the open air helped him as much as anything. When the grayness oppressed him too severely, he would summon his coach and drive about the countryside. So one day, as he drove through a small country village in the hills beyond Remo, it happened. It was nobody's fault; the bishop's least of all. He saw to it that he had a skilful coachman and good horses as he saw to all such matters. But when a tall, gangling boy darts across the street right under the nose of the horses, the most skilful coachman cannot always save him. There was a cry and a scream and a soft jar. Then, where the coach had passed, the boy lay writhing in the street.

The bishop always showed at his best in emergency. When he got out of the coach, the angry shouts of the crowd died away to a respectful murmur. He lifted the boy into the coach with his strong arms and drove back with him to Remo. On the way he talked to him soothingly, though the boy was in too much pain to pay much attention to this graciousness. When they got to Remo, he had the boy carried to a servant's room in the palace and doctors summoned for him. Later on he gave instructions about cleaning the coach.

At dinner his secretary recounted the little incident, and all men praised the kindliness of the bishop. The bishop passed it off pleasantly, but, at heart, he felt a trifle irritated. He had not felt particularly drawn toward the boy; on the other hand, he could not have left him lying in the road.

By the next day, as such things do, the story had gone all over Remo, and there were unusual demonstrations of good will as the bishop passed to the cathedral. The bishop received them with dignity, but his irritation remained. He disliked ostentatious shows of virtue and distrusted the fickleness of crowds. Nevertheless, it was his duty to see the boy, and he did so.

Washed, combed, and rid of his vermin, the boy looked ordinary enough, though somewhat older than the bishop had thought him. His body was slight and emaciated, but he had a well-shaped head and large liquid eyes. These stared at the bishop with some intensity; indeed, with such intensity that the bishop wondered, at first, if the boy might not be an idiot. But a little conversation proved him sound of mind, though rustic in speech.

His name was Luigi and he was an orphan, living as best he could. In the summer he tended goats; in the winter he lived with his uncle and aunt, the tavern-keepers, who fed him and beat him. His age was about nineteen. He had made his Easter duty as a Christian. He would never walk again.

Such were the facts of the case, and the bishop thought them over clearheadedly. He wondered what to do with the boy.

"Luigi," he said, "would you like to go back to your village?"

"Oh, no," said the boy. "It is a very good village, but now that I can no longer herd goats, there is no place in it for me. Besides, one eats better in Remo—I have had white cheese twice already." And he smacked his lips. His voice was remarkably strong and cheerful, the bishop noticed with surprise.

"Very well," said the bishop patiently. "You need not go back if you do not choose. You are now, in some sense, a ward of the Church, and the wings of the Church are sheltering." He looked at the boy's legs, lying limp and motionless under the covers, and felt, though against his will, the natural distaste of the hale man for the maimed. "You might learn some useful trade," he said thoughtfully. "There are many trades where the hands do all—a cobbler's, a tailor's, a basket-weaver's."

The boy shook his head joyfully. "Oh, no, your lordship," he said. "Trades take so long to learn and I am very stupid. It would not be worth the expense; your lordship would be embarrassed."

"My lordship, perhaps, is the best judge of that," said the bishop a trifle grimly. He kept thinking of the boy's remark about white cheese; it must be a spare life indeed where white cheese was such a treat. "But we are reasonable," he said. "Come, what would you be?"

"A beggar!" said the boy, and his dark eyes shone with delight.

"A beggar?" said the bishop, astonished and somewhat revolted.

"Why, yes," said the boy, as if it were the most natural thing in the world. "For ten years my father begged on the cathedral steps. That was before your lordship's time, but he was an excellent beggar and a master of his craft. True, he was subject to continual persecutions and jealousies from the honorable corporation of the beggars of Remo, coming, as he did, from outside the city. It was that which caused the ruin of our fortunes, for, in the end, when he had begun to fail, they threw him down a well, where he caught a bad cold and died of it. But in his good days he could outbeg any two of them. If your lordship would care to have me demonstrate his celebrated fainting fit, when his eyeballs rolled backward in his head—"

"I can think of nothing I should like less," said the bishop, shocked and disgusted, for it seemed to him an unworthy thing that a sturdy young man, though a cripple, should think of nothing better than beggary. "Besides," he said, "these other beggars you speak of—if they persecuted your father, no doubt they would persecute you."

"Me?" said the boy, and laughed. "Oh, once they understood, they would not dare touch me—not even Giuseppe, the Hook. I would be your lordship's beggar—the bishop's beggar!" And a light as of great peace and contentment spread over his countenance.

The bishop stared at him for a long time in silence. "That is what you wish?" he said, and his voice was dry.

"That is what I wish, your lordship," said the boy, nodding his head.

"So be it," said the bishop with a sigh, and left him. But when his coachman came to him the next morning for orders, it was all he could do to keep from reviling the man.

The bishop was not the sort of man who liked beggars. Indeed, were it not for custom and Christian charity, he would long since have cleared them from the steps of his cathedral. He could not very well do that; he knew what an impression such a move would make. Nevertheless, when he passed among them, as he must at times, he saw to it that his almoner made a suitable distribution of small coins, but he himself did his best to see and smell them as little as possible. Their whines and their supplications, their simulated sores, and their noisome rags—these were a fret and a burden to him.

Now, it seemed, he was to have a beggar of his own. He would have it taken it as a suitable humiliation for pride, but he did not feel himself to be a proud man. Nor could he think of the accident as anything but an accident. Had he deliberately trodden the lad beneath the hoofs of his horses—but he had not. He was well liked, able, decisive, a rising son of the Church. Nevertheless, he was to have a beggar—every day he must see his beggar on the steps of the cathedral, living reproach, a living lesson in idleness and heedlessness. It was a small thing, to be sure, but it darkened his dinner and made him sore at heart.

Therefore, being the man he was, he put a mask upon his face. He meant to speak of the thing, so it should be known—at least *that* might ward off ridicule. He spoke of it to his secretary; the secretary agreed that it was a very seemly and Christian idea of his lordship's, while the bishop wondered if the man laughed at him in his sleeve. He spoke of it to others; there were compliments, of course. Each time he spoke of it, it turned a small knife in his breast. But that did not keep him from speaking of it, nor from seeing that every care was given Luigi.

Nevertheless, he dreaded the day when Luigi would take up his post on the steps of the cathedral. He dreaded and yearned for it, both. For then, at last, the thing would be done. After that, like many things, it would become a custom, and in time Luigi himself would fade into the mass of whining beggary that haunted the steps of the cathedral. But things were not to be quite that way.

He admired, while he detested, the thoroughness with which Luigi prepared himself for his profession. He heard the whine ring out from the servants' quarters—"Ten scudi for Luigi!"—he saw the little cart and the crutches Luigi had made for himself. Now and then he heard his own servants laugh at the beggar's stories. This was hard enough to bear. But at last the day of parting came.

To his disgust, the bishop found the boy neither clean nor well-clad, as he had been since his accident, but dirty and dressed in tatters. He opened his mouth to reprove the boy, then he shut it again, for it seemed pitifully true that a beggar must dress his part. Nevertheless, the bishop did not like it. He asked Luigi, coolly, how he meant to live.

"Oh, your lordship's secretary has found me a very suitable chamber," said Luigi eagerly. "It is on the ground floor of a rookery by the river and it has room for crutches, my gear, and my cart. He will move me there tonight. Tomorrow I will be at my post on the steps of the cathedral." And he smiled gratefully at the bishop. "That will be a great day," he said.

"So," said the bishop, who could not trust himself to say anything further.

"Yet before I go," said Luigi, "I must thank your lordship for his kindness, and ask your lordship's blessing on my work. That is only suitable."

The bishop stiffened. "I may bless you, Luigi," he said, "but your work I cannot bless. I cannot give the blessing of the Church to the work of a man who lives by beggary when he might live otherwise."

"Well, then, I must go unblessed," said Luigi cheerfully. "After all, your lordship has already done so much for me! The bishop's beggar! How my uncle and aunt will stare!"

Now, of all the vainglorious, self-seeking, worthless, rascally sons of iniquity—and to think that I stand your sponsor, said the bishop, but, fortunately, he did not say it aloud. Silently he extended his ring and Luigi kissed it with such innocent reverence that the bishop was sorely moved to give him his blessing after all. But he summoned up his principles and departed in silence.

The bishop slept ill that night, tormented by dreams of Luigi. He dreamed that, for his sins, he must carry Luigi on his back all the way up the steps of the cathedral. And as he mounted each step, the weight upon his back became more crushing, till at last he woke, unrefreshed.

The next day he went to the cathedral in great state, though it was an ordinary Sunday. Yet he felt the state to be, in some measure, a protection. When he passed by the steps of the cathedral, the beggars set up their usual supplications. He sent his almoner among them; it was over quicker than he thought. He did not look for Luigi and yet he felt Luigi's eyes upon him as he stood there for a moment, splendid in robe and miter. Then the thing was finished.

In the cathedral that same day, he preached passionately against the sins of idleness and heedlessness. Seldom had he been so moving—he could feel that from his congregation. When Mass was over he retired to his palace, exhausted. Yet it was pleasant for him to walk about the palace and know that Luigi was not there.

It was just after vespers when his secretary came to him and told him that a man called Giuseppe, self-styled provost of the company of the beggars of Remo, requested an audience. The bishop sighed wearily and ordered the man brought before him. He was a squat fellow of great strength and an evil cast of countenance, for one side of his face had been so burned in a fire that it was as if he had two faces, one of them inhuman. Also, his left arm terminated in an iron hook.

"This is Giuseppe, the beggar, your lordship," said the secretary with repugnance.

"Giuseppe, called Double-Face, also called the Hook, provost of the honorable company of the beggars of Remo," said Giuseppe in a rusty voice, and plumped on his knees.

The bishop raised him and asked his business.

"Well, your lordship, it's this new fellow, Luigi Lamelegs," said Giuseppe. "I've got nothing against him personal—I wouldn't hurt a fly myself in a personal way"—and he grinned horribly—"but there he is in a good place on the steps, and your lordship's servants put him there. Well, now, if he's your lordship's beggar, that's one thing—though, even so, there's fees and vails to be paid, for that's the custom. But if he isn't your lordship's beggar—and your lordship paid him no attention this morning—"

"Stop!" said the bishop with anger. "Do you mean to tell me that the very steps of the cathedral are bartered and sold among you? Why, this is simony—this is the sin of simony!"

"Your lordship can call it hard words," said Giuseppe stolidly, "but that's been the way it's been done ever since there were beggars in Remo. I paid twenty crowns for my own place, and fought old Marco too. But that's beside the point. Your lordship has a right to a beggar if your lordship wants one—we're all agreed on that. But the question is: Is this man your lordship's beggar or isn't he?"

"And supposing I said he was not my beggar?" said the bishop, trembling.

"Well, that's all we'd want to know," said Giuseppe. "And thank your lordship kindly. I had my own suspicions of the man from the first. But we've got him down by the river now—Carlo and Benito and old blind Marta; she's a tough one, old blind Marta—and once we're through with him, he'll trouble your lordship no more." And sketching a clumsy salute, the man turned to go.

"Stop!" said the bishop again. "Would you have the guilt of murder upon your conscience?"

"Oh, your lordship takes it too hard," said Giuseppe, shuffling his feet. "What's one beggar more or less? We're not rich folk or learned folk to bother a mind like your lordship's. We breed and we die, and there's an end. And even at the best, it's no bed of roses on the steps of the cathedral."

The bishop wished to say many things, but he could think of only one.

"I declare to you that this man is my beggar," he said. "I stretch my hand over him."

"Well, that's very nicely spoken of your lordship," said Giuseppe in a grumbling voice, "and I dare say we can make room for him. But if the man's to keep a whole skin, your lordship had best come with me—old Marta was talking of ear-slitting when I left her."

So they found Luigi, bound but cheerful, in his first-floor chamber by the river, guarded by the persons Giuseppe had described—a hunchback, a dwarf, and a blind woman. The window which gave upon the river was open, and a large sack, weighted with stones, lay in one corner of the room. The bishop's arrival produced a certain consternation on the part of all but Luigi, who seemed to take it as a matter of course. After the boy had been unbound, the bishop addressed the beggars with some vivacity, declared that Luigi was his beggar, and gave him a piece of silver before them all, in token. This seemed to satisfy the company, who then crept away in silence.

"And yet have I done right? Have I done right?" said the bishop, striding up and down the chamber. "I greatly fear I have condoned the sin of simony! I have spent Mother Church's substance among the unworthy! And yet, even so, your blood may be upon my head," and he looked at Luigi doubtfully.

"Oh, your lordship need not take it so hard," said Luigi, rubbing his arms. "All is safe enough now. I arranged about the dues and vails with Giuseppe while your lordship was discussing her state of grace with Marta. He's an honest fellow enough, and his point is reasonable. One should not take a good place without money to keep it up. Had your lordship given me alms with your own hand this morning, our little difficulty would never have arisen. That was my fault—I assumed that your lordship knew."

"Knew?" said the bishop. "What should I know of such things? And yet, God forgive me, I am a priest and I should have knowledge of evil."

"It is merely a difference in knowledge," said Luigi gently. "Now, your lordship, doubtless, has never been in a room quite like this before."

The bishop stared at the damp walls and the mean chamber. He smelled the smell that cannot be aired from a room, the smell of poverty itself. He had never doubted his own experience before—when he had been first made a priest, he had gone on certain works of charity. Now it seemed to him that those works must have been rather carefully selected.

"No," he said, "I have never been in a room just like this one."

"And yet there are many of us who live in such rooms—and not all beggars," said Luigi. He changed his tone. "That was a fine rousing sermon your lordship gave us on idleness and heedlessness this morning," he said. "Hey, it brought the scudi forth from the goodfolks' pockets! An admirable sermon!"

"I am grateful for your encomiums," said the bishop bitterly. He glanced around the room again. "Is there nought else I can do?" he asked unwillingly.

"No, thank your lordship," said Luigi, and his eyes were smiling. "I have a woman to cook my dinner—it is true she is a thief, but she will not steal from a cripple—and soon, with your lordship's patronage, I shall be able to afford a charcoal brazier. Moreover, my friends seem to have left me a sack. So, after dinner

I shall say my prayers and go to bed to refresh myself for tomorrow's labor."

I shall say mine, too, for I need them, said the bishop, though he did not say it to Luigi.

So that was how it began. Soon enough, the bishop's beggar was a familiar figure on the steps of the cathedral—one of the admitted curiosities of the town. He was well-liked in his trade, for he always had a merry word or a sharp one for his clients— and it passed around until "Luigi says" became a byword. The bishop became used to him as one becomes used to a touch of rheumatism. Other men had their difficulties; he had his beggar. Now and then it seemed odd to the bishop that he had ever thought of the beggars on the steps as a vague and indistinguishable heap of misery and rags. He knew them all by now—blind Marta and Carlo, the dwarf, Giuseppe Double-Face, and Benito, the hunchback. He knew their ways and their thoughts. He knew the hovels where they lived and the bread they ate. For every week or so he would slip from his palace to visit Luigi's chamber.

It was necessary for him to do so, for to him Luigi represented the gravest problem of the soul that he had yet encountered. Was the man even a Christian? The bishop was not sure. He professed religion, he followed the rites of the Church. Yet sometimes when he confessed him, the bishop was appalled. Every sin that could ravage the human heart was there—if not in act, then in desire—and all told so gaily! Sometimes the bishop, angrily, would tax him with wilful exaggeration, and Luigi, with a smile, would admit the charge and ask for still another penance. This left the bishop confused.

Yet through the years there grew up between the two men a singular bond. The bishop may have been heedless, he was not stupid. Very soon he began to realize that there was another Remo than the city he had come to first—a city not of lords and scholars and tradesmen and pious ladies, but a city of the poor and the ignorant, the maimed and the oppressed. For, as Luigi said, when one lay all day on the steps of the cathedral one heard stories, and anyone will talk to a beggar. Some of the stories struck the bishop to the heart. He could hardly believe them at first, yet, when he investigated them, they were true. When he was convinced they were true, he set himself stubbornly to remedy them. He was not always successful—pleasant sinners like the Church to keep its own place. Now and then he discussed his efforts with Luigi, who listened, it seemed to the bishop, with an air of perfect cynicism. His attitude seemed to be that it was all very well for a man like the bishop to concern himself about these things and, if other folk starved and died, it was none of his concern. This irritated the bishop inordinately and made him more determined than ever.

Gradually, he noticed, the composition of his table changed. There were fewer courtiers and scholars; there were more priests from the county, smelling of poverty and chestnut bread. They came in their tattered cassocks, with their big red wrists; at first they were strange and ill at ease at his table. But the bishop was able to talk to them. After all, were they not like the old parish priest that Luigi talked of so often? When the ceremony of his table disturbed them he saw to it that there was less ceremony. Luigi mocked him for this and told him bluntly what his richer clients were saying. The bishop rebuked him for impertinence to his spiritual director and persisted.

It is strange how time flies when the heart is occupied. In no time at all, it seemed to the bishop, he was a middle-aged man with gray at his temples, and Luigi a man in his thirties. That seemed odd to the bishop; he did not know where the time had gone. He thought of it, one morning, with a sense of loss. He had meant to do many things—he was still ambitious. Now, when night came, he was often too tired to think. The troubles of many people weighed upon his heart—the troubles of the peasants in the hills, who lived from hand to mouth; the troubles of Domenico, the shoemaker, who had too pretty a daughter; the troubles of Tessa, the flower-seller, whose son was a thief. When he had first come to Remo, he had not had all these troubles. He picked up a letter on his desk—a letter that had lain there for days—and, having read it, sat staring.

The dreams of his youth came back to him, doubly hot, doubly dear. While he idled his life away in Remo, his brother and his friends had been busy. They had not forgotten him, after all. Cardinal Malaverni, the great, sage statesman whose hand was ever upon the strings of policy, meant to pass by Remo on his way to Rome. The bishop knew the cardinal—once, long ago, he had

THE BISHOP'S BEGGAR

been one of the cardinal's promising young men. There was a letter also from the bishop's brother, the lord—a letter that hinted of grave and important matters. The bishop almost sobbed when he thought how long both letters had lain unanswered. He summoned his secretary and set himself about an unaccustomed bustle of preparation.

It often occurred to him, sorrowfully, within the next few days, how foolish it was to leave one's letters unopened. The preparations went forward for the cardinal's visit, yet it seemed to him that they went forward ill, though he could not put his finger upon the cause. Somehow he had got out of the way of the world where such things go forward smoothly; he was more used to his country priests than to entertaining distinguished visitors. Nevertheless, he botched together a few Latin verses, saw to it that the hangings in the guestchambers were cleaned and mended, drove his choirmaster nearly frantic, and got in the way of his servants. He noticed that these were no longer afraid of him, but treated him with tolerant patience, more like a friend than a master, and this irked him oddly. What irked him even more, perhaps, was Luigi's shameless and undisguised self-interest in the whole affair.

"Ah, your lordship, we've waited a long time for this," he said, "but it's come at last. And everyone knows that a great man like Cardinal Malaverni doesn't come to a place like Remo for nothing. So all we have to do is to play our cards well, and then, when we move on, as we doubtless shall—well, I, for one, won't be sorry."

"Move on?" said the bishop, astonished.

The beggar yawned.

"But how else?" he said. "I have been the bishop's beggar. When your lordship is made a cardinal I will be the cardinal's beggar. The post will entail new responsibilities, no doubt, but I have confidence in my abilities. Perhaps I shall even employ an assistant for my actual begging—after all, it is often drafty on the steps of the cathedral."

The bishop turned and left him without a word. Yet what Luigi had said caused trouble and disquiet in his heart, for he knew that Luigi often had news of things to come before even the Count of Remo had an inkling of them.

At last the great day of the cardinal's visit came.

Like all such days, it passed as a dream passes, with heat and ceremony and worry about small things. The Latin verses of welcome were unexpectedly well read; on the other hand, the choristers were nervous and did not sing their best. Two gentlemen of the cardinal's suite had to be lodged over the stables, much to the bishop's distress, and the crayfish for dinner had been served without sauce.

The bishop hoped that all had gone well, but he did not know. As he sat, at last, alone with his old friend in his study that overlooked the garden, he felt at once wrought-up and drowsy.

This should be the real pleasure of the day, to sit with his old friend in the cool of the evening and renew contact with the great world. But the bishop was used to country hours by now, and the feast had broken up late. He should be listening to the cardinal with the greatest attention, and yet those accursed crayfish kept coming into his mind.

"Well, Gianfrancesco," said the cardinal, sipping delicately at his wine, "you have given your old tutor a most charming welcome. Your wine, your people, your guests—it reminds me somehow of one of those fine Virgilian Eclogues we used to parse together. *'Tityre, tu patulae recubans—'*"

"The choir," said the bishop—"the choir usually is—"

"Why, they sang very well!" said the cardinal. "And what good, honest, plain-spoken priests you have in your charge!" He shook his head sadly. "I fear that we do not always get their like in Rome. And yet, each man to his task."

"They have a hard charge in these hills," said the bishop wearily. "It was a great honor for them to see Your Eminence."

"Oh, honor!" said the cardinal. "To see an old man with the gout—yes, I have the gout these days, Gianfrancesco—I fear we both are not so young as we were." He leaned forward and regarded the bishop attentively. "You, too, have altered, my old friend," he said softly.

"Your Eminence means that I have rusticated," said the bishop a trifle bitterly. "Well, it is true."

"Oh, not rusticated," said the cardinal, with a charming gesture. "Not at all. But there has been a change—a perceptible one —from the Gianfrancesco I knew." He took a walnut and began to crack it. "That Gianfrancesco was a charming and able young man," he said. "Yet I doubt if he would have made the Count of his city do penance in his shirt, for his sins, before the doors of his cathedral!"

"I can explain about that," said the bishop hurriedly. "The shirt was a silk one and the weather by no means inclement. Moreover, the Count's new tax would have ruined my poor. It is true we have not always seen eye to eye since then, yet I think he respects me more than he did before."

"That is just what I said to your brother, Piero," said the cardinal comfortably. "I said, 'You are wrong to be perturbed about this, Piero; it will have a good effect.' Yes, even as regards the beggar."

"My beggar?" said the bishop, and sighed.

"Oh, you know how small things get about," said the cardinal. "Some small thing is seized upon; it even travels to Rome. The bishop's beggar—the beggars' bishop—the bishop who humbles his soul to protect the poor."

"But it was not like that at all," said the bishop. "I—"

The cardinal waved him aside. "Do not hide your good works beneath a bushel, Gianfrancesco," he said. "The Church herself has need of them. These are troubled times we live in. The French king may march any day. There is heresy and dissension abroad. You have no idea what difficult days may lie ahead." He watched the bishop intently. "Our Holy Father leans much upon my unworthy shoulder," he said, "and our Holy Father is beginning to age."

"That is sore news for us all," said the bishop.

"Sore indeed," said the cardinal. "And yet, one must face realities. Should our Holy Father die, it will be necessary for those of us who truly love the Church to stand together—more especially in the college of cardinals." He paused and with a silver nutpick extracted the last meat from the walnut. "I believe that our Holy Father is disposed to reward your own labors with the see of Albano," he said.

"The see of Albano?" said the bishop as if in a dream, for, as all men knew, Albano was an old and famous diocese outside the walls of Rome, and he who was bishop of Albano wore a cardinal's hat.

"It might have a most excellent effect," said the cardinal. "I myself think it might. We have clever and able men who are sons of the Church. Indeed. And yet, just at this moment, with both the French and the German parties so active—well, there is perhaps need for another sort of man—at least as regards the people." He smiled delightfully. "You would be very close to me as cardinal-bishop of Albano—very close to us all," he said. "I should lean upon you, Gianfrancesco."

"There is nought that would please me more!" cried the bishop, like a boy. He thought for a moment of the power and the glory, of the great, crowded streets of Rome and the Church that humbles kings. "I would have to leave Remo," he said.

"Well, yes, naturally, it would mean your having to leave Remo," said the cardinal. "Your new duties would demand it."

"That would be hard," said the bishop. "I would have to leave Luigi and all my people." He thought of them suddenly—the lame, the halt, the oppressed.

"Your people, perhaps," said the cardinal, "but certainly not Luigi. He should come with you by all means, as a living example."

"Oh, no, no, that would never do," said the bishop. "Your Eminence does not understand. Luigi is difficult enough as a bishop's beggar. As a cardinal's beggar, he would be overweening. You have no idea how overweening he would be."

The cardinal regarded him with a puzzled stare.

"Am I dreaming, Gianfrancesco?" he said. "Or are you declining the see of Albano and a cardinal's hat for no more reason than that you are attached to a beggar?"

"Oh, no, no, no!" cried the bishop, in an agony. "I am not in the least attached to him—he is my cross and my thorn. But you see, it would be so bad for him if I were to be made a cardinal. I tremble to think what would happen to his soul. And then there are all his companions—Giuseppe, the Hook, is dead, but there is still blind Marta, and Benito, the hunchback, and the new ones. No, I must stay in Remo."

The cardinal smiled—a smile of exasperation. "I think you have forgotten something, Gianfrancesco," he said. "I think you have forgotten that obedience is the first law of the Church."

"I am five times obedient," said the bishop. "Let our Holy

Father do with me as he wills. Let him send me as a missionary to savages; let him strip me of my bishopric and set me to work in the hills. I shall be content. But while I have been given Remo, I have work to do in Remo. I did not expect it to be so when I first came here," he said in a low voice, "and yet, somehow, I find that it is so."

The cardinal said nothing at all for a long time.

Then at last he rose, and, pressing the bishop's hand, he retired to his own quarters. The bishop hoped that he was comfortable in them, though it occurred to him, in the uneasy sleep before dawn, that the chimney smoked.

Next morning the cardinal departed on his journey toward Rome without speaking of these matters further. The bishop felt sorry to see him go, and yet relieved. He had been very glad to see his old friend again—he told himself that. Yet from the moment of the cardinal's arrival there had been an unfamiliar grayness upon his spirit, and now that grayness was gone. Nevertheless, he knew that he must face Luigi—and that thought was hard for him.

Yet it went well enough, on the whole.

The bishop explained to him, as one explains to a child, that it did not seem as if God had intended him to be a cardinal, only bishop of Remo, and with that Luigi had to be content. Luigi grumbled about it frequently and remarked that if he had known all this in the first place, he might never have accepted the position of bishop's beggar. But he was not any more overweening than before, and with that the bishop had to be satisfied.

Then came the war with the French, and that was hard upon the bishop. He did not like wars, he did not like the thought of his people being killed. Yet, when the Count of Remo fled with most of his soldiery, and the mayor locked himself in his house and stayed there, shaking, there was no one to take over the rule of the town but the bishop. The very beggars in the streets cried out for him; he could not escape the task.

He took it with a heavy heart, under the mocking eyes of Luigi. With Luigi in his cart, he inspected the walls and defenses.

"Well, your lordship has a very pretty problem," said Luigi. "Half a dozen good cannon shot and the city will be taken by storm."

"I thought so, I feared so," said the bishop, sighing. "And yet my people are my people."

"Your lordship might easily compromise with the enemy," said Luigi. "They are angry with the Count, it is true—they thought they had him bought over. Yet it would mean but two score hangings or so, and a tribute, properly assessed."

"I cannot permit my flock to be harried and persecuted," said the bishop.

"Well, if your lordship must die, I will die with your lordship," said Luigi. "Meanwhile, we might set the townsfolk to work on the walls—at least it will give them something to do. And yet, there may be another way."

So it was done, and the bishop worked day and night, enheartening and encouraging his people. For once, all Remo was one, and the spirit and will that burned within it were the bishop's. Yet it seemed no time at all before the French sat down before Remo.

They sent a trumpet and a flag to demand the surrender of the city. The bishop received the young officer who came with the trumpet—a dark-faced man he was, with a humorous twist to his mouth. The bishop even took him on a tour of the walls, which seemed to surprise him a little.

"You are well defended," said the Frenchman politely.

"Oh, no, we are very ill defended," said the bishop. "My good children have been trying to strengthen the wall with sandbags, but, as you perceive, it is rotten and needs rebuilding. Moreover, the Count was badly cheated on his powder. I must speak to him of it sometime, for hardly a gun we have is fit to fire."

The Frenchman's astonishment grew. "I do not wish to doubt your lordship's word," he said, "but if those things are so, how does your lordship propose to defend Remo?"

"By the will of God," said the bishop very simply. "I do not wish my poor people killed; neither do I wish them oppressed. If needs must, I shall die in their stead, but they shall go scatheless. Ere you hang one man of Remo, I shall take the noose from around his neck and put it around my own."

"Your lordship makes things very difficult," said the Frenchman, thoughtfully. "My King has no desire to attack the Church—

and, indeed, the walls of Remo seem stronger than your lordship reckons."

Then he was conscious of a plucking at his sleeve. It was Luigi, the beggar, in his little cart, who, by signs and grimaces, seemed to wish the Frenchman to follow him.

"What is it, Luigi?" said the bishop wearily. "Ah, yes, you wish to show our friend the room where we store the powder. Very well. Then he may see how little we have."

When the Frenchman rejoined the bishop, he was wiping sweat from his forehead, and his face was white. The bishop pressed him to stay for a glass of wine, but he said he must return to his camp, and departed, muttering something incoherent about it being indeed the will of God that defended Remo.

When he had gone, the bishop looked severely upon Luigi. "Luigi," he said sternly, "I fear you have been up to some of your tricks."

"How your lordship mistakes me," said the beggar. "It is true I showed him three of my fellow-beggars—and they did not seem to him in the best of health. But I did not say they had plague; I let him draw his own conclusions. It took me four days to school them in their parts, but that I did not tell him either."

"That was hardly honest, Luigi," said the bishop. "We know there is no plague in the town."

"We know also that our walls are rotten," said Luigi, "but the French will not believe that, either. Men of war are extremely suspicious—it is their weakness. We shall wait and see."

They waited and saw, for that night a council of war was held in the French camp and the officer who had come with the trumpet reported (a) that Remo was held in great force and strongly defended; (b) that its bishop was resolved to die in the breach, and (c) that there was plague in the city. Taking all these factors into account, the French wisely decided, after some forty-eight hours' delay, to strike camp and fall back on their main army—which they did just in time to take part in the historic defeat of the whole French invasion a week later. This defeat sealed for all time the heroic defense of Remo; for, had the part of the French army occupied before Remo rejoined their main body before, the historic defeat might have been as historic a victory for the French. As it was, all Italy rang with the name of the bishop of Remo.

But of all this the bishop knew nothing, for his beggar, Luigi, was dying.

As the French moved away they had loosed off a few cannon shot, more in irritation than for any real military purpose. However, one of the cannon shot, heedlessly aimed, struck the steps of the cathedral, and you may still see the scars. It also struck the cart wherein Luigi lay directing his beggars at one task of defense or another. When the bishop first heard that his beggar was hurt, he went to him at once. But there was little that a man could do but wait, and the waiting was long. It was not until seven weeks later that Luigi passed from this earth. He endured, indeed, till the messengers came from Rome.

After they had talked with the bishop, the bishop went alone to his cathedral and prayed. Then he went to see Luigi.

"Well?" said the dying man eagerly, staring at him with limpid eyes.

"His Holiness has been graciously pleased to make of me the first archbishop of Remo, placing under my staff, as well, the dioceses of Ugri and Soneto," said the bishop slowly. "But I have the news from Cardinal Malaverni, and I may remain here till I die." He stared at Luigi. "I do not understand," he said.

"It is well done. You have stood by the poor in their poverty and the wretched in their hour of trial," said Luigi, and for once there was no trace of mockery in his voice.

"I do not understand. I do not understand at all," said the bishop again. "And yet I think you deserve recompense rather than I, Luigi."

"No," said Luigi, "that I do not."

The bishop passed his hand across his brow. "I am not a fool," he said. "It was well done, to humble my spirit. And yet, why did you do so, Luigi?"

"Why, that was my great sin," said Luigi. "I have confessed many vain and imaginary sins, but never the real one till now." He paused, as if the words hurt him. "When your lordship's coach rolled over my legs, I was very bitter," he said. "A poor man has little. To lose that little—to lose the air on the hills and the springing step, to lie like a log forever because a bishop's coachman was careless—that made me very bitter. I had rather your lordship had driven over me again than taken me back to your palace and treated me with kindness. I hated your lordship for your indifferent kindness—I hated you for everything."

"Did you so, Luigi?" said the bishop.

"Yes," said Luigi. "And I could see that your lordship hated me—or, if not hated, loathed, like a crippled dog that one must be kind to without liking. So I set myself out to tease and torment your lordship—at first by being your beggar, then in other ways. I could not believe in goodness; I could not believe there would not come a moment when your lordship would turn upon me and drive me forth."

He paused a moment and wiped his mouth with a cloth.

"Yes, I could not believe that at all," he said. "But you were not to be broken, Gianfrancesco, my brother. The evil I showed you daily was like a knife in your heart and a burden on your back, but you bore the knife and the burden. I took delight in showing you how ill things went in your city—how, below the fair surface, there was misery and pain. And had you once turned aside from that misery and pain, I would have been satisfied, for then, bishop or no bishop, you would have lost your soul. Was that evil of me, Gianfrancesco?"

"Very evil in intent," said the bishop steadily, "for, while it is permitted to be tempted, it is evil to tempt. And yet proceed."

"Well," said Luigi, with a sudden and childlike stare, "it did not work. The more I tried to make you a bad man, the better man you became. You would not do what was ill; you would not depart from your poor, once you had known them—not even for a red hat or a count's favor. You would not do ill at all. So now we have defended Remo, the two of us, and I am dying." He stirred uneasily in his bed. "It is just as well," he said, with a trace of his old mockery. "I told my uncle I would live to be a cardinal's beggar, but I am not sure that I would have liked it. I have been the bishop's beggar so long. And yet, from the first I have loved you also, Gianfrancesco. Will you give me your blessing now, on me and my work—the blessing you denied me once?"

The bishop's face was wrung. Yet he lifted his hand and absolved and blessed Luigi. He blessed Luigi and his work in the name of the Father and of the Son and of the Holy Ghost. When that had been done, a smile appeared on Luigi's face.

"A very fine blessing," he said. "I must tell that to the Hook when I see him; he will be envious. I wonder is it drafty on the steps of heaven? A very fine blessing, your lordship . . . ten . . . scudi . . . for . . . Luigi." And with that his jaw dropped, and it was over. But the bishop knelt beside the bed with streaming eyes.

And all that, to be sure, was a long time ago. But they still tell the story in Remo when they show the bishop's tomb. He lies upon it, fairly carven in marble. But carved all around the tomb are a multitude of beggars, lame, halt, and misshapen, yet all praising God. And there are words in Latin which say, "It is not enough to have knowledge—these also are my sheep." Of the tomb of Luigi, the beggar—that no man knows. They say it is beside the bishop's but, in one war or another, it was destroyed and there is no trace of it now. Yet Luigi was an arrogant spirit; perhaps he would have liked that best.

THE CURFEW TOLLS

"It is not enough to be the possessor of genius—the time and the man must conjoin. An Alexander the Great, born into an age of profound peace, might scarce have troubled the world—a Newton, grown up in a thieves' den, might have devised little but a new and ingenious picklock. . . ."

DIVERSIONS OF HISTORICAL THOUGHT BY
JOHN CLEVELAND COTTON.

(The following extracts have been made from the letters of General Sir Charles William Geoffrey Estcourt, C.B., to his sister Harriet, Countess of Stokely, by permission of the Stokely family. Omissions are indicated by triple dots, thus . . .)

St. Philippe-des-Bains, September 3d, 1788.

My Dear Sister: . . . I could wish that my excellent Paris physician had selected some other spot for my convalescence. But he swears by the waters of St. Philip and I swear by him, so I must resign myself to a couple of yawning months ere my constitution mends. Nevertheless, you will get long letters from me, though I fear they may be dull ones. I cannot bring you the gossip of Baden or Aix—except for its baths, St. Philip is but one of a dozen small white towns on this agreeable coast. It has its good inn and its bad inn, its dusty, little square with its dusty, fleabitten beggar, its posting-station and its promenade of scrubby lindens and palms. From the heights one may see Corsica on a clear day, and the Mediterranean is of an unexampled blue. To tell the truth, it is all agreeable enough, and an old Indian campaigner, like myself, should not complain. I am well treated at the Cheval Blanc—am I not an English milord?—and my excellent Gaston looks after me devotedly. But there is a blue-bottle drowsiness about small watering places out of season, and our gallant enemies, the French, know how to bore themselves more exquisitely in their provinces than any nation on earth. Would you think that the daily arrival of the diligence from Toulon would be an excitement? Yet it is to me, I assure you, and to all St. Philip. I walk, I take the waters, I read Ossian, I play piquet with Gaston, and yet I seem to myself but half-alive. . . .

. . . You will smile and say to me, "Dear brother, you have always plumed yourself on being a student of human nature. Is there no society, no character for you to study, even in St. Philippe-des-Bains?" My dear sister, I bend myself earnestly to that end, yet so far with little result. I have talked to my doctor —a good man but unpolished; I have talked to the curé—a good man but dull. I have even attempted the society of the baths, beginning with Monsieur le Marquis de la Percedragon, who has ninety-six quarterings, soiled wristbands, and a gloomy interest in my liver, and ending with Mrs. Macgregor Jenkins, a worthy and red-faced lady whose conversation positively cannonades with dukes and duchesses. But, frankly, I prefer my chair in the garden and my Ossian to any of them, even at the risk of being considered a bear. A witty scoundrel would be the veriest godsend to me, but do such exist in St. Philip? I trow not. As it is, in my weakened condition, I am positively agog when Gaston comes in every morning with his budget of village scandal. A pretty pass to come to, you will say, for a man who has served with Eyre Coote and but for the mutabilities of fortune, not to speak of a most damnable cabal . . . (A long passage dealing with General Estcourt's East Indian services and his personal and unfavorable opinion of Warren Hastings is here omitted from the manuscript.) . . . But, at fifty, a man is either a fool or a philosopher. Nevertheless, unless Gaston provides me with a character to try my wits on, shortly, I shall begin to believe that they too have deteriorated with Indian suns. . . .

September 21st, 1788.

My Dear Sister: . . . Believe me, there is little soundness in the views of your friend, Lord Martindale. The French monarchy is not to be compared with our own, but King Louis is an excellent and well-beloved prince, and the proposed summoning of the States-General cannot but have the most salutary effect. . . . (Three pages upon French politics and the possibility of cultivating sugar-cane in Southern France are here omitted.) . . . As for news of myself, I continue my yawning course, and feel a decided improvement from the waters. . . . So I shall continue them though the process is slow. . . .

You ask me, I fear a trifle mockingly, how my studies in human nature proceed?

Not so ill, my dear sister—I have, at least, scraped acquaintance with one odd fish, and that, in St. Philip, is a triumph. For some time, from my chair in the promenade, I have observed a pursy little fellow, of my age or thereabouts, stalking up and down between the lindens. His company seems avoided by such notables of the place as Mrs. Macgregor Jenkins and at first I put him down as a retired actor, for there is something a little theatrical in his dress and walk. He wears a wide-brimmed hat of straw, loose nankeen trousers and a quasi-military coat, and takes his waters with as much ceremony as Monsieur le Marquis, though not quite with the same *ton*. I should put him down as a Meridional, for he has the quick, dark eye, the sallow skin, the corpulence and the rodomontish airs that mark your true son of the Mid, once he has passed his lean and hungry youth.

And yet, there is some sort of unsuccessful oddity about him, which sets him off from your successful bourgeois. I cannot put my finger on it yet, but it interests me.

At any rate, I was sitting in my accustomed chair, reading

Ossian, this morning, as he made his solitary rounds of the promenade. Doubtless I was more than usually absorbed in my author, for I must have pronounced some lines aloud as he passed. He gave me a quick glance at the time, but nothing more. But on his next round, as he was about to pass me, he hesitated for a moment, stopped, and then, removing his straw hat, saluted me very civilly.

"Monsieur will pardon me," he said, with a dumpy hauteur, "but surely monsieur is English? And surely the lines that monsieur just repeated are from the great poet, Ossian?"

I admitted both charges, with a smile, and he bowed again.

"Monsieur will excuse the interruption," he said, "but I myself have long admired the poetry of Ossian"—and with that he continued my quotation to the end of the passage, in very fair English, too, though with a strong accent. I complimented him, of course, effusively—after all, it is not every day that one runs across a fellow-admirer of Ossian on the promenade of a small French watering place—and after that, he sat down in the chair beside me and we fell into talk. He seems, astonishingly for a Frenchman, to have an excellent acquaintance with our English poets—perhaps he has been a tutor in some English family. I did not press him with questions on this first encounter, though I noted that he spoke French with a slight accent also, which seems odd.

There is something a little rascally about him, to tell you the truth, though his conversation with me was both forceful and elevated. An ill man, too, and a disappointed one, or I miss my mark, yet his eyes, when he talks, are strangely animating. I fancy I would not care to meet him in a *guet-apens,* and yet, he may be the most harmless of broken pedagogues. We took a glass of waters together, to the great disgust of Mrs. Macgregor Jenkins, who ostentatiously drew her skirts aside. She let me know, afterward, in so many words, that my acquaintance was a noted bandit, though, when pressed, she could give no better reason than that he lives a little removed from the town, that "nobody knows where he comes from" and that his wife is "no better than she should be," whatever that portentous phrase entails. Well, one would hardly call him a gentleman, even by Mrs. Macgregor's somewhat easy standards, but he has given me better conversation than I have had in a month—and if he is a bandit, we might discuss thuggee together. But I hope for nothing so stimulating, though I must question Gaston about him. . . .

October 11th.

. . . But Gaston could tell me little, except that my acquaintance comes from Sardinia or some such island originally, has served in the French army and is popularly supposed to possess the evil eye. About Madame he hinted that he could tell me a great deal, but I did not labor the point. After all, if my friend has been c-ck-ld-d—do not blush, my dear sister!—that, too, is the portion of a philosopher, and I find his wide range of conversation much more palatable than Mrs. Macgregor Jenkins' rewarmed London gossip. Nor has he tried to borrow money from me yet, something which, I am frank to say, I expected and was prepared to refuse. . . .

November 20th.

. . . Triumph! My character is found—and a character of the first water, I assure you! I have dined with him in his house, and a very bad dinner it was. Madame is not a good housekeeper, whatever else she may be. And what she has been, one can see at a glance—she has all the little faded coquetries of the garrison coquette. Good-tempered, of course, as such women often are, and must have been pretty in her best days, though with shocking bad teeth. I suspect her of a touch of the tarbrush, though there I may be wrong. No doubt she caught my friend young— I have seen the same thing happen in India often enough—the experienced woman and the youngster fresh from England. Well, 'tis an old story—an old one with him, too—and no doubt Madame has her charms, though she is obviously one reason why he has not risen.

After dinner, Madame departed, not very willingly, and he took me into his study for a chat. He had even procured a bottle of port, saying he knew the Englishman's taste for it, and while it was hardly the right Cockburn, I felt touched by the attention. The man is desperately lonely—one reads that in his big eyes. He is also desperately proud, with the quick, touchy sensitiveness of the failure, and I quite exerted myself to draw him out.

And indeed, the effort repaid me. His own story is simple enough. He is neither bandit nor pedagogue, but, like myself, a broken soldier—a major of the French Royal Artillery, retired on half pay for some years. I think it creditable of him to have reached so respectable a rank, for he is of foreign birth—Sardinian, I think I told you—and the French service is by no means as partial to foreigners as they were in the days of the first Irish Brigade. Moreover, one simply does not rise in that service, unless one is a gentleman of quarterings, and that he could hardly claim. But the passion of his life has been India, and that is what interests me. And, 'pon my honor, he was rather astonishing about it.

As soon as, by a lucky chance, I hit upon the subject, his eyes lit up and his sickness dropped away. Pretty soon he began to take maps from a cabinet in the wall and ply me with questions about my own small experiences. And very soon indeed, I am abashed to state, I found myself stumbling in my answers. It was all book knowledge on his part, of course, but where the devil he could have got some of it, I do not know. Indeed, he would even correct me, now and then, as cool as you please. "Eight twelve pounders, I think, on the north wall of the old fortifications of Madras—" and the deuce of it is, he would be right. Finally, I could contain myself no longer.

"But, major, this is incredible," I said. "I have served twenty years with John Company and thought that I had some knowledge. But one would say you had fought over every inch of Bengal!"

He gave me a quick look, almost of anger, and began to roll up his maps.

"So I have, in my mind," he said, shortly, "but, as my superiors have often informed me, my hobby is a tedious one."

"It is not tedious to me," I said boldly. "Indeed, I have often marveled at your government's neglect of their opportunities in India. True, the issue is settled now—"

"It is by no means settled," he said, interrupting me rudely. I stared at him.

"It was settled, I believe, by Baron Clive, at a spot named Plassey," I said frigidly. "And afterward, by my own old general, Eyre Coote, at another spot named Wandewash."

"Oh, yes—yes—yes," he said impatiently, "I grant you Clive—

Clive was a genius and met the fate of geniuses. He steals an empire for you, and your virtuous English Parliament holds up its hands in horror because he steals a few lakhs of rupees for himself as well. So he blows out his brains in disgrace—you inexplicable English!—and you lose your genius. A great pity. I would not have treated Clive so. But then, if I had been Milord Clive, I would not have blown out my brains."

"And what would you have done, had you been Clive?" I said, for the man's calm, staring conceit amused me.

His eyes were dangerous for a moment and I saw why the worthy Mrs. Macgregor Jenkins had called him a bandit.

"Oh," he said coolly, "I would have sent a file of grenadiers to your English Parliament and told it to hold its tongue. As Cromwell did. Now there was a man. But your Clive—faugh!—he had the ball at his feet and he refused to kick it. I withdraw the word genius. He was a nincompoop. At the least, he might have made himself a rajah."

This was a little too much, as you may imagine. "General Clive had his faults," I said icily, "but he was a true Briton and a patriot."

"He was a fool," said my puffy little major, flatly, his lower lip stuck out. "As big a fool as Dupleix, and that is saying much. Oh, some military skill, some talent for organization, yes. But a genius would have brushed him into the sea! It was possible to hold Arcot, it was possible to win Plassey—look!" and, with that, he ripped another map from his cabinet and began to expound to me eagerly exactly what he would have done in command of the French forces in India, in 1757, when he must have been but a lad in his twenties. He thumped the paper, he strewed corks along the table for his troops—corks taken from a supply in a tin box, so it must be an old game with him. And, as I listened, my irritation faded, for the man's monomania was obvious. Nor was it, to tell the truth, an ill-designed plan of campaign, for corks on a map. Of course these things are different, in the field.

I could say, with honesty, that his plan had features of novelty, and he gulped the words down hungrily—he has a great appetite for flattery.

"Yes, yes," he said. "That is how it should be done—the thickest skull can see it. And, ill as I am, with a fleet and ten thousand picked men—" He dreamed, obviously, the sweat of his exertions on his waxy face—it was absurd and yet touching to see him dream.

"You would find a certain amount of opposition," I said, in an amused voice.

"Oh, yes, yes," he said quickly, "I do not underrate the English. Excellent horse, solid foot. But no true knowledge of cannon, and I am a gunner—"

I hated to bring him down to earth and yet I felt that I must.

"Of course, major," I said, "you have had great experience in the field."

He looked at me for a moment, his arrogance quite unshaken.

"I have had very little," he said, quietly, "but one knows how the thing should be done or one does not know. And that is enough."

He stared at me for an instant with his big eyes. A little mad, of course. And yet I found myself saying, "But surely, major—what happened?"

"Why," he said, still quietly, "what happens to folk who have naught but their brains to sell? I staked my all on India when I was young—I thought that my star shone over it. I ate dirty puddings—*corpo di Baccho!*—to get there—I was no De Rohan or Soubise to win the king's favor! And I reached there indeed, in my youth, just in time to be included in the surrender of Pondicherry." He laughed, rather terribly, and sipped at his glass.

"You English were very courteous captors," he said. "But I was not released till the Seven Years War had ended—that was in '63. Who asks for the special exchange of an unknown artillery lieutenant? And then ten years odd of garrison duty at Mauritius. It was there that I met Madame—she is a Creole. A pleasant spot, Mauritius. We used to fire the cannon at the sea birds when we had enough ammunition for target practice," and he chuckled drearily. "By then I was thirty-seven. They had to make me a captain—they even brought me back to France. To garrison duty. I have been on garrison duty, at Toulon, at Brest, at—" He ticked off the names on his fingers but I did not like his voice.

"But surely," I said, "the American war, though a small affair—there were opportunities—"

"And who did they send?" he said quickly. "Lafayette—Rochambeau—De Grasse—the sprigs of the nobility. Oh, at Lafayette's age, I would have volunteered like Lafayette. But one should be successful in youth—after that, the spring is broken. And when one is over forty, one has responsibilities. I have a large family, you see, though not of my own begetting," and he chuckled as if at a secret joke. "Oh, I wrote the Continental Congress," he said reflectively, "but they preferred a dolt like Von Steuben. A good dolt, an honest dolt, but there you have it. I also wrote your British War Office," he said in an even voice. "I must show you that plan of campaign—sometime—they could have crushed General Washington with it in three weeks."

I stared at him, a little appalled.

"For an officer who has taken his king's shilling to send to an enemy nation a plan for crushing his own country's ally," I said, stiffly—"well, in England, we would call that treason."

"And what is treason?" he said lightly. "If we call it unsuccessful ambition we shall be nearer the truth." He looked at me, keenly. "You are shocked, General Estcourt," he said. "I am sorry for that. But have you never known the curse"—and his voice vibrated—"the curse of not being employed when you should be employed? The curse of being a hammer with no nail to drive? The curse—the curse of sitting in a dusty garrison town with dreams that would split the brain of a Caesar, and no room on earth for those dreams?"

"Yes," I said, unwillingly, for there was something in him that demanded the truth, "I have known that."

"Then you know hells undreamed of by the Christian," he said, with a sigh, "and if I committed treason—well, I have been punished for it. I might have been a brigadier, otherwise—I had Choiseul's ear for a few weeks, after great labor. As it is, I am here on half pay, and there will not be another war in my time. Moreover, M. de Ségur has proclaimed that all officers now must show sixteen quarterings. Well, I wish them joy of those officers, in the next conflict. Meanwhile, I have my corks, my maps and my family ailment." He smiled and tapped his side. "It killed my father at thirty-nine—it has not treated me quite so ill, but it will come for me soon enough."

And indeed, when I looked at him, I could well believe it, for the light had gone from his eyes and his cheeks were flabby. We chatted a little on indifferent subjects after that, then I left him, wondering whether to pursue the acquaintance. He is indubitably a character, but some of his speeches leave a taste in my mouth. Yet he can be greatly attractive—even now, with his mountainous failure like a cloak upon him. And yet why should I call it mountainous? His conceit is mountainous enough, but what else could he have expected of his career? Yet I wish I could forget his eyes. . . . To tell the truth, he puzzles me and I mean to get to the bottom of him. . . .

February 12th, 1789.

. . . I have another sidelight on the character of my friend, the major. As I told you, I was half of a mind to break off the acquaintance entirely, but he came up to me so civilly, the following day, that I could find no excuse. And since then, he has made me no embarrassingly treasonable confidences, though whenever we discuss the art of war, his arrogance is unbelievable. He even informed me, the other day, that while Frederick of Prussia was a fair general, his tactics might have been improved upon. I merely laughed and turned the question. Now and then I play a war game with him, with his corks and maps, and when I let him win, he is as pleased as a child. . . . His illness increases visibly, despite the waters, and he shows an eagerness for my company which I cannot but find touching. . . . After all, he is a man of intelligence, and the company he has had to keep must have galled him at times. . . .

Now and then I amuse myself by speculating what might have happened to him, had he chosen some other profession than that of arms. He has, as I have told you, certain gifts of the actor, yet his stature and figure must have debarred him from tragic parts, while he certainly does not possess the humors of the comedian. Perhaps his best choice would have been the Romish church, for there, the veriest fisherman may hope, at least, to succeed to the keys of St. Peter. . . . And yet, Heaven knows, he would have made a very bad priest! . . .

But, to my tale. I had missed him from our accustomed walks for some days and went to his house—St. Helen's it is called; we live in a pother of saints' names hereabouts—one evening to inquire. I did not hear the quarreling voices till the tousle-haired servant had admitted me and then it was too late to retreat. Then my friend bounced down the corridor, his sallow face bored and angry.

"Ah, General Estcourt!" he said, with a complete change of expression as soon as he saw me. "What fortune! I was hoping you would pay us a call—I wish to introduce you to my family!"

He had told me previously of his pair of stepchildren by Madame's first marriage, and I must confess I felt curious to see them. But it was not of them he spoke, as I soon gathered.

"Yes," he said. "My brothers and sisters, or most of them, are here for a family council. You come in the nick of time!" He pinched my arm and his face glowed with the malicious naïveté of a child. "They do not believe that I really know an English general—it will be a great blow to them!" he whispered as we passed down the corridor. "Ah, if you had only worn your uniform and your Garters! But one cannot have everything in life!"

Well, my dear sister, what a group, when we entered the salon! It is a small room, tawdrily furnished in the worst French taste, with a jumble of Madame's femininities and souvenirs from the Island of Mauritius, and they were all sitting about in the French after-dinner fashion, drinking tisane and quarreling. And, indeed, had the room been as long as the nave of St. Peter's, it would yet have seemed too small for such a crew! An old mother, straight as a ramrod and as forbidding, with the burning eyes and the bitter dignity one sees on the faces of certain Italian peasants— you could see that they were all a little afraid of her except my friend, and he, I must say, treated her with a filial courtesy that was greatly to his credit. Two sisters, one fattish, swarthy and spiteful, the other with the wreck of great beauty and the evident marks of a certain profession on her shabby-fine *toilette* and her pinkened cheeks. An innkeeper brother-in-law called Buras or Durat, with a jowlish, heavily handsome face and the manners of a cavalry sergeant—he is married to the spiteful sister. And two brothers, one sheep-like, one fox-like, yet both bearing a certain resemblance to my friend.

The sheep-like brother is at least respectable, I gathered—a provincial lawyer in a small way of business whose great pride is that he has actually appeared before the Court of Appeals at Marseilles. The other, the fox-like one, makes his living more

THE CURFEW TOLLS

dubiously—he seems the sort of fellow who orates windily in taprooms about the Rights of Man, and other nonsense of M. Rousseau's. I would certainly not trust him with my watch, though he is trying to get himself elected to the States-General. And, as regards family concord, it was obvious at first glance that not one of them trusted the others. And yet, that is not all of the tribe. There are, if you will believe me, two other brothers living, and this family council was called to deal with the affairs of the next-to-youngest, who seems, even in this mélange, to be a black sheep.

I can assure you, my head swam, and when my friend introduced me, proudly, as a Knight of the Garters, I did not even bother to contradict him. For they admitted me to their intimate circle at once—there was no doubt about that. Only the old lady remained aloof, saying little and sipping her camomile tea as if it were the blood of her enemies. But, one by one, the others related to me, with an unasked-for frankness, the most intimate and scandalous details of their brothers' and sisters' lives. They seemed united only on two points, jealously of my friend, the major, because he is his mother's favorite, and dislike of Madame Josephine because she gives herself airs. Except for the haggard beauty—I must say, that, while her remarks anent her sister-in-law were not such as I would care to repeat, she seemed genuinely fond of her brother, the major, and expounded his virtues to me through an overpowering cloud of scent.

It was like being in a nest of Italian smugglers, or a den of quarrelsome foxes, for they all talked, or rather barked at once, even the brother-in-law, and only Madame Mère could bring silence among them. And yet, my friend enjoyed it. It was obvious he showed them off before me as he might have displayed the tricks of a set of performing animals. And yet with a certain fondness, too—that is the inexplicable part of it. I do not know which sentiment was upmost in my mind—respect for this family feeling or pity for his being burdened with such a clan.

For though not the eldest, he is the strongest among them, and they know it. They rebel, but he rules their family conclaves like a petty despot. I could have laughed at the farce of it, and yet, it was nearer tears. For here, at least, my friend was a personage.

I got away as soon as I could, despite some pressing looks from the haggard beauty. My friend accompanied me to the door.

"Well, well," he said, chuckling and rubbing his hands, "I am infinitely obliged to you, general. They will not forget this in a hurry. Before you entered, Joseph"—Joseph is the sheep-like one—"was boasting about his acquaintance with a *sous-intendant*, but an English general, bah! Joseph will have green eyes for a fortnight!" And he rubbed his hands again in a perfect paroxysm of delight.

It was too childlike to make me angry. "I am glad, of course, to have been of any service," I said.

"Oh, you have been a great service," he said. "They will not plague my poor Josie for at least half an hour. Ah, this is a bad business of Louis'—a bad business!"—Louis is the black sheep—"but we will patch it up somehow. Hortense is worth three of him—he must go back to Hortense!"

"You have a numerous family, major," I said, for want of something better to say.

"Oh, yes," he said, cheerfully. "Pretty numerous—I am sorry you could not meet the others. Though Louis is a fool—I pampered him in his youth. Well! He was a baby—and Jerome a mule. Still, we haven't done so badly for ourselves; not badly. Joseph makes a go of his law practice—there are fools enough in the world to be impressed by Joseph—and if Lucien gets to the States-General, you may trust Lucien to feather his nest! And there are the grandchildren, and a little money—not much," he said, quickly. "They mustn't expect that from me. But it's a step up from where we started—if papa had lived, he wouldn't have been so ill-pleased. Poor Elisa's gone, but the rest of us have stuck together, and, while we may seem a little rough, to strangers, our hearts are in the right place. When I was a boy," and he chuckled again, "I had other ambitions for them. I thought, with luck on my side, I could make them all kings and queens. Funny, isn't it, to think of a numskull like Joseph as a king! Well, that was the boy of it. But, even so, they'd all be eating chestnuts back on the island without me, and that's something."

He said it rather defiantly, and I did not know which to marvel at most—his preposterous pride in the group or his cool contempt of them. So I said nothing but shook his hand instead. I could not help doing the latter. For surely, if anyone started in life with a millstone about his neck . . . and yet they are none of them ordinary people. . . .

March 13th, 1789.

. . . My friend's complaint has taken a turn for the worse and it is I who pay him visits now. It is the act of a Christian to do so and, to tell the truth, I have become oddly attached to him, though I can give no just reason for the attachment. He makes a bad patient, by the way, and is often abominably rude to both myself and Madame, who nurses him devotedly though unskillfully. I told him yesterday that I could have no more of it and he looked at me with his strangely luminous eyes. "So," he said, "even the English desert the dying." . . . Well, I stayed; after that, what else might a gentleman do? . . . Yet I cannot feel that he bears me any real affection—he exerts himself to charm, on occasion, but one feels he is playing a game . . . yes, even upon his deathbed, he plays a game . . . a complex character. . . .

April 28th, 1789.

. . . My friend the major's malady approaches its term—the last few days find him fearfully enfeebled. He knows that the end draws nigh; indeed he speaks of it often, with remarkable calmness. I had thought it might turn his mind toward religion, but while he has accepted the ministrations of his Church, I fear it is without the sincere repentance of a Christian. When the priest had left him, yesterday, he summoned me, remarking, "Well, all that is over with," rather more in the tone of a man who has just reserved a place in a coach than one who will shortly stand before his Maker.

"It does no harm," he said, reflectively. "And, after all, it might be true. Why not?" and he chuckled in a way that repelled me. Then he asked me to read to him—not the Bible, as I had expected, but some verses of the poet Gray. He listened attentively, and when I came to the passage, "Hands that the rod of empire might have swayed," and its successor, "Some mute inglorious Milton here may rest," he asked me to repeat them. When I had done so, he said, "Yes, yes. That is true, very true. I did not think so in boyhood—I thought genius must force its own way. But your poet is right about it."

I found this painful, for I had hoped that his illness had brought him to a juster, if less arrogant, estimate of his own abilities.

"Come, major," I said, soothingly, "we cannot all be great men, you know. And you have no need to repine. After all, as you say, you have risen in the world—"

"Risen?" he said, and his eyes flashed. "Risen? Oh, God, that I should die alone with my one companion an Englishman with a soul of suet! Fool, if I had had Alexander's chance, I would have bettered Alexander! And it will come, too, that is the worst of it. Already Europe is shaking with a new birth. If I had been born under the Sun-King, I would be a Marshal of France; if I had been born twenty years ago, I would mold a new Europe with my fists in the next half-dozen years. Why did they put my soul in my body at this infernal time? Do you not understand, imbecile? Is there no one who understands?"

I called Madame at this, as he was obviously delirious, and, after some trouble, we got him quieted.

May 8th, 1789.

. . . My poor friend is gone, and peacefully enough at the last. His death, oddly enough, coincided with the date of the opening of the States-General at Versailles. The last moments of life are always painful for the observer, but his end was as relatively serene as might be hoped for, considering his character. I was watching at one side of the bed and a thunderstorm was raging at the time. No doubt, to his expiring consciousness, the cracks of the thunder sounded like artillery, for, while we were waiting the death-struggle, he suddenly raised himself in the bed and listened intently. His eyes glowed, a beatific expression passed over his features. "The army! Head of the army!" he whispered ecstatically, and, when we caught him, he was lifeless . . . I must say that, while it may not be very Christian, I am glad that death brought him what life could not, and that, in the very article of it, he saw himself at the head of victorious troops. Ah, Fame—delusive spectre . . . (A page of disquisition by General Estcourt on the vanities of human ambition is here omitted.) . . . The face, after death, was composed, with a certain majesty, even

... one could see that he might have been handsome as a youth. ...

May 26th, 1789.

... I shall return to Paris by easy stages and reach Stokely sometime in June. My health is quite restored and all that has kept me here this long has been the difficulty I have met with in attempting to settle my poor friend, the major's affairs. For one thing, he appears to have been originally a native of Corsica, not of Sardinia as I had thought, and while that explains much in his character, it has also given occupation to the lawyers. I have met his rapacious family, individually and in conclave, and, if there are further gray hairs on my head, you may put it down to them. ... However, I have finally assured the major's relict of her legitimate rights in his estate, and that is something—my one ray of comfort in the matter being the behavior of her son by the former marriage, who seems an excellent and virtuous young man. ...

... You will think me a very soft fellow, no doubt, for wasting so much time upon a chance acquaintance who was neither, in our English sense, a gentleman nor a man whose Christian virtues counterbalanced his lack of true breeding. Yet there was a tragedy about him beyond his station, and that verse of Gray's rings in my head. I wish I could forget the expression on his face when he spoke of it. Suppose a genius born in circumstances that made the development of that genius impossible—well, all this is the merest moonshine. ...

... To revert to more practical matters, I discover that the major has left me his military memoirs, papers and commentaries, including his maps. Heaven knows what I shall do with them! I cannot, in courtesy, burn them *sur-le-champ,* and yet they fill two huge packing cases and the cost of transporting them to Stokely will be considerable. Perhaps I will take them to Paris and quietly dispose of them there to some waste-paper merchant. ... In return for his unsought legacy, Madame has consulted me in regard to a stone and epitaph for her late husband, and, knowing that otherwise the family would squabble over the affair for weeks, I have drawn up a design which I hope meets with their approval. It appears that he particularly desired that the epitaph should be writ in English, saying that France had had enough of him, living—a freak of dying vanity for which one must pardon him. However, I have produced the following, which I hope will answer.

Here lies
NAPOLEONE BUONAPARTE
Major of the Royal Artillery
of France.
Born August 15th, 1737
at Ajaccio, Corsica.
Died May 5th, 1789
at St. Philippe-des-Bains
"Rest, perturbed spirit . . ."

. . . I had thought, for some hours, of excerpting the lines of Gray's—the ones that still ring in my head. But, on reflection, though they suit well enough, they yet seem too cruel to the dust.

INTO EGYPT

It had finally been decided to let them go and now, for three days, they had been passing. The dust on the road to the frontier had not settled for three days or nights. But the strictest orders had been given and there were very few incidents. There could easily have been more.

Even the concentration camps had been swept clean, for this thing was to be final. After it, the State could say "How fearless we are—we let even known conspirators depart." It is true that, in the case of those in the concentration camps, there had been a preliminary rectification—a weeding, so to speak. But the news of that would not be officially published for some time and the numbers could always be disputed. If you kill a few people, they remain persons with names and identities, but if you kill in the hundreds, there is simply a number for most of those who read the newspapers. And, once you start arguing about numbers, you begin to wonder if the thing ever happened at all. This too had been foreseen.

In fact, everything had been foreseen—and with great acuteness. There had been the usual diplomatic tension, solved, finally, by the usual firm stand. At the last moment, the other Powers had decided to co-operate. They had done so unwillingly, grudgingly, and with many representations, but they had done so. It was another great victory. And everywhere the trains rolled and the dust rose on the roads, for, at last and at length, the Accursed People were going. Every one of them, man, woman and child, to the third and the fourth generation—every one of them with a drop of that blood in his veins. And this was the end of it all and, by sunset on the third day, the land would know them no more. It was another great victory—perhaps the greatest. There would be a week of celebration after it, with appropriate ceremonies and speeches, and the date would be marked in the new calendar, with the date of the founding of the State and other dates.

Nevertheless, and even with the noteworthy efficiency of which the State was so proud, any mass evacuation is bound to be a complicated and fatiguing affair. The lieutenant stationed at the crossroads found it so—he was young and in the best of health but the strain was beginning to tell on him, though he would never have admitted it. He had been a little nervous at first— a little nervous and exceedingly anxious that everything should go according to plan. After all, it was an important post, the last crossroads before the frontier. A minor road, of course—they'd be busier on the main highways and at the ports of embarkation —but a last crossroads, nevertheless. He couldn't flatter himself it was worth a decoration—the bigwigs would get those. But, all the same, he was expected to evacuate so many thousands—he knew the figures by heart. Easy enough to say one had only to follow the plan! That might do for civilians—an officer was an officer. Would he show himself enough of an officer, would he make a fool of himself in front of his men? Would he even, perhaps, by some horrible, unforeseen mischance, get his road clogged with fleeing humanity till they had to send somebody over from Staff to straighten the tangle out? The thought was appalling.

He could see it happening in his mind—as a boy, he had been imaginative. He could hear the staff officer's words while he stood at attention, eyes front. One's first real command and a black mark on one's record! Yes, even if it was only police work—that didn't matter—a citizen of the State, a member of the Party must be held to an unflinching standard. If one failed to meet that standard there was nothing left in life. His throat had been dry and his movements a little jerky as he made his last dispositions and saw the first black specks begin to straggle toward the crossroads.

He could afford to laugh at that now, if he had had time. He could even afford to remember old Franz, his orderly, trying to put the brandy in his coffee, that first morning. "It's a chilly morning, Lieutenant," but there had been a question in Franz's eyes. He'd refused the brandy, of course, and told Franz off properly, too. The new State did not depend on Dutch courage but on the racial valor of its citizens. And the telling-off had helped—it had made his own voice firmer and given a little fillip of anger to his pulse. But Franz was an old soldier and imperturbable. What was it he had said, later? "The lieutenant must not worry. Civilians are always sheep—it is merely a matter of herding them." An improper remark, of course, to one's lieutenant, but it had helped settle his mind and make it cooler. Yes, an orderly like Franz was worth something, once one learned the knack of keeping him in his place.

Then they had began to come, slowly, stragglingly, not like soldiers. He couldn't remember who had been the first. It was strange but he could not—he had been sure that he would remember. Perhaps a plodding family, with the scared children looking at him—perhaps one of the old men with long beards and burning eyes. But, after three days, they all mixed, the individual faces. As Franz had said, they became civilian sheep—sheep that one must herd and keep moving, keep moving always through day and night, moving on to the frontier. As they went, they wailed. When the wailing grew too loud, one took measures; but, sooner or later it always began again. It would break out down the road, die down as it came toward the post. It seemed to come out of their mouths without their knowledge—the sound of broken wood, of wheat ground between stones. He had tried to stop it completely at first, now he no longer bothered. And yet there were many—a great many—who did not wail.

At first, it had been interesting to see how many different types there were. He had not thought to find such variety among the Accursed People—one had one's own mental picture, reinforced by the pictures in the newspapers. But, seeing them was different. They were not at all like the picture. They were tall and short, plump and lean, black-haired, yellow-haired, red-haired. It was obvious, even under the film of dust, that some had been rich, others poor, some thoughtful, others active. Indeed, it was often hard to tell them, by the looks. But that was not his affair —his affair was to keep them moving. All the same, it gave you a shock, sometimes, at first.

Perhaps the queerest thing was that they all looked so ordinary, so much a part of everyday. That was because one had been used to seeing them—it could be no more than that. But, under the film of dust and heat, one would look at a face. And then one would think, unconsciously, "Why, what is that fellow doing, so far from where he lives? Why, for heaven's sake, is he straggling along this road? He doesn't look happy." Then the mind would resume control and one would remember. But the thought would come, now and then, without orders from the mind.

He had seen very few that he knew. That was natural—he came from the South. He had seen Willi Schneider, to be sure —that had been the second day and it was very dusty. When he was a little boy, very young, he had played in Willi's garden with Willi, in the summers, and, as they had played, there had come to them, through the open window, the ripple of a piano and the clear, rippling flow of Willi's mother's voice. It was not a great voice—not a Brunhild voice—but beautiful in *lieder* and beautifully sure. She had sung at their own house; that was odd to remember. Of course, her husband had not been one of them —a councilor, in fact. Needless to say, that had been long before the discovery that even the faintest trace of that blood tainted. As for Willi and himself, they had been friends—yes, even through the first year or so at school. Both of them had meant to run away and be cowboys, and they had had a secret password. Naturally, things had changed, later on.

For a horrible moment, he had thought that Willi would speak to him—recall the warm air of summer and the smell of linden and those young, unmanly days. But Willi did not. Their eyes met, for an instant, then both had looked away. Willi was helping an old woman along, an old woman who muttered fretfully as she walked, like a cat with sore paws. They were both of them covered with dust and the old woman went slowly. Willi's mother had walked with a quick step and her voice had not been cracked or fretful. After play, she had given them both cream buns, laughing and moving her hands, in a bright green dress. It was not permitted to think further of Willi Schneider.

That was the only real acquaintance but there were other, recognizable faces. There was the woman who had kept the newsstand, the brisk little waiter at the summer hotel, the taxi chauffeur with the squint and the heart specialist. Then there was the former scientist—one could still tell him from his pictures—and the actor one had often seen. That was all that one knew and not all on the same day. That was enough. He had not imagined the taxi chauffeur with a wife and children and that the youngest child should be lame. That had surprised him—surprised him almost as much as seeing the heart specialist walking along the road like any man. It had surprised him, also, to see the scientist led along between two others and to recognize the fact that he was mad.

But that also mixed with the dust—the endless, stifling cloud of the dust, the endless, moving current. The dust got in one's throat and one's eyes—it was hard to cut, even with brandy, from one's throat. It lay on the endless bundles people carried; queer bundles, bulging out at the ends, with here a ticking clock, and there a green bunch of carrots. It lay on the handcarts a few of them pushed—the handcarts bearing the sort of goods that one would snatch, haphazard, from a burning house. It rose and whirled and penetrated—it was never still. At night, slashed by the efficient searchlights that made the night bright as day, it was still a mist above the road. As for sleep—well, one slept when one could, for a couple of hours after midnight, when they too slept, ungracefully, in heaps and clumps by the road. But, except for the first night, he could not even remember Franz pulling his boots off.

His men had been excellent, admirable, indefatigable. That

was, of course, due to the Leader and the State, but still, he would put it in his report. They had kept the stream moving, always. The attitude had been the newly prescribed one—not that of punishment, richly as that was deserved, but of complete aloofness, as if the Accursed People did not even exist. Naturally, now and then, the men had had their fun. One could not blame them for that—some of the incidents had been extremely comic. There had been the old woman with the hen—a comedy character. Of course, she had not been permitted to keep the hen. They should have taken it away from her at the inspection point. But she had looked very funny, holding on to the squawking chicken by the tail feathers, with the tears running down her face.

Yes, the attitude of the men would certainly go in his report. He would devote a special paragraph to the musicians also—they had been indefatigable. They had played the prescribed tunes continually, in spite of the dust and the heat. One would hope that those tunes would sink into the hearts of the Accursed People, to be forever a warning and a memory. Particularly if they happened to know the words. But one could never be sure about people like that.

Staff cars had come four times, the first morning, and once there had been a general. He had felt nervous, when they came, but there had been no complaint. After that, they had let him alone, except for an occasional visit—that must mean they thought him up to his work. Once, even, the road had been almost clear, for a few minutes—he was moving them along faster than they did at the inspection point. The thought had gone to his head for an instant, but he kept cool—and, soon enough, the road had been crowded again.

As regarded casualties—he could not keep the exact figure in his head, but it was a minor one. A couple of heart attacks— one of the man who had been a judge, or so the others said. Unpleasant but valuable to see the life drain out of a face like that. He had made himself watch it—one must harden oneself. They had wanted to remove the body—of course, that had not been allowed. The women taken in childbirth had been adequately dealt with—one could do nothing to assist. But he had insisted, for decency's sake, on a screen, and Franz had been very clever at rigging one up. Only two of those had died, the rest had gone on—they showed a remarkable tenacity. Then there were the five executions, including the man suddenly gone crazy, who had roared and foamed. A nasty moment, that—for a second the whole current had stopped flowing. But his men had jumped in at once—he himself had acted quickly. The others were merely incorrigible stragglers and of no account.

And now, it was almost over and soon the homeland would be free. Free as it never had been—for, without the Accursed People, it would be unlike any other country on earth. They were gone, with their books and their music, their false, delusive science and their quick way of thinking. They were gone, all the people like Willi Schneider and his mother, who had spent so much time in talking and being friendly. They were gone, the willful people, who clung close together and yet so willfully supported the new and the untried. The men who haggled over pennies, and the others who gave—the sweater, the mimic, the philosopher, the discoverer—all were gone. Yes, and with them went their slaves' religion, the religion of the weak and the humble, the religion that fought so bitterly and yet exalted the prophet above the armed man.

One could be a whole man, with them gone, without their doubts and their mockery and their bitter, self-accusing laughter, their melancholy, deep as a well, and their endless aspiration for something that could not be touched with the hand. One could be solid and virile and untroubled, virile and huge as the old, thunderous gods. It was so that the Leader had spoken, so it must be true. And the countries who weakly received them would be themselves corrupted into warm unmanliness and mockery, into a desire for peace and a search for things not tangible. But the homeland would stand still and listen to the beat of its own heart —not even listen, but stand like a proud fierce animal, a perfect, living machine. To get children, to conquer others, to die gloriously in battle—that was the end of man. It had been a long time forgotten, but the Leader had remembered it. And, naturally, one could not do that completely with them in the land, for they had other ideas.

He thought of these things dutifully because it was right to think of them. They had been repeated and repeated in his ears till they had occupied his mind. But, meanwhile, he was very tired and the dust still rose. They were coming by clumps and groups, now—the last stragglers—they were no longer a solid, flowing current. The afternoon had turned hot—unseasonably hot. He didn't want any more brandy—the thought of it sickened his stomach. He wanted a glass of beer—iced beer, cold and dark, with foam on it—and a chance to unbutton his collar. He wanted to have the thing done and sit down and have Franz pull off his boots. If it were only a little cooler, a little quieter—if even these last would not wail, so, now and then—if only the dust would not rise! He found himself humming, for comfort, a Christmas hymn—it brought a little, frail coolness to his mind.

"Silent night, holy night,
All is calm, all is bright. . . ."

The old gods were virile and thunderous, but, down in the South, they would still deck the tree, in kindliness. Call it a custom—call it anything you like—it still came out of the heart. And it was a custom of the homeland—it could not be wrong. Oh, the beautiful, crisp snow of Christmas Day, the greetings between friends, the bright, lighted tree! Well, there'd be a Christmas to come. Perhaps he'd be married, by then—he had thought of it, often. If he were, they would have a tree—young couples were sentimental, in the South. A tree and a small manger beneath it, with the animals and the child. They carved the figures out of wood, in his country, with loving care—the thought of them was very peaceful and cool. In the old days, he had always given Willi Schneider part of his almond cake—one knew it was not Willi's festival but one was friendly, for all that. And that must be forgotten. He had had no right to give Willi part of his almond cake—it was the tree that mattered, the tree and the tiny candles, the smell of the fresh pine and the clear, frosty sweetness of the day. They would keep that, he and his wife, keep it with rejoicing, and Willi would not look in through the window, with his old face or his new face. He would not look in at all, ever any more. For now the homeland was released, after many years.

Now the dust was beginning to settle—the current in the road had dwindled to a straggling trickle. He was able to think, for the first time, of the land to which that trickle was going—a hungry land, the papers said, in spite of its boastful ways. The road led blankly into it, beyond the rise of ground—hard to tell what it was like. But they would be dispersed, not only here, but over many lands. Of course, the situation was not comparable—all the same, it must be a queer feeling. A queer feeling, yes, to start out anew, with nothing but the clothes on your back and what you could push in a handcart, if you had a handcart. For an instant the thought came, unbidden. "It must be a great people that can bear such things." But they were the Accursed People—the thought should not have come.

He sighed and turned back to his duty. It was really wonderful—even on the third day there was such order, such precision. It was something to be proud of—something to remember long. The Leader would speak of it, undoubtedly. The ones who came now were the very last stragglers, the weakest, but they were being moved along as promptly as if they were strong. The dust actually no longer rose in a cloud—it was settling, slowly but surely.

He did not quite remember when he had last eaten. It did not matter, for the sun was sinking fast, in a red warm glow. In a moment, in an hour, it would be done—he could rest and undo his collar, have some beer. There was nobody on the road now—nobody at all. He stood rigidly at his post—the picture of an officer, though somewhat dusty—but he knew that his eyes were closing. Nobody on the road—nobody for a whole five minutes . . . for eight . . . for ten.

He was roused by Franz's voice in his ear—he must have gone to sleep, standing up. He had heard of that happening to soldiers on the march—he felt rather proud that, now, it had happened to him. But there seemed to be a little trouble on the road—he walked forward to it, stiffly, trying to clear his throat.

It was a commonplace grouping—he had seen dozens like it in the course of the three days—an older man, a young woman, and, of course, the child that she held. No doubt about them, either—the man's features were strongly marked, the woman had the liquid eyes. As for the child, that was merely a wrapped bundle. They should have started before—stupid people—the man looked strong enough. Their belongings were done up like all poor people's belongings.

He stood in front of them, now, erect and a soldier. "Well,"

INTO EGYPT

he said. "Don't you know the orders? No livestock to be taken. Didn't they examine you, down the road?" ("And a pretty fool I'll look like, reporting one confiscated donkey to Headquarters," he thought, with irritation. "We've been able to manage, with the chickens, but this is really too much! What can they be thinking of at the inspection point? Oh, well, they're tired too, I suppose, but it's my responsibility.")

He put a rasp in his voice—he had to, they looked at him so stupidly. "Well?" he said. "Answer me! Don't you know an officer when you see one?"

"We have come a long way," said the man, in a low voice. "We heard there was danger to the child. So we are going. May we pass?" The voice was civil enough, but the eyes were dark and large, the face tired and worn. He was resting one hand on his staff, in a peasant gesture. The woman said nothing at all and one felt that she would say nothing. She sat on the back of the gray donkey and the child in her arms, too, was silent, though it moved.

The lieutenant tried to think rapidly. After all, these were the last. But the thoughts buzzed around his head and would not come out of his mouth. That was fatigue. It should be easy enough for a lieutenant to give an order.

He found himself saying, conversationally, "There are just the three of you?"

"That is all," said the man and looked at him with great simplicity. "But we heard there was danger to the child. So we could not stay any more. We could not stay at all."

"Indeed," said the lieutenant and then said again, "indeed."

"Yes," said the man. "But we shall do well enough—we have been in exile before." He spoke patiently and yet with a certain authority. When the lieutenant did not answer, he laid his other hand on the rein of the gray donkey. It moved forward a step and with it, also, the child stirred and moved. The lieutenant, turning, saw the child's face now, and its hands, as it turned and moved its small hands to the glow of the sunset.

"If the lieutenant pleases—" said an eager voice, the voice of the Northern corporal.

"The lieutenant does not please," said the lieutenant. He nodded at the man. "You may proceed."

"But Lieutenant—" said the eager voice.

"Swine and dog," said the lieutenant, feeling something snap in his mind, "are we to hinder the Leader's plans because of one gray donkey? The order says—all out of the country by sunset. Let them go. You will report to me, Corporal, in the morning."

He turned on his heel and walked a straight line to the field hut, not looking back. When Franz, the orderly, came in a little later, he found him sitting in a chair.

"If the lieutenant would take some brandy—" he said, respectfully.

"The lieutenant has had enough brandy," said the lieutenant, in a hoarse, dusty voice. "Have my orders been obeyed?"

"Yes, Lieutenant."

"They are gone—the very last of them?"

"Yes, Lieutenant."

"They did not look back?"

"No, Lieutenant."

The lieutenant said nothing, for a while, and Franz busied himself with boots. After some time, he spoke.

"The lieutenant should try to sleep," he said. "We have carried out our orders. And now, they are gone."

"Yes," said the lieutenant, and, suddenly he saw them again, the whole multitude, dispersed among every country—the ones who had walked his road, the ones at the points of embarkation. There were a great many of them, and that he had expected. But they were not dispersed as he had thought. They were not dispersed as he had thought, for, with each one went shame, like a visible burden. And the shame was not theirs, though they carried it—the shame belonged to the land that had driven them forth—his own land. He could see it growing and spreading like a black blot—the shame of his country spread over the whole earth.

"The lieutenant will have some brandy," he said. "Quickly, Franz."

When the brandy was brought, he stared at it for a moment, in the cup.

"Tell me, Franz," he said. "Did you know them well? Any of them? Before?"

"Oh, yes, Lieutenant," said Franz, in his smooth, orderly's

voice. "In the last war, I was billeted—well, the name of the town does not matter, but the woman was one of them. Of course that was before we knew about them," he said, respectfully. "That was more than twenty years ago. But she was very kind to me—I used to make toys for her children. I have often wondered what happened to her—she was very considerate and kind. Doubtless I was wrong, Lieutenant? But that was in another country."

"Yes, Franz," said the lieutenant. "There were children, you say?"

"Yes, Lieutenant."

"You saw the child today? The last one?"

"Yes, Lieutenant."

"Its hands had been hurt," said the lieutenant. "In the middle. Right through. I saw them. I wish I had not seen that. I wish I had not seen its hands."

BY THE WATERS OF BABYLON

The north and the west and the south are good hunting ground, but it is forbidden to go east. It is forbidden to go to any of the Dead Places except to search for metal and then he who touches the metal must be a priest or the son of a priest. Afterwards, both the man and the metal must be purified. These are the rules and the laws; they are well made. It is forbidden to cross the great river and look upon the place that was the Place of the Gods—this is most strictly forbidden. We do not even say its name though we know its name. It is there that spirits live, and demons—it is there that there are the ashes of the Great Burning. These things are forbidden—they have been forbidden since the beginning of time.

My father is a priest; I am the son of a priest. I have been in the Dead Places near us, with my father—at first, I was afraid. When my father went into the house to search for the metal, I stood by the door and my heart felt small and weak. It was a dead man's house, a spirit house. It did not have the smell of man, though there were old bones in a corner. But it is not fitting that a priest's son should show fear. I looked at the bones in the shadow and kept my voice still.

Then my father came out with the metal—a good, strong piece. He looked at me with both eyes but I had not run away. He gave me the metal to hold—I took it and did not die. So he knew that I was truly his son and would be a priest in my time. That was when I was very young—nevertheless, my brothers would not have done it, though they are good hunters. After that, they gave me the good piece of meat and the warm corner by the fire. My father watched over me—he was glad that I should be a priest. But when I boasted or wept without a reason, he punished me more strictly than my brothers. That was right.

After a time, I myself was allowed to go into the dead houses and search for metal. So I learned the ways of those houses—and if I saw bones, I was no longer afraid. The bones are light and old—sometimes they will fall into dust if you touch them. But that is a great sin.

I was taught the chants and the spells—I was taught how to stop the running of blood from a wound and many secrets. A priest must know many secrets—that was what my father said. If the hunters think we do all things by chants and spells, they may believe so—it does not hurt them. I was taught how to read in the old books and how to make the old writings—that was hard and took a long time. My knowledge made me happy—it was like a fire in my heart. Most of all, I liked to hear of the Old Days and the stories of the gods. I asked myself many questions that I could not answer, but it was good to ask them. At night, I would lie awake and listen to the wind—it seemed to me that it was the voice of the gods as they flew through the air.

We are not ignorant like the Forest People—our women spin wool on the wheel, our priests wear a white robe. We do not eat grubs from the tree, we have not forgotten the old writings, although they are hard to understand. Nevertheless, my knowledge and my lack of knowledge burned in me—I wished to know more. When I was a man at last, I came to my father and said, "It is time for me to go on my journey. Give me your leave."

He looked at me for a long time, stroking his beard, then he said at last, "Yes. It is time." That night, in the house of the priesthood, I asked for and received purification. My body hurt but my spirit was a cool stone. It was my father himself who questioned me about my dreams.

He bade me look into the smoke of the fire and see—I saw and told what I saw. It was what I have always seen—a river and, beyond it, a great Dead Place and in it the gods walking. I have always thought about that. His eyes were stern when I told him—he was no longer my father but a priest. He said, "This is a strong dream."

"It is mine," I said, while the smoke waved and my head felt light. They were singing the Star song in the outer chamber and it was like the buzzing of bees in my head.

He asked me how the gods were dressed and I told him how they were dressed. We know how they were dressed from the book, but I saw them as if they were before me. When I had finished, he threw the sticks three times and studied them as they fell.

"This is a very strong dream," he said. "It may eat you up."

"I am not afraid," I said and looked at him with both eyes. My voice sounded thin in my ears but that was because of the smoke.

He touched me on the breast and the forehead. He gave me the bow and the three arrows.

"Take them," he said. "It is forbidden to travel east. It is forbidden to cross the river. It is forbidden to go to the Place of the Gods. All these things are forbidden."

"All these things are forbidden," I said, but it was my voice that spoke and not my spirit. He looked at me again.

"My son," he said. "Once I had young dreams. If your dreams do not eat you up, you may be a great priest. If they eat you, you are still my son. Now go on your journey."

I went fasting, as is the law. My body hurt but not my heart. When the dawn came, I was out of sight of the village. I prayed and purified myself, waiting for a sign. The sign was an eagle. It flew east.

Sometimes signs are sent by bad spirits. I waited again on the flat rock, fasting, taking no food. I was very still—I could feel the sky above me and the earth beneath. I waited till the sun was beginning to sink. Then three deer passed in the valley, going east—they did not wind me or see me. There was a white fawn with them—a very great sign.

I followed them, at a distance, waiting for what would happen. My heart was troubled about going east, yet I knew that I must go. My head hummed with my fasting—I did not even see the panther spring upon the white fawn. But, before I knew it, the bow was in my hand. I shouted and the panther lifted his head from the fawn. It is not easy to kill a panther with one arrow but the arrow went through his eye and into his brain. He died as he tried to spring—he rolled over, tearing at the ground. Then I knew I was meant to go east—I knew that was my journey. When the night came, I made my fire and roasted meat.

It is eight suns' journey to the east and a man passes by many Dead Places. The Forest People are afraid of them but I am not. Once I made my fire on the edge of a Dead Place at night and, next morning, in the dead house, I found a good knife, little rusted. That was small to what came afterward but it made my heart feel big. Always when I looked for game, it was in front of my arrow, and twice I passed hunting parties of the Forest People without their knowing. So I knew my magic was strong and my journey clean, in spite of the law.

Toward the setting of the eighth sun, I came to the banks of the great river. It was half-a-day's journey after I had left the god-road—we do not use the god-roads now for they are falling apart into great blocks of stone, and the forest is safer going. A long way off, I had seen the water through trees but the trees were thick. At last, I came out upon an open place at the top of a cliff. There was the great river below, like a giant in the sun. It is very long, very wide. It could eat all the streams we know and still be thirsty. Its name is Ou-dis-sun, the Sacred, the Long. No man of my tribe had seen it, not even my father, the priest. It was magic and I prayed.

Then I raised my eyes and looked south. It was there, the Place of the Gods.

How can I tell what it was like—you do not know. It was there, in the red light, and they were too big to be houses. It was there with the red light upon it, mighty and ruined. I knew that in another moment the gods would see me. I covered my eyes with my hands and crept back into the forest.

Surely, that was enough to do, and live. Surely it was enough to spend the night upon the cliff. The Forest People themselves do not come near. Yet, all through the night, I knew that I should have to cross the river and walk in the places of the gods, although the gods ate me up. My magic did not help me at all and yet there was a fire in my bowels, a fire in my mind. When the sun rose, I thought, "My journey has been clean. Now I will go home from my journey." But, even as I thought so, I knew I could not. If I went to the Place of the Gods, I would surely die, but, if I did not go, I could never be at peace with my spirit again. It is better to lose one's life than one's spirit, if one is a priest and the son of a priest.

Nevertheless, as I made the raft, the tears ran out of my eyes. The Forest People could have killed me without fight, if they had come upon me then, but they did not come. When the raft was made, I said the sayings for the dead and painted myself for death. My heart was cold as a frog and my knees like water, but the burning in my mind would not let me have peace. As I pushed the raft from the shore, I began my death song—I had the right. It was a fine song.

"I am John, son of John," I sang. "My people are the Hill People.
    They are the men.
I go into the Dead Places but I am not slain.
I take the metal from the Dead Places but I am not blasted.
I travel upon the god-roads and am not afraid. E-yah! I have
    killed the panther, I have killed the fawn!
E-yah! I have come to the great river. No man has come there
    before.
It is forbidden to go east, but I have gone, forbidden to go on
    the great river, but I am there.
Open your hearts, you spirits, and hear my song.
    Now I go to the Place of the Gods, I shall not return.
My body is painted for death and my limbs weak, but my heart
    is big as I go to the Place of the Gods!"

All the same, when I came to the Place of the Gods, I was afraid, afraid. The current of the great river is very strong—it gripped my raft with its hands. That was magic, for the river itself is wide and calm. I could feel evil spirits about me, in the bright morning; I could feel their breath on my neck as I was swept down the stream. Never have I been so much alone—I tried to think of my knowledge, but it was a squirrel's heap of winter nuts. There was no strength in my knowledge any more and I felt small and naked as a new-hatched bird—alone upon the great river, the servant of the gods.

Yet, after a while, my eyes were opened and I saw. I saw both banks of the river—I saw that once there had been god-roads across it, though now they were broken and fallen like broken vines. Very great they were, and wonderful and broken—broken in the time of the Great Burning when the fire fell out of the sky. And always the current took me nearer to the Place of the Gods, and the huge ruins rose before my eyes.

I do not know the customs of rivers—we are the People of the Hills. I tried to guide my raft with the pole but it spun around. I thought the river meant to take me past the Place of the Gods and out into the Bitter Water of the legends. I grew angry then—my heart felt strong. I said aloud, "I am a priest and the son of a priest!" The gods heard me—they showed me how to paddle with the pole on one side of the raft. The current changed itself—I drew near to the Place of the Gods.

When I was very near, my raft struck and turned over. I can swim in our lakes—I swam to the shore. There was a great spike of rusted metal sticking out into the river—I hauled myself up upon it and sat there, panting. I had saved my bow and two arrows and the knife I found in the Dead Place but that was all. My raft went whirling downstream toward the Bitter Water. I looked after it, and thought if it had trod me under, at least I would be safely dead. Nevertheless, when I had dried my bow-string and re-strung it, I walked forward to the Place of the Gods.

It felt like ground underfoot; it did not burn me. It is not true what some of the tales say, that the ground there burns forever, for I have been there. Here and there were the marks and stains of the Great Burning, on the ruins, that is true. But they were old marks and old stains. It is not true either, what some of our priests say, that it is an island covered with fogs and enchantments. It is not. It is a great Dead Place—greater than any Dead Place we know. Everywhere in it there are god-roads, though most are cracked and broken. Everywhere there are the ruins of the high towers of the gods.

How shall I tell what I saw? I went carefully, my strung bow in my hand, my skin ready for danger. There should have been the wailings of spirits and the shrieks of demons, but there were not. It was very silent and sunny where I had landed—the wind and the rain and the birds that drop seeds had done their work—the grass grew in the cracks of the broken stone. It is a fair island—no wonder the gods built there. If I had come there, a god, I also would have built.

How shall I tell what I saw? The towers are not all broken—here and there one still stands, like a great tree in a forest, and the birds nest high. But the towers themselves look blind, for the gods are gone. I saw a fish-hawk, catching fish in the river. I saw a little dance of white butterflies over a great heap of broken stones and columns. I went there and looked about me—there was a carved stone with cut-letters, broken in half. I can read letters but I could not understand these. They said UBTREAS. There was also the shattered image of a man or a god. It had been made of white stone and he wore his hair tied back like a woman's. His name was ASHING, as I read on the cracked half of a stone. I thought it wise to pray to ASHING, though I do not know that god.

How shall I tell what I saw? There was no smell of man left, on stone or metal. Nor were there many trees in that wilderness of stone. There are many pigeons, nesting and dropping in the towers—the gods must have loved them, or, perhaps, they used them for sacrifices. There are wild cats that roam the god-roads, green-eyed, unafraid of man. At night they wail like demons but they are not demons. The wild dogs are more dangerous, for they hunt in a pack, but them I did not meet till later. Everywhere there are the carved stones, carved with magical numbers or words.

I went North—I did not try to hide myself. When a god or a demon saw me, then I would die, but meanwhile I was no longer afraid. My hunger for knowledge burned in me—there was so much that I could not understand. After awhile, I knew that my belly was hungry. I could have hunted for my meat, but

I did not hunt. It is known that the gods did not hunt as we do—they got their food from enchanted boxes and jars. Sometimes these are still found in the Dead Places—once, when I was a child and foolish, I opened such a jar and tasted it and found the food sweet. But my father found out and punished me for it strictly, for, often, that food is death. Now, though, I had long gone past what was forbidden, and I entered the likeliest towers, looking for the food of the gods.

I found it at last in the ruins of a great temple in the mid-city. A mighty temple it must have been, for the roof was painted like the sky at night with its stars—that much I could see, though the colors were faint and dim. It went down into great caves and tunnels—perhaps they kept their slaves there. But when I started to climb down, I heard the squeaking of rats, so I did not go—rats are unclean, and there must have been many tribes of them, from the squeaking. But near there, I found food, in the heart of a ruin, behind a door that still opened. I ate only the fruits from the jars—they had a very sweet taste. There was drink, too, in bottles of glass—the drink of the gods was strong and made my head swim. After I had eaten and drunk, I slept on the top of a stone, my bow at my side.

When I woke, the sun was low. Looking down from where I lay, I saw a dog sitting on his haunches. His tongue was hanging out of his mouth; he looked as if he were laughing. He was a big dog, with a gray-brown coat, as big as a wolf. I sprang up and shouted at him but he did not move—he just sat there as if he were laughing. I did not like that. When I reached for a stone to throw, he moved swiftly out of the way of the stone. He was not afraid of me; he looked at me as if I were meat. No doubt I could have killed him with an arrow, but I did not know if there were others. Moreover, night was falling.

I looked about me—not far away there was a great, broken god-road, leading North. The towers were high enough, but not so high, and while many of the dead-houses were wrecked, there were some that stood. I went toward this god-road, keeping to the heights of the ruins, while the dog followed. When I had reached the god-road, I saw that there were others behind him. If I had slept later, they would have come upon me asleep and torn out my throat. As it was, they were sure enough of me;

they did not hurry. When I went into the dead-house, they kept watch at the entrance—doubtless they thought they would have a fine hunt. But a dog cannot open a door and I knew, from the books, that the gods did not like to live on the ground but on high.

I had just found a door I could open when the dogs decided to rush. Ha! They were surprised when I shut the door in their faces—it was a good door, of strong metal. I could hear their foolish baying beyond it but I did not stop to answer them. I was in darkness—I found stairs and climbed. There were many stairs, turning around till my head was dizzy. At the top was another door—I found the knob and opened it. I was in a long small chamber—on one side of it was a bronze door that could not be opened, for it had no handle. Perhaps there was a magic word to open it but I did not have the word. I turned to the door in the opposite side of the wall. The lock of it was broken and I opened it and went in.

Within, there was a place of great riches. The god who lived there must have been a powerful god. The first room was a small ante-room—I waited there for some time, telling the spirits of the place that I came in peace and not as a robber. When it seemed to me that they had had time to hear me, I went on. Ah, what riches! Few, even, of the windows had been broken—it was all as it had been. The great windows that looked over the city had not been broken at all though they were dusty and streaked with many years. There were coverings on the floors, the colors not greatly faded, and the chairs were soft and deep. There were pictures upon the walls, very strange, very wonderful—I remember one of a bunch of flowers in a jar—if you came close to it, you could see nothing but bits of color, but if you stood away from it, the flowers might have been picked yesterday. It made my heart feel strange to look at this picture—and to look at the figure of a bird, in some hard clay, on a table and see it so like our birds. Everywhere there were books and writings, many in tongues that I could not read. The god who lived there must have been a wise god and full of knowledge. I felt I had right there, as I sought knowledge also.

Nevertheless, it was strange. There was a washing-place but no water—perhaps the gods washed in air. There was a cooking-place but no wood, and though there was a machine to cook food, there was no place to put fire in it. Nor were there candles or lamps—there were things that looked like lamps but they had neither oil nor wick. All these things were magic, but I touched them and lived—the magic had gone out of them. Let me tell one thing to show. In the washing-place, a thing said "Hot" but it was not hot to the touch—another thing said "Cold" but it was not cold. This must have been a strong magic but the magic was gone. I do not understand—they had ways—I wish that I knew.

It was close and dry and dusty in their house of the gods. I have said the magic was gone but that is not true—it had gone from the magic things but it had not gone from the place. I felt the spirits about me, weighing upon me. Nor had I ever slept in a Dead Place before—and yet, tonight, I must sleep there. When I thought of it, my tongue felt dry in my throat, in spite of my wish for knowledge. Almost I would have gone down again and faced the dogs, but I did not.

I had not gone through all the rooms when the darkness fell. When it fell, I went back to the big room looking over the city and made fire. There was a place to make fire and a box with wood in it, though I do not think they cooked there. I wrapped myself in a floor-covering and slept in front of the fire—I was very tired.

Now I tell what is very strong magic. I woke in the midst of the night. When I woke, the fire had gone out and I was cold. It seemed to me that all around me there were whisperings and voices. I closed my eyes to shut them out. Some will say that I slept again, but I do not think that I slept. I could feel the spirits drawing my spirit out of my body as a fish is drawn on a line.

Why should I lie about it? I am a priest and the son of a priest. If there are spirits, as they say, in the small Dead Places near us, what spirits must there not be in that great Place of the Gods? And would not they wish to speak? After such long years? I know that I felt myself drawn as a fish is drawn on a line. I had stepped out of my body—I could see my body asleep in front of the cold fire, but it was not I. I was drawn to look out upon the city of the gods.

It should have been dark, for it was night, but it was not dark.

Everywhere there were lights—lines of light—circles and blurs of light—ten thousand torches would not have been the same. The sky itself was alight—you barely see the stars for the glow in the sky. I thought to myself "This is strong magic" and trembled. There was a roaring in my ears like the rushing of rivers. Then my eyes grew used to the light and my ears to the sound. I knew that I was seeing the city as it had been when the gods were alive.

That was a sight indeed—yes, that was a sight: I could not have seen it in the body—my body would have died. Everywhere went the gods, on foot and in chariots—there were gods beyond number and counting and their chariots blocked the streets. They had turned night to day for their pleasure—they did not sleep with the sun. The noise of their coming and going was the noise of many waters. It was magic what they could do—it was magic what they did.

I looked out of another window—the great vines of their bridges were mended and the god-roads went East and West. Restless, restless, were the gods and always in motion! They burrowed tunnels under rivers—they flew in the air. With unbelievable tools they did giant works—no part of the earth was safe from them, for, if they wished for a thing, they summoned it from the other side of the world. And always, as they labored and rested, as they feasted and made love, there was a drum in their ears—the pulse of the giant city, beating and beating like a man's heart.

Were they happy? What is happiness to the gods? They were great, they were mighty, they were wonderful and terrible. As I looked upon them and their magic, I felt like a child—but a little more, it seemed to me, and they would pull down the moon from the sky. I saw them with wisdom beyond wisdom and knowledge beyond knowledge. And yet not all they did was well done—even I could see that—and yet their wisdom could not but grow until all was peace.

Then I saw their fate come upon them and that was terrible past speech. It came upon them as they walked the streets of their city. I have been in the fights with the Forest People—I have seen men die. But this was not like that. When gods war with gods, they use weapons we do not know. It was fire falling out of the sky and a mist that poisoned. It was the time of the

Great Burning and the Destruction. They ran about like ants in the streets of their city—poor gods, poor gods! Then the towers began to fall. A few escaped—yes, a few. The legends tell it. But even after the city had become a Dead Place, for many years the poison was still in the ground. I saw it happen, I saw the last of them die. It was darkness over the broken city and I wept.

All this, I saw. I saw it as I have told it, though not in the body. When I woke in the morning, I was hungry, but I did not think first of my hunger for my heart was perplexed and confused. I knew the reason for the Dead Places but I did not see why it had happened. It seemed to me it should not have happened, with all the magic they had. I went through the house looking for an answer. There was so much in the house I could not understand—and yet I am a priest and the son of a priest. It was like being on one side of the great river, at night, with no light to show the way.

Then I saw the dead god. He was sitting in his chair, by the window, in a room I had not entered before and, for the first moment, I thought that he was alive. Then I saw the skin on the back of his hand—it was like dry leather. The room was shut, hot and dry—no doubt that had kept him as he was. At first I was afraid to approach him—then the fear left me. He was sitting looking out over the city—he was dressed in the clothes of the gods. His age was neither young nor old—I could not tell his age. But there was wisdom in his face and great sadness. I could see that he would have not run away. He had sat at his window, watching his city die—then he himself had died. But it is better to lose one's life than one's spirit—and you could see from the face that his spirit had not been lost. I knew, that, if I touched him, he would fall into dust—and yet, there was something unconquered in the face.

That is all of my story, for then I knew he was a man—I knew then that they had been men, neither gods nor demons. It is a great knowledge, hard to tell and believe. They were men—they went a dark road, but they were men. I had no fear after that—I had no fear going home, though twice I fought off the dogs and once I was hunted for two days by the Forest People. When I saw my father again, I prayed and was purified. He touched my lips and my breast, he said, "You went away a boy.

You come back a man and a priest." I said, "Father, they were men! I have been in the Place of the Gods and seen it! Now slay me, if it is the law—but still I know they were men."

He looked at me out of both eyes. He said, "The law is not always the same shape—you have done what you have done. I could not have done it in my time, but you come after me. Tell!"

I told and he listened. After that, I wished to tell all the people but he showed me otherwise. He said, "Truth is a hard deer to hunt. If you eat too much truth at once, you may die of the truth. It was not idly that our fathers forbade the Dead Places." He was right—it is better the truth should come little by little. I have learned that, being a priest. Perhaps, in the old days, they ate knowledge too fast.

Nevertheless, we make a beginning. It is not for the metal alone we go to the Dead Places now—there are the books and the writings. They are hard to learn. And the magic tools are broken—but we can look at them and wonder. At least, we make a beginning. And, when I am chief priest we shall go beyond the great river. We shall go to the Place of the Gods—the place newyork—not one man but a company. We shall look for the images of the gods and find the god ASHING and the others—the gods Lincoln and Biltmore and Moses. But they were men who built the city, not gods or demons. They were men. I remember the dead man's face. They were men who were here before us. We must build again.

THREE

Criticism and Letters

FOREWORD TO MURIEL RUKEYSER'S THEORY OF FLIGHT

Some people are born with their craft already in their hand, and, from her first book, Miss Rukeyser seems to be one of these. There is little of the uncertainty, the fumbling, the innocently direct imitation of admirations which one unconsciously associates with a first book of verse. It is, some of it, work in a method, but the method is handled maturely and the occasional uncertainties are rather from experimentation than any technical insufficiency. Moreover, there is a great deal of power—a remarkable power for twenty-one. I don't know quite what Miss Rukeyser will do with the future but she certainly will be a writer. It sticks out all over the book.

Politically, she is a Left Winger and a revolutionary. She speaks for her part of the generation born "in Prinzip's year" that found the world they grew up in too bitterly tainted by that year to accept.

"We focus on our times, destroying you, fathers
in the long ground—you have given strange birth
to us who turn against you in our blood,"

she says in "The Blood Is Justified" and again

FOREWORD TO MURIEL RUKEYSER'S THEORY OF FLIGHT

"I do not say : Forgive, to my kindred dead,
only : Understand my treason, See I betray you kissing,
I overthrow your milestones weeping among your tombs."

I do not intend to add, in this preface, to the dreary and unreal discussion about unconscious fascists, conscious proletarians, and other figures of straw which has afflicted recent criticism with head noises and small specks in front of the eyes. But I will remark that when Miss Rukeyser speaks her politics—and she speaks with sincerity and fire—she does so like a poet, not like a slightly worn phonograph record, and she does so in poetic terms. For evidence, I offer the section "The Lynchings of Jesus" in the long poem "Theory of Flight"; the short "shot" of the coal-mine in the elegy for Ruth Lehman and the poem "The Blood Is Justified," among others. They are worth reading, to see what a young and talented person thinks of certain contemporary things—and how a poet of talent can make poetry out of them.

I use the word "shot" advisedly—for the mind behind these poems is an urban and a modern one. It has fed on the quick jerk of the news-reel, the hard lights in the sky, the long deserted night-street, the take-off of the plane from the ground. It knows nature as well—the look of landscape, the quietness of hills. But its experience has been largely an urban experience, and it is interesting to see the poetry of youth so based. When Miss Rukeyser thinks of energy, she thinks of a dynamo rather than a river, an electric spark rather than a trampling hoof—and that is interesting, too.

Perhaps that makes her verse sound like verse of the "Oh, Grandmother Dynamo, what great big wheels you have!" school—and that, most decidedly, it is not. Witness "Song for Dead Children," "Breathing Landscape," and the beautiful and original "Thousands of Days," with its serene and successful assonance. She can write powerfully; she can also write delicately, to a new and light-footed pattern. Her technique is sure, and is developing in original directions. Her long poem, "Theory of Flight," is a rather unusual achievement for a girl in her twenties. It has passages of confusion and journalistic passages, it also has passages that remind one of structural steel. There is a largeness of attempt about it which is one of the surest signs of genuine ability.

Her later lyrics, particularly the ones I have mentioned, are more successfully and surely integrated. But only an original mind could have accomplished both.

Miss Rukeyser is twenty-one. She was born and brought up in New York City and has attended Vassar, the Columbia Summer School, and the Roosevelt School of the Air (the latter to gather material for "Theory of Flight"). At present, she is on the staff of "New Theatre." I think we may expect a good deal from her in the future. And it would seem to me that in this first book she displays an accomplishment which ranks her among the most interesting and individual of our younger poets.

EPIC ON AN AMERICAN THEME

STEPHEN VINCENT BENÉT
AND THE GUGGENHEIM FOUNDATION

[Editor's Note: "Epic on an American Theme" is reprinted from *The New Colophon*, which asked Rosemary Benét to supply the introductory note.]

These letters need no comment. They paint a clear picture. In Steve's own way, he tells how it was with him then and how much the Guggenheim meant to us. All I can do is to add a fact or two for the background. When he applied for the Guggenheim Fellowship in December, 1925, he was twenty-seven years old. He had a wife, and a child under two. Another child was to be born in early fall. He lived entirely by his writing and he wanted very much to take time to write a long poem. To say the Fellowship meant a great deal to us under those particular circumstances is to deal in understatement. It was, in this case, exactly the reverse of Dr. Johnson's bitter definition of a patron: "One who looks with unconcern on a man struggling for life in the water, and, when he has reached ground, encumbers him with help."

The backward look is easy. Too easy perhaps. People are apt to say to me now, "It was inevitable for him to write a long poem." So it was. But I remember how it was then, when we were trying to look forward, and there was no backward look. It would have taken longer, been more difficult, been much more of a strain on the spirit in every way, without the Fellowship. I remember just how it was with us at that time. . . . We were both grateful then and always will be. That Fellowship, since it resulted in John Brown's Body, proved, I think, to be bread upon the waters. Well, it should have been! it was *bread upon the waters.*

ROSEMARY BENÉT

I PLAN FOR STUDY

[SUBMITTED TO THE JOHN SIMON GUGGENHEIM
MEMORIAL FOUNDATION]

[*Pencilled date Dec. 11, '25, not in SVB's hand*]

As regards the plan of study, I shall try to outline my aims as clearly and succinctly as possible, realizing, however, that any plan which deals with unaccomplished creative work cannot be charted quite as definitely as if it dealt with research.

For the past ten years, my chief interest has been the writing of poetry and I feel that I have now reached a point in the development of my work where, if I were financially able, I should devote myself exclusively to that one task for a period of some years. It is, however, practically impossible for an author, under present-day conditions of writing and publishing, to support himself solely by the writing of verse. At least I know that it is impossible for me. This means that the work which I do best and to which I should like to give all the time and energy possible, must instead be done in spare-hours, with what energy is left after doing other and more lucrative work, and seldom except under a feeling of financial strain. This is not a complaint—it is merely a statement of fact. I know that if I could count on even a few free months out of a year, relieved from economic pressure and the necessity of writing hack short-stories for a living, I could do more work in my chosen field and of a better quality than I am doing now. And I feel, with some conviction, that the next few years may be of particular importance to me in the development of my craft, if it is to develop at all.

As for the projected work itself—I have three subjects for long poems under consideration, and have had for some time. All three would require labor, time and experimentation which it would be difficult for me to give under present conditions—and all three would need, besides, a certain leisure and freshness of mind which, at present, I doubt if I should be able to give at all. One is a long narrative poem on an American historical subject for which I have collected material over a considerable period—one a modern narrative laid in New York City—and one a somewhat erratic romance in a vein I have not tried before. I should also like to round out with four or five additional poems the series of American ballads begun in *Tiger Joy*. I have other projects in mind—but those are the most important. There is, in addition, for instance, a historical novel, to be called "The Singing Sword," the greater part of which is laid in Europe—and it would be of the greatest value to me to visit some of the places I wish to deal with—but doing so would not interrupt the main course of my work, once I felt free to pursue that work without having to think too constantly of a definite financial reward.

If awarded a scholarship, I should go to France to carry out my plans and probably live either in or near Paris, or in some small place in the provinces, depending on circumstance. I have lived in France before (1920-1921 and 1921-1922, returning to America for the summer of 1921)—I am familiar with the life—the atmosphere is congenial to me—and I know that I can work there under the most favorable conditions. My wife finished her education at the Government Ecole Normale at Sèvres, having received one of the French Government fellowships awarded by the Committee of Collegiate Alumnae (1919-1920), and we would not find the slightest difficulty in living abroad on a minimum amount of funds. The scale of living there, for Americans, with the present exchange on the dollar, would more than compensate for any actual diminution in income incurred by my giving up the greater part of my present hack-work, and I would be able to do what I want to do in comparative peace of mind. At the same time, living within reaching distance of Paris, I would be in touch with adequate facilities for any needed research and with those sources of artistic stimulation by contact with other arts than those of the writer which are of such service to any worker in the field of letters.

I cannot promise accomplishment—no writer with a degree of honesty can. I can promise work, and I think I can promise, with some definiteness, better work and a greater amount of it, under such conditions, than it seems likely I shall be able to produce without them. I should intend to finish at least one book of narrative poems at the end of the year—with, possibly, other work mapped out or in train—that is all that I can say. I realize that to do that, in the way I should wish to do it, would take more energy and harder labor than I have yet expended on any single object—but I should be more than grateful for the opportunity. My ultimate purpose in study, or, for that matter, in existence, is to attempt to write good poetry, and, given the opportunity, I shall do the best I can to further that purpose.

I should therefore like to apply for a fellowship on the John Simon Guggenheim Memorial Foundation for the one year period beginning January 1, 1926.

In case the above information does not fully cover the requirements of the questionnaire, I should be glad to furnish any additional information that may be necessary.

Very sincerely, STEPHEN VINCENT BENÉT

II

February 1st 1927

89 Avenue de Neuilly
Neuilly-sur-Seine, Seine, France.

Dear Mr. Moe:—

I am taking the liberty of applying for a six months' renewal of my fellowship, should the Foundation see fit to grant it, and enclosing a preliminary report and a formal application herewith. The poem is getting along very well, but I've had to do such a lot of preliminary reading for it, among other things, that I won't be able to finish it in the time. I was hoping some private windfall would happen along, so I could finish it on my own funds, and so delayed, but nothing seems to be in sight, and I don't want to hold the poem back or break it off to write short stories if I can help it, which is what I'll have to do without luck or a renewal. This is a nice quiet place here, near the Bois which is good for the children, and with a separate room for me to work in. So all goes well in spite of the decline of the dollar.

With all best wishes
Sincerely, STEPHEN VINCENT BENÉT

III

February 1st, 1927

89 Avenue de Neuilly,
Neuilly-sur-Seine, France

John Simon Guggenheim Memorial Foundation

Dear Sirs:—

I wish to submit my formal application for a six months' renewal of the John Simon Guggenheim Memorial Fellowship awarded me for 1926-1927, the renewal to run six months from July 15th 1927 when the present fellowship expires.

My reasons for wishing a renewal of this fellowship are stated in the attached preliminary report covering work already done to February 1st 1927.

Very sincerely, STEPHEN VINCENT BENÉT

IV PRELIMINARY REPORT

Stephen Vincent Benét
89 Avenue de Neuilly,
Neuilly-sur-Seine,
Seine, France

I reached France on August first, 1926, sailing from New York July 22nd, and went immediately to Paris. Until January first, 1927, I lived in Paris itself at 14 bis Rue Jadin, XVII. Since then I have been living at 89 Avenue de Neuilly, Neuilly, a ten minutes' walk from one of the gates of the city, and a place where I find working-conditions even more favorable than in the city itself.

My work has progressed favorably and in spite of the fall of the dollar in regard to the franc and the consequent rise in the price of living for Americans drawing their income in dollars, I find it possible for myself and my family to live perfectly comfortably for something like a half to two-thirds of what we were paying in New York. I have a separate room to work in—one of the servant's rooms at the top of the building—and the American Library has been most kind in helping me with the research I have had to do.

When I first applied for a Guggenheim fellowship, I stated in the plan submitted, that what I hoped to do was to complete in the given year at least one long poem or volume of poems, with such incidental work as might naturally arise.

I had, at that time, several projects for a long poem upon an American theme. One was to deal with De Soto, or to deal in general with some of the Spanish explorers, and the curious color and flare of the Spanish adventure in the New World. It was for that reason that I thought tentatively of going to Spain, and making certain historical researches there. But there were other projects—in particular a project for a long poem dealing with the Civil War, which I had then thought about for almost a year—and it is upon this last that I am working now.

As regards the poem itself. I have planned it in a prologue, eight books or sections, and an epilogue. The working-title I have for it at present is "The Horses of Anger," but I am not entirely satisfied with it and may change it before publication. Each section or book will run to between thirty and forty pages of typewritten manuscript. The prologue runs to five. There is an average of about fifty lines of verse to a page. The completed book should make between 280 and 300 pages of my manuscript or between 14,000 and 15,000 lines.

Except for the prologue and epilogue, the action of the poem is a continuous action, beginning shortly before the John Brown raid and ending shortly after the surrender at Appomattox. But, naturally, it does not follow history in the strict sense—that is to say I have not described and do not mean to describe every battle, every fluctuation of fortune, every event. I have spent a good deal of space on various men and incidents relatively unimportant to history and dealt scantly or not at all with others of greater textbook importance. That is to say—it is a poem, an attempt at an interpretation, not a history or a recital of events.

The poem is schemed, I suppose, as an epic—an epic on an American theme. I do not particularly like the word—it instantly suggests a portentousness and a presumption which I do not wish to claim. The events of the time were epic, and I have tried to keep their epic quality—but to deal with them as well with enough boldness and freshness to make them real, and not a dim struggle between distant men, who had no likeness to us, but were steel-engravings in a book.

There are many characters in the poem, some real, some fictional. In every case I have endeavored to treat them as individuals and not conscious representatives of a type or a mood. The main thread of the plot is carried by six characters, two Northern, three Southern, and one from the West. Others, real or fictional, come in for a while to drop out or reappear as the poem needs them or does not need them. But I think the main thread is strong enough and clear enough to stand out against the shifting background without either dominating it unduly or being lost in its details.

In a way, the form of the book bears some resemblance to the form employed by Hardy in "The Dynasts." In a way it might be said to bear some resemblance to such books as "Our Times" and "The Mauve Decade," though written in neither mood. But neither comparison is particularly close. The form is a large pattern made of many shifting threads—certain threads run through and carry the strength of the verse. Some threads are real men, some people I have invented. I think I can claim that, successful or unsuccessful, it is a new form for long narrative verse—and that, if it can be classed as an epic, it is an epic told in a new way.

I have employed various metres and verse-forms in the writing and used various devices of interlude and change of pace in an attempt to keep the thing from growing monotonous. But there is a foundation or backbone of rather rough blank verse combined with a dactyllic or anapestic pentameter-form that takes the chief load and binds the whole project together.

I have now finished the prologue and the first two books in first draft. I am hoping by the first of July to finish four more books or sections, and if granted a renewal of the fellowship would propose to finish the whole first draft by October and devote three months to necessary revision, checking of references, and the reshaping that can and must be done when one sees the thing as a whole and cannot be done while the individual parts are still in the mill.

It may be reasonably advanced that I have asked for a year in which to do a certain piece of work and now confess myself unable to complete that work within the year. That is true. But, in the first place, the mere planning of such a lengthy poem as I have attempted, its difference in scheme and manner from any model that could be followed and anything I had done before, necessitated a great deal of preliminary thought and experimentation. I had to feel my way at first, and do it uncertainly, trying various expedients and rejecting many. That is one reason why the drafting of the first two parts has taken such a disproportionate amount of time.

In the second place, it is difficult to predict the completion of any piece of creative work while the thing is still in embryo. There are too many factors that have to be taken as they come. It has always seemed to me that of any writer's time at least half is necessarily wasted, in the stricter sense of the word. But without that wasted motion, the work somehow does not get born full-bodied—the pump must bring up dirty water before it brings up clean.

In the third place, I have, of necessity, had to do a great deal more research than I would have if I had been engaged upon a purely imaginative theme. I had, I think, at least rather better than an average layman's knowledge of the Civil War before I began—because the period had always interested me. But even so, what I had was entirely inadequate. And, without wishing to swamp my poem in unnecessary detail, I have had and will have to read hard and widely to get what I want from the books. Fortunately, the American Library and the Library of the American Chamber of Commerce have adequate material for what I want.

It may also seem curious to be writing an American poem of American events in the center of France. But I can give my whole time to it here—in America I could not. I would not have the time or the money which is time. As for the actual places described, I happen to have seen some of them—I have lived in the South, in New England and in the West. And seeing the battlefield of Gettysburg as it is today will not necessarily help you to write a poem about it as it was sixty years ago or so.

I think that is all there is to say about the poem itself. I have only shown the drafted portions of it to one other person. I value his opinion and he thinks it likely to be the best work I have done. I can hardly report on it without prejudice—no writer is supposed to be the best judge of his own work. I should be very glad to submit the drafted portions to the committee or to anyone they might select, should they think it advisable.

In conclusion, may I submit my project for the summer, in case my fellowship should be renewed. I should then go about June first to Bizy-Vernon and remain there till October. Bizy is a small town on the fringes of Normandy, about an hour and a quarter from Paris. The climate is healthy, rents are cheap, it is near enough to Paris so I could come in for books, and there are no distractions and no tourists. In October I would come back to Paris, probably to this address unless I could find a cheaper one, and devote the last three months to the revision, reworking etc., as stated above. I cannot go too far away from a good reference library and yet I do not want to get into the more expensive sections, especially during the summer when the tourists come and the prices rise.

As for the month's vacation which I see is optional with the various holders of fellowships, I consider that I have used that up in getting my family settled and making two moves. Besides, now I see my way clear and have finished the preliminaries, I want to get the work done.

Incidentally I have written half a dozen or so short poems since coming here, one of which is coming out in the "New Republic" shortly.

Very sincerely
STEPHEN VINCENT BENÉT